W9-BVJ-625

DATE DUE			
APR 30			
NOV 28			
APR 11 78			
JAN 0 6 2012			
DEC 1 2 20			

63391
Laer

St. Procopius College Library
Maple Ave. & College Rd.
Lisle, Illinois

DUQUESNE STUDIES
Philosophical Series

14

PHILOSOPHY OF SCIENCE

PART TWO
A STUDY OF THE DIVISION AND NATURE
OF VARIOUS GROUPS OF SCIENCES

DUQUESNE STUDIES
Philosophical Series

14

PHILOSOPHY OF SCIENCE

by

P. Henry van Laer, D.Sc.

Part Two

A STUDY OF THE DIVISION AND NATURE OF VARIOUS GROUPS OF SCIENCES

1962
Duquesne University Press, Pittsburgh, Pa.
Editions E. Nauwelaerts, Louvain

Q
175
.L18

DUQUESNE STUDIES
Philosophical Series

Andrew G. van Melsen, D.Sc., D.Ed., and Henry J. Koren, C.S.Sp., S.T.D., editors.

Volume One—*Andrew G. van Melsen,* From Atomos to Atom. Pp. XII and 240. Price: paper $3.50, cloth $4.25. Published also in Dutch, German, Spanish, and Italian.

Volume Two—*Andrew G. van Melsen,* The Philosophy of Nature. Pp. XII and 265. Third edition, fourth impression. Price: paper $3.75, cloth $4.50. Published also in Italian and Dutch. Polish edition in preparation.

Volume Three—*P. Henry van Laer,* Philosophico-Scientific Problems. Out of print.

Volume Four—*Cajetan's,* The Analogy of Names and The Concept of Being. Pp. X and 93. Second edition. Price: $2.25, cloth.

Volume Five—*Louis de Raeymaeker and others,* Truth and Freedom. Pp. VII and 132. Second impression. Price: $3.00, cloth. Published also in French.

Volume Six—*P. Henry van Laer,* The Philosophy of Science. Part One: Science in General. Pp. XVII and 164. Price: cloth $3.75.

Volume Seven—*Stephan Strasser,* The Soul in Metaphysical and Empirical Psychology. Pp. X and 275. Second impression. Price: cloth $6.00. Published also in German, Dutch, and French.

Volume Eight—*Albert Dondeyne,* Contemporary European Thought and Christian Faith. Pp. XI and 211. Price: paper $5.00, cloth $5.75. Published also in French.

Volume Nine—*Maxwell J. Charlesworth,* Philosophy and Linguistic Analysis. Pp. XIII and 234. Second impression. Price: paper $4.75, cloth $5.50.

Volume Ten—*Remy C. Kwant,* Philosophy of Labor. Pp. XI and 163. Price: paper $4.50, cloth $5.25.

Library of Congress Catalog Card Number: 56-14599

All rights reserved
©1962, by Duquesne University
Printed in the United States of America by
The Ad Press, Ltd., New York, N. Y.

63391

Volume Eleven—*Remy C. Kwant,* ENCOUNTER. Pp. VIII and 85. Price: cloth $3.25. Published also in Dutch.

Volume Twelve—*William A. Luijpen,* EXISTENTIAL PHENOMENOLOGY. Pp. XIII and 355. Second impression. Price: paper $6.00, cloth $6.75. Published also in Dutch.

Volume Thirteen—*Andrew G. van Melsen,* SCIENCE AND TECHNOLOGY. Pp. X and 373. Price: paper $6.20, cloth $6.95. Published also in Dutch.

Volume Fourteen—*P. Henry van Laer,* THE PHILOSOPHY OF SCIENCE. Part Two: A STUDY OF THE DIVISION AND NATURE OF VARIOUS GROUPS OF SCIENCES. Pp. XIII and 342. Price: paper $5.75, cloth $6.50.

Other series of Duquesne Studies:

Philological Series

Spiritan Series

Annuale Mediaevale

Psychological Series (in preparation)

Theological Series (in preparation)

Periodicals published by Duquesne University Press:

Duquesne Science Counselor

Duquesne Hispanic Review

Duquesne Review. A Journal of the Social Sciences

Review of Existential Psychology and Psychiatry

TABLE OF CONTENTS

vii

PREFACE

When in 1956 the first part of the PHILOSOPHY OF SCIENCE appeared under the subtitle, *Science in General,* we announced that we were preparing the second part, to be called, *A Study of the Division and Nature of Various Groups of Sciences.* All kinds of circumstances caused this preparation to last much longer than we had expected and hoped for. One of the main reasons for the delay was the fact that, to be even somewhat complete, the second part would have to become much longer than we had originally planned. Even as it is, the book, which we are now happy to present to the reader, does not offer much more than a brief survey of the subject matter.

The two parts of the work constitute a single whole, and for this reason we are justifiably entitled to refer to the first part in appropriate circumstances. Nevertheless, the second part has been set up in such a way that it can be used separately without giving rise to great inconveniences. It is our hope that the book will, as the phrase goes, fill a vacancy and that it will receive the same benevolent reception as the first part.

We may use this opportunity to express once more our heartfelt gratitude to the Reverend Henry J. Koren, C.S.Sp., S.T.D., Professor of Philosophy at Duquesne University. His pertinent remarks have caused us to modify many points and to add supplementary considerations. He has taken care of translating the text into English and adapting it, wherever necessary, to the needs of the English-speaking world. Moreover, most of the work involved in preparing the text for printing and publication has fallen upon his shoulders. Despite his gratefully accepted help, however, the responsibility for the content of this book remains entirely our own.

Finally we would like to express our sincere gratitude to our colleague, Dr. Ferdinand L. R. Sassen, Professor of Philosophy at the University of Leyden, for his continuous and stimulating interest in the preparation of this book and for his many valuable remarks and critical observations, especially with respect to the chapters which we submitted to his authoritative scrutiny.

P. HENRY VAN LAER, D.Sc.
Professor at the State University of
Leyden, Netherlands

GENERAL INTRODUCTION

Title and Content of this Book. As in the general introduction to Part One, we want to make a few remarks here about the main title of the book, THE PHILOSOPHY OF SCIENCE. For such a title can easily be misunderstood and lead to expectations which will not be fulfilled.

First of all, the term 'science' is not limited here to mathematics and physical science, as is so often the case in French and English writings. 'Science' is used here in the broad sense, a sense which was generally attributed to it in former centuries and which we have indicated in the second chapter of Part One. It applies therefore also to philosophy and theology. A simple glance at the table of content will suffice to give the reader an idea of the broad scope assigned to the term 'science' in this work.

Secondly, the combination of the terms 'philosophy' and 'science' into 'philosophy of science' may easily give rise to misunderstanding, because nowadays this expression is often understood in a narrower sense, not only because, as we have just said, a restricted realm is assigned to 'science', but also because of the divergences of views that exist regarding the nature and task of philosophy. Recent publications, for example, often limit the use of the expression 'philosophy of science' to treatises concerned with the examination of the foundations and structure of the sciences or to the analysis of scientific language. Although the great value of such studies cannot be denied and there is some reason for calling these studies 'philosophy of science', it remains regrettable that the underlying conception of 'philosophy' usually leads to the neglect of important aspects of the sciences and even to the disregard of entire groups of sciences.

It is very deliberately that in this book we devote our attention to philosophical consideration in a more traditional sense, because in our opinion—which is shared by many—there still is a great need for such a study of the sciences. Perhaps this need is even greater now than ever before. As the subtitle indicates, the general subject matter of this philosophical reflection is concerned with the division of the sciences into various groups and with the proper character of these groups. The table of contents and the perusal of the book will show the reader what kind of subjects and aspects we have considered in this context. Our considerations often allow us to rely upon what we have said in Part One about 'science' in general and about the characteristics which, in an analogous sense, pertain to all sciences.

There are many subjects which could be considered under the broad title of 'philosophy of science', but which in this book are not considered at all or only in a passing way. To name a few examples, the relationship of science and society, the psychology of the scientist, the responsibility of the man of research with respect to the practical application of his discoveries, subjectivity and objectivity in the pursuit of science, and the analysis of scientific language. All these subjects, however, have been treated extensively in numerous publications.

As will be explained more fully in Chapter One, the reflection upon the totality of the sciences offered here is woefully neglected and often even despised; yet such a reflection is desirable and necessary if one is to attain to the maturity of judgment that is required to avoid one-sidedness in the pursuit of science and to remain open without prejudice for all aspects presented by scientific material. Moreover, the reader with philosophical interest will be enabled to attain to a more profound understanding of the phenomenon 'science' and its various forms and thus be lead to a more complete outlook upon the totality of scientific endeavor. In this way he may reach also a greater knowledge of man himself, who appears endowed with so many intellectual potentialities, and who through his cognitive contact with the richly varied wealth of reality is able to discover and realize his potentialities in so many different fashions. Thus, we hope, the book will be able to make a contribution also to a better knowledge of the 'microcosmos' which man is.

Remarks About the Way of Considering the Subject Matter. In the writing of this second part it became soon evident that extensive treatment of the subject matter would make the book grow beyond permissible limits. For this reason there were all kinds of restrictions both in the choice of topics and in the length of their consideration. As a rule, such restrictions are explicitly indicated and accompanied by indications of the direction in which the topics can be complemented. I hope that this will encourage the reader to further personal work. Accordingly, this book should be viewed as an introduction rather than as an exhaustive study of the philosophy of the sciences. It goes without saying that the writing of such an introduction is much more difficult than that of a complete study which has a more restricted scope. There are constantly all kinds of difficult decisions to be made about the inclusion or exclusion of topics—decisions which will easily deviate from the views and desires of the readers. Many will not find here what they are looking for, while what they find appears to them too elaborate or even wholly superfluous. There is no way in which this difficulty can be overcome.

Moreover, the character of this book, which in a relatively brief space had to compress many things, offers a certain danger of superficiality and lack of sufficient differentiation, which may dissatisfy specialists in certain areas and lead them to critical remarks. The risk of such a critique cannot be avoided. There are many ways in which the subject can be treated, but each of them has its own particular objections. The main point is that the accepted plan be as rigorously as possible adhered to.

We hope that this book may prove its usefulness both as a text for philosophical instruction in the present subject matter, e.g., in a college or university course, and as a guide in independent study. We flatter ourselves with the thought that perhaps even professional philosophers may discover something of value in it.

References. The content of this work has grown little by little over the course of years, mainly in connection with courses given at the university. Part of it owes its origin to the reading of books and articles concerning the subject matter, but most of it ripened under the influence of our own thinking. When such a process of slow growth and maturing is involved, it is not always possible later to indicate exactly what has been derived from one's own reflection and what has been borrowed from others, for all of it has become the personal indivisible thought of the writer. Wherever possible, however, we have endeavored to indicate the publications of which we have made use. We will name here especially two because, years ago, they gave rise to our interest in this branch of philosophy—namely, J. Hoogveld, *Inleiding tot de Wijsbegeerte*, revised by F. Sassen, vol. I, 4th ed., Utrecht-Nijmegen, 1947, vol. II, 2nd ed., *ibid.*, 1949; and Erich Becher, *Geisteswissenschaften und Naturwissenschaften*, München, 1921.

For practical reasons we abstain from appending a bibliography for the use of readers interested in further study. Although the importance of such a list cannot be denied, it appeared impossible to us to assemble a bibliography which would be justified in all respects. It is at present hardly possible to be well-informed about all publications that appear throughout the world even in a limited realm of science. Thus attempting a bibliography could very easily lead to the enumeration of less valuable works and the omission of important books or articles. Moreover, with the appearance of this work in English there would be no point in mentioning, e.g., books in Dutch. We think, however, that the reader whose interest is aroused through this book and who wants to secure further information about any of the topics treated in it will have little difficulty in finding the necessary literature in the language or languages he knows. We trust therefore that he will not be unduly disturbed by the omission of a bibliography.

CHAPTER ONE

THE IMPORTANCE OF A GOOD DIVISION OF THE SCIENCES

On considering the divisions of the sciences that were proposed in the past—some examples will be given in the next chapter—or the more or less successful attempted divisions of our time, many will ask themselves whether all this trouble is really necessary. Is it so important to classify the sciences or to divide them according to their mutual resemblances or differences? Is such a division not merely a peculiar hobby of some queer minds which, undeterred by the total uselessness of their labor, persist in doing a work that can offer a measure of satisfaction only to themselves? Is it not sufficient to dominate the realm of one's own science without meddling in others? These and similar questions can be raised and de facto sometimes are raised. For this reason it will be useful to devote an introductory chapter to the importance of division in general (Section I) and that of the sciences in particular (Section II).

I. The Importance of Division in General

A Good Division Has Practical Use. First of all, a division of the objects contained in a given realm is desirable from the purely practical point of view. It makes it possible to survey the realm which otherwise would be chaotic because of the manifold diversity of the objects it contains. Such a division can be made by grouping similar objects of the same kind together and separating them from groups of a different kind. A contractor, for instance, will not stack the necessary building materials in a disorderly way, because otherwise it would be impossible to survey the available material and it would take too much time to find a particular item as it is required. In a similar way, it will be impossible to study a science without a suitable arrangement of the subject matter. The impossibility of surveying the disordered material would make it very difficult or even impossible to achieve any scientific results. Without an orderly disposition of the subject matter, one could not even write a scientific book or a systematic encyclopedia.

5

A Good Division Facilitates the Understanding of the Subject Matter. The above-mentioned practical motive is by no means the most important reason for making a correct division, especially when the man of science or the philosopher is concerned. A more important reason is that every effort to come to a suitable division increases the understanding of the realm in question, because it forces the intellect to take into consideration the relevance or irrelevance of certain observed characteristics. The study of this relevancy will reveal, first of all, whether these characteristics possess an internal necessity or are merely contingent, i.e., whether they are determined by the specific nature of the object or by its individual structure. Next, it will become clear whether a division according to a given principle is reasonable or not—reasonable, in the sense that it terminates in groups which also in other important respects constitute a clearly distinct whole; unreasonable, if such a division produces an unsatisfactory result because, for instance, some objects cannot be assigned to any of the groups or perhaps have to be placed in more than one. Moreover, in general, a division will have to be rejected as useless if in a queer way it runs across other divisions that are based upon different but important criteria.

Examples. To clarify the matter, let us give a few examples. A first instance of an unsuitable division was Linnaeus' classification of plants based on the number of stamina and the structure of the pistils of flowers. Although such a criterion could be useful in helping lovers of nature determine the kind of plant they were looking at, it was unsuitable for scientific purposes, because some plants have no stamina and pistils or possess a variable number of stamina. Moreover, the division did not run parallel with the classification of plants by other important characteristics. For this reason modern botanists base their divisions more on the total organic structure of plants (incidentally, this method also offers many difficulties).

Another example may be taken from mineralogy. Minerals have been classified by color. But a more essential division takes its principle from their chemical composition or crystalline structure, which cross the division by color in a strange way. Obviously, the classification by structure or composition presupposes a more profound knowledge of minerals.

An example of divisions that cross one another is provided by the classification of animals. If they are grouped together according to their anatomic structure, the division results in classes that differ considerably from those that are based on physiological criteria, such as their method of breathing or assimilating food, the presence or absence of the capacity to fabricate their own albumen. In such a case the question has to be asked which of the two divisions deserves scientific preference.

The preceding considerations should make it clear that a good division can be useful for obtaining a better understanding of the scientific subject matter covered by it. Every effort to arrive at a division presupposes a certain amount of knowledge regarding the realm in which it applies. This understanding grows together with the attempt to divide, whether this attempt succeeds or not. At first, as in the above-mentioned examples, one will begin to work with a division by clear sense perceptible characteristics, without knowing whether they are relevant or not for the nature of the objects. As the investigation makes progress, understanding grows and slowly one arrives at a more 'natural' division, i.e., one that is based on distinctions in the nature or essence of the objects. A division which satisfies this demand will be permanently useful not only from a purely scientific standpoint but also for didactic purposes.

II. The Importance of a Good Division of the Sciences

Evidently, what has been said about the usefulness of division in general applies also to that of the sciences and to the subsequent consideration of the various groups resulting from the classification of the sciences.

Practical Importance. A rational division of the sciences is desirable or even necessary for practical reasons—namely, to make possible a comprehensive view of the whole of the sciences. Such a view, obtained by grouping together related and connected branches of learning will be necessary, for instance, for the editing of a systematic encyclopedia of the sciences, the arrangement of a library, and more even for the purposive organization and functioning of an institute of higher learning. For universities, it is a matter of sheer necessity to make a rational division by types of study, each of which contains a number of connected sciences, taught in distinct 'schools' or 'departments'.

Theoretical Value for the Philosophy of Science. More important than its practical usefulness is the theoretical value which a rational division of the sciences has for any philosopher of science. Every time a responsible attempt is made to arrive at a division, we are aided in obtaining a better understanding of the phenomenon 'science' as such, the totality of all sciences, and the special characters of the various groups. And a successful classification—one that is really based on essential characteristics—will be of permanent value for the philosophers of science.

Importance for the Specialized Man of Science. Hardly anyone will deny the preceding points. But there is still another urgent reason of a theoretico-practical nature which is not so readily seen and therefore deserves to be considered somewhat more extensively. This reason concerns the specialists in a particular branch of learning. In our opinion, it is very useful and even necessary for them to have some understanding of the sciences in their totality and their mutual differences. Otherwise these specialists are in danger of being hampered by a narrowness of outlook which could become fatal with respect to both their scientific orientation and often also their attitude as human beings. Although this point will become clearer when we shall consider the physical and moral sciences more in detail, even at this stage a few remarks on the question should not be out of order.

Ever since the special sciences have broken their ties with philosophy, and more still since through progressive specialization the realm that one cultivates and dominates has constantly shrunk, the specialist is tempted to make his own particular science the absolute norm for all the others. He is in danger of looking at the whole of the sciences in a very one-sided way, applying to it the view point that is proper only to the limited particular realm of science which he himself dominates and studies. In modern times, from being a temptation, this danger has progressed more and more to becoming a reality in large groups of specialists, notably in the realm of the physical sciences. We consider this phenomenon so dangerous both for the healthy study of the sciences and for the general outlook on facts and events that we cannot omit to draw attention to it here by means of a few examples.

Examples. The striking results reached by the physical sciences in the past century and more even in our own times have given rise to a feeling of superiority in many of their students. This feeling finds expression in the conviction that, strictly speaking, physical science is the only true science, and that its methods alone can lead to indisputable results. Traditional philosophy is simply brushed aside, because its conclusions cannot at all be verified by the methods of physical science. The sciences of experience which consider man and his culture are thus held to be scientific only insofar as they are capable of proceeding according to the methods of the physical sciences. The difference in character that still sets the sciences of man apart from the others is often attributed to their relatively recent origin—briefly, to inevitable childhood diseases. Utterances of this kind are usually accompanied by the expectation and prediction that these sciences will gradually acquire more and more the character proper to the physical sciences.

Although even in the past there were some efforts to treat such sciences as linguistics and history by physical methods, it is especially in the last few decades that these views have been cultivated under the aegis of certain positivistic philosophical trends. The aim of these trends is to promote a 'unity of science' and to seek it, of course, in a unification patterned on the physical sciences. But such an attitude is an illegitimate usurpation, perpetrated in the name of the physical sciences, which misjudges the proper value and character of the other disciplines. By assuming such an attitude, the man of research will not allow the typically proper features of the human object of his study to assert themselves. He will make, for example, a study of human activities and human language, but use methods that are wholly inadequate to lay hold on the typically human element. Such a procedure necessarily mutilates the object studied, for certain aspects of it are deliberately left out of consideration, so that the object can no longer be seized in its totality. This one-sided attitude usually results from a conscious or unconscious philosophical frame of mind which wants to eliminate as undesirable or harmful certain aspects of reality, such as the typically human feature that reveals itself in intellectual and free activities. In this way they are led to view human events as fully determined processes which obey fixed laws, so that nothing can be done about their outcome. Such a world view leads logically to a kind of materialism, whether of a dialectical nature or of a different kind.

Moreover, the above-mentioned narrowness of vision easily leads to the alarmingly arrogant mentality which causes some men of science to consider that their own area of study is wholly autonomous and does not permit 'outsiders' to interfere in the least. Any critique coming from them is simply brushed aside as irrelevant. Such a mental attitude is always unreasonable, for it is quite possible that the specialists of other sciences, e.g., of philosophy, have retained a broader view and thus are able to see the mutual connection and relative subordination of the different sciences. For example, misled by the similarity of body structures and functions of man and animal, a biologist may easily conclude to a complete likeness and overlook the essential differences, despite the fact that the psychologist and the philosophical anthropologist will sound a warning based on their more complete view of man.

Where man himself is chosen as the object of study, the scientist should assume a frame of mind which is in accord with the unique value of the human person and accept the limitations that are demanded by the dignity of man. If the experimentalist personally lacks the necessary understanding of these points, he should refer to the judgment of other men of science who are capable of judging the ethical issues involved. Anyone who is acquainted with biological and medical literature knows how often such experiments trespass the limits imposed by ethics. These transgressions arise from the defective vision of the over-specialized scientist or from a kind of professional pride which on the basis of the autonomy attributed to one's own science does not brook any 'outside interference'.

Apart from these consequences, the too one-sided scientific vision has also the result that the specialists in different branches become strangers to one another because they see one another with a lack of understanding and with distrust and therefore prefer to lock themselves up in their ivory tower where they can continue their hobby without being disturbed by the irrelevant interference of others.

For all these and other reasons which will be considered in the course of this study, it is beneficial for every man of science to survey the whole realm of all the sciences, to endeavor to learn the proper nature and character of the various areas, and to realize that the nature and limits of a certain group of sciences do not always have to be arbitrary and changeable, but may be determined from within by the very character of the sciences contained in such a group. To obtain this understanding, it is necessary to study the proper nature of various groups of sciences, how they differ by foundation, object, degree of abstraction, inner purpose, methods, etc., so as to arrive at a purposive division and a well-founded synthesis of the sciences. The understanding reached in this way will broaden the view and prevent too much one-sidedness. It will become apparent then that, for instance, physical science occupies only a very modest place in the totality of all sciences—whence it would be foolish to reserve the term 'science' for it alone and to consider that only the methods of this science deserve to be called 'scientific'.

Further Division of this Book. As was indicated in the general Introduction, the purpose of this book is to explain, insofar as this is possible within the limitation of a single book, some divisions of the sciences that in our opinion are well-founded and to examine the typical characteristics of the various groups of sciences which arise from these divisions. However, before undertaking this explanation, we will first devote a chapter to survey without much commentary a number of divisions proposed by philosophers of the past. Apart from its historical value, such a survey has the advantage of offering a first orientation in the problems of division and the possible criteria that can be used for such a purpose. In the subsequent chapter we will begin the philosophical study of the division of the sciences with an explanation of the norms and criteria to be used in a satisfactory division. The remaining chapters will be dedicated to some of the important divisions of the sciences and a consideration of the character proper to the different groups resulting from these divisions.

CHAPTER TWO

HISTORICAL SURVEY OF SOME IMPORTANT DIVISIONS OF THE SCIENCES

It appears that from the very moment when man began to apply himself to science he realized how important it was for his theories to possess a good division of the scientific realm. At least, attempts to make such divisions may be found in the first centuries of Western philosophy and science, for instance, in the works of Plato and Aristotle. We will record here some divisions of the sciences proposed by philosophers of the past which show how they viewed this question and what principles they followed in their divisions.

Although some of the proposed divisions retain only historical interest, others still possess actual significance for our times. So far as Greek antiquity and the Middle Ages are concerned, it may be noted that there is usually question of dividing 'philosophy'. One should keep in mind here that for the men of science and the philosophers of these periods there was no difference between philosophy and specialized sciences in the modern sense of the term. They used the word 'philosophy' to indicate the totality of human knowledge.

We may conveniently present the main historical divisions in four groups, adding here and there a brief word of explanation.[1]

I. THE DIVISIONS OF PLATO AND ARISTOTLE

Western philosophy and science originated in pre-Christian times among the Greeks. The main personalities of this period who exercised an inestimable influence on the subsequent development of philosophy were Plato and Aristotle. For both, the term 'philosophy' indicated the highest knowledge of the divinity, of man and the cosmos. The heterogeneous nature of this knowledge led them spontaneously to the making of distinctions and the defining of areas to which they assigned special names. In this way the first division of 'philosophy' came into existence.

---

[1]Apart from the works quoted in the footnotes of this chapter, we have made use of E. Becher, *Geisteswissenschaften und Naturwissenschaften*, Leipzig-Muenchen, 1921; J. Hoogveld-F. Sassen, *Inleiding tot de Wijsbegeerte*, vol. I, 4th ed., Utrecht-Nijmegen, 1947; Wilhelm Wundt, *Einleitung in die Philosophie*, Leipzig, 1901, pp. 40-85.

Plato (427-347 B.C.)

The first man who deserves to be named here is Plato. However, the division of 'philosophy' usually attributed to him was proposed by his disciple Xenocrates.[2] This scholar divided Plato's philosophy into dialectics, physics, and ethics. The term 'dialectics' indicated the whole theory of ideas with all its implications; hence it comprised almost as much as is conveyed by the modern usage of the terms metaphysics, epistemology, logic, and even theodicy. 'Physics' covered the areas that in modern terminology are called philosophy of nature, philosophical anthropology, and physical science. 'Ethics' implied not only the general theory of morality, but also social and political philosophy.

Undoubtedly, Xenocrates' division is in harmony with Plato's philosophical thought. It is related with his doctrine regarding the tripartite distinction of man's mental capacities, viz., intellectual knowledge, sense perception, which puts us into contact with the objects of nature, and man's appetitive power that is the source of human action. With these three capacities correspond dialectics, physics, and ethics. However, these sciences do not occupy positions of equality. Just as intellectual knowledge pervades the other two powers and illuminates their activities, so also dialectics cannot be dispensed with by physics and ethics. Thus in a sense these two sciences are subordinated to dialectics.

Surprisingly enough, no special place was assigned to the special sciences that existed already in Plato's time, such as astronomy and especially mathematics, to which the Platonic Academy attached a very great importance. Probably the reason is that the object of astronomy was considered to belong to the cosmos and, according to Plato, the cosmos itself had a mathematical structure. Thus his physics, which occupied itself with general cosmological questions, contained in a general way also astronomy and mathematics.

The Platonic tripartite division recurred repeatedly in subsequent centuries, although the distinction was not always made in the same way and the same terms did not always carry the same meaning. We may cite here, e.g., Albert the Great (cf. p. 18) and Leibniz (1646-1716), who divided the realm of science into "three great provinces", viz., physics, moral science, and logic.

---

[2]Cf. F. Sassen, *Geschiedenis van de wijsbegeerte der Grieken en Romeinen*, Antwerp-Nijmegen, 4th ed., 1949, pp. 57 f.

Aristotle (384-322 B. C.)

The second Greek philosopher who made an important contribution to the division of 'philosophy' was Aristotle. Although he did not propose a systematically developed division of the sciences, there are several places in his works where he makes valuable remarks about this classification and formulates principles that can serve as the basis of such a division. He accepted Plato's distinction of man's mental capacities, but alongside it he paid attention to the various purposes at which man's thinking may aim. Thus in his *Metaphysics* he says that "all thought is either practical or productive or theoretical".[3] And in *Topics*: "This [epistēmē] is classed as speculative, practical, and productive; and each of these denotes a relation, for it speculates upon something, and produces something, and does something".[4] The threefold orientation of the intellect and the character of knowledge are the basis for a tripartite division of the sciences into *practical, poietic* and *theoretical*. Elsewhere in his works Aristotle distinguishes only two groups of sciences, viz., theoretical and practical.[5] Apparently, he combines here practical and poietic knowledge into a single group. As we will see later in Chapter IV, such a combination is fully justifiable.

The *theoretical thinking* that gives rise to the theoretical sciences has as its object a kind of being which can be of a threefold nature and thus give rise to three different sciences or theoretical 'philosophies' —*physics, mathematics,* and *theology.*[6] According to Aristotle, this division is based on a difference in the nature of the object. "For physics deals with things which exist separately but are not immovable, and some parts of mathematics deal with things which are immovable but presumably do not exist separately, but as embodied in matter; while the first science [i.e. metaphysics] deals with things which both exist separately and are immovable".[7] There is, moreover, as Aristotle

---

[3] *Metaphysica,* E, 1; 1025b 25. Here and elsewhere we quote the text of W. D. Ross, *The Works of Aristotle Translated into English.*

[4] *Topica,* VI, 6; 145a 15.

[5] *Topica,* VII, 1; 152b 4.

[6] *Metaphysica,* E, 1; 1026a, 18-21. The term 'metaphysics' instead of 'theology' is post-Aristotelian. It owes its origin to Andronicus of Rhodes (c. 70 B.C.). This scholar joined Aristotle's works concerning the subject in question together and placed them after the books about physics (*meta ta physica*). In this way 'metaphysics' became the accepted term for what Aristotle himself had called 'first science' or 'theology', for "if the divine is present anywhere, it is present in things of this sort".

[7] *Metaphysica,* E, 1; 1026a, 13-17.

indicates elsewhere, in the object of these sciences a difference in degree of abstraction, but it was only in the Middle Ages that the particulars of this difference were worked out.

As should be clear from these considerations, for Aristotle, theoretical thought comprised the dialectics and physics of Plato's division, and mathematics is given a special place.

Practical thought is directed toward regulating man's acts of will, his doings (*prattein*), and gives rise to the ethical sciences. *Poietic* or *productive thinking,* on the other hand, aims at arranging man's transitive activity and finds its completion in the creating or making (*poiein*) of a concrete technical or artistic object. The disciplines that are concerned with this realm may be called poietic sciences. Accordingly, Aristotle's practical and poietic sciences have a broader scope than Plato's ethics.

Aristotle's division of the sciences into theoretical, practical, and poietic is very much in accord with reason, for it is based on the threefold character of man's thought. The subdivision also of the theoretical sciences into physics, mathematics, and metaphysics has a solid foundation, as we have seen in Chapter III of Part One. Later, in Chapter IV, we will return to this division in more detail and make it the basis of more extensive considerations.

II. A FEW MEDIEVAL DIVISIONS

Passing over the next fourteen centuries, which did not make any important contribution to the question under consideration, we find ourselves well advanced into the Middle Ages. Although at this time philosophy was still considered as the all-embracing science, mathematics and some of the sciences that deal directly with the data of experience had gradually undergone some growth and development. As a result, they had come to acquire a measure of autonomy. Thus a division of the realms of learning could no longer be satisfied with subdividing philosophy, but had to pay attention also to these more or less independent sciences. As will appear from the examples to be quoted, this is exactly what happened. Nevertheless, the medievals tried to hold fast to the Platonic and Aristotelian divisions and nomenclatures.

Hugo of St. Victor (1096-1141)

The first man to be named here in chronological order is Hugo, the principal scholar of the Abbey of St. Victor. In his *Didascalion*[8] he proposed a division which was related to that of Aristotle. He distinguished 'philosophy', which for him also still comprised the totality of all sciences, into the following groups: 1) *'theoretica'* or 'speculativa', containing 'theology' (i.e., metaphysics), mathematics and physics; 2) *'practica'*, also called 'activa', 'ethica' or 'moralis', whose object was the *opus internum,* the acts of will; 3) *'mechanica'*, which was concerned with the *opus externum,* the *humana opera* or objects of man's transitive activity and corresponded with Aristotle's poietic sciences. These three groups gave rise to several subdivisions.

Logic was added as a fourth group by Hugo, contrary to Aristotle. He divided it into 'grammatica', 'dialectica' and 'rhetorica'. Aristotle did not have this group because he did not include logic in philosophy but considered it merely a propaedeutic study.

Dominicus Gundisalinus (c. 1170)

Another scholar who deserves to be named here is Dominicus Gundisalinus (Gundisalvi), whose book *De divisione philosophiae*[9] was dedicated to the division of the sciences. An important point is that he began to make a distinction between *'sciencia divina'* and *'sciencia humana'*. 'Divine science' had as its object whatever God has revealed, as the Old and the New Testament. It is called 'sciencia divina' after its most noble part, viz., the one concerned with the existence and nature of God. Sometimes this science is called 'philosophia prima' and 'causa causarum' because it is the science of God as the first cause of everything. It is known also as 'metaphysica', as 'post physicam', because it is concerned with what lies 'beyond nature'.

'Human science' extends to everything which can be discovered by means of man's reason, such as the so-called *'artes liberales'*. Some of these 'artes' belong to *'eloquencia'*; for instance, 'grammatica', 'poetica' and 'rhetorica', which are strongly propaedeutic. Others pertain to *'sapiencia*—namely, those which illuminate the human mind

---

[8]*Hugonis de Sancto Victore Didascalion.* A Critical Text. Edited by Charles Henry Buttimer, The Catholic University of America Press, Washington, 1939.
[9]Edited by Ludwig Baur in *Beiträge zur Geschichte der Philosophie des Mittelalters,* Münster, 1903.

to know the truth or lead man to love the good. There is no science which is not a part of philosophy. According to Gundisalvi, logic is both a part of philosophy and its instrument.

The author divides philosophy into *'philosophia theoretica'*, which makes us understand intelligible things, and *'philosophia practica'*, which makes us know what we have to do. With a reference to Boethius and Aristotle, Gundisalvi splits theoretical philosophy into 1) 'sciencia phisica' sive 'naturalis', 2) 'sciencia mathematica', and 3) 'theologia' sive 'sciencia prima' sive 'philosophia prima' sive 'metaphysica'. The first two are, of course, subdivided into different groups. Practical philosophy is divided into 1) 'politica sciencia', which establishes the correct norms guiding the interrelationship of all human beings, the governance of the state, and the knowledge of civil rights; 2) the science of the correct order in one's own home and family; and 3) 'ethica' or 'moralis', which teaches man to adapt his way of life to the dignity of his soul.

Albert the Great (1206-1280)

This scholar divided his treatises in a way corresponding with the distinction into three groups—namely, 1) logical sciences, 2) philosophy, which contained the physical sciences, mathematics, and metaphysics, 3) moral sciences. His division recalls Xenocrates' partition of Plato's philosophy. However, its first two groups do not coincide with those of Xenocrates for, as explained above, Plato's dialectics contained much more than the logical sciences and, on the other hand, the physics of the Platonic system are only partially equivalent to Albert's second group. It is with Aristotle's subdivision of the theoretical sciences that Albert the Great's subdivision of the second group coincides.

Thomas Aquinas (1225-1274)

In his commentaries on Aristotle and also in other works Albert's disciple Thomas Aquinas adhered to the Aristotelian division into theoretical or speculative and practical or operative sciences. The latter included the poietic disciplines. Thomas took over also the division of the theoretical sciences into metaphysics, mathematics, and physics. He devoted extensive considerations to this distinction in his commentaries on Boethius' treatise *De Trinitate*. However, we will not dwell on it here to any extent, for these divisions have already been touched upon in Part I, Chapter III, and will again be the object of our attention in Chapter IV.

III. Francis Bacon's Division

According as the special sciences continued to develop and new ones came into existence for which the earlier classifications had made no provisions, the scholars of the time slowly began to see that the traditional framework of 'philosophy' was too narrow to embrace all sciences. They could no longer limit themselves to a division of 'philosophy', but had to search for a rational division of the 'sciences' in which philosophy would assume a position alongside the other sciences, but in a privileged place.

As an example of such a division we may quote here the one proposed by Francis Bacon (1561-1626) in his book *De dignitate et augmentis scientiarum,* 1623.[10]

General Division. First of all, Bacon distinguishes the sciences acquired by man's natural capacities (*doctrina humana*) from sciences based on the data of Revelation (*doctrina theologica* or *theologia inspirata seu sacra*).

As the dividing principle of these two main groups he uses the three powers of the soul called memory (*memoria*), imagination (*phantasia*) and reason (*ratio*). Although these three always function together, the degree in which they share in the common work varies. According as the activities of one predominate, they give rise to a new group of sciences. Thus the *doctrina humana* is subdivided into history (*historia*), poetry (*poesis*), and philosophy (*philosophia*).

History, which is subdivided into history of nature (*historia naturalis*) and history of man (*historia civilis*), is concerned primarily with individual things that can be circumscribed by place and time. If the history of nature often seems to speak about species, the reason is that individuals of the same species resemble one another so closely. However, if there are individuals that are unique in their species, such as the sun and the moon, their description belongs just as much to the history of nature as that of individual human beings finds its proper place in the history of man.

Poetry, by which Bacon means the representation of imagined objects and the science of fables and myths, also is concerned with individual things. However, contrary to what happens in history, these individuals arise in an arbitrary way, as can be clearly seen, for instance, in the art of painting.

---

[10]The edition we have made use of is that of Leyden, 1645.

Philosophy leaves aside the individual and has as its object the general concepts that are abstracted from the individual. Here we are in the domain of reason. It studies the abstract objects and joins òr separates the concepts in a judgment in accord with the law of nature or the demands of evidence.

Bacon admits that a similar tripartition can be made in theology: it consists of sacred history, parables that play the role of poetry, and precepts and dogmas which constitute, as it were, an eternal philosophy.

Main Subdivisions. After this general division, Bacon devotes many chapters to numerous subdivisions of the above-mentioned main sciences.

History is distinguished into the history of man (*historia civilis*) and the history of nature (*historia naturalis*). Man's history is sub-divided into political, ecclesiastical, and literary history, each of which gives rise to new branches. The history of nature likewise permits subdivisions.

Philosophy is divided by its triple object, God, nature, and man, into a philosophy of God (*doctrina de Numine*), of nature (*doctrina de natura* or *philosophia naturalis*), and of man (*doctrina de homine*). Moreover, this division refers to different modes of knowing. Nature is known directly (*radio directo*), God indirectly through an inade-quate medium (*radio refracto*), and man makes himself known to himself (*radio reflexo*).

These three branches of philosophy have a common trunk indi-cated by the term 'first philosophy' or 'wisdom' (*prima philosophia* or *sapientia*). It functions as the science of the principles that do not properly belong to a single science but serve as the foundation of several. In addition, it investigates transcendental concepts such as many, few, similar, dissimilar, possible, impossible, being, non-being etc.

Each of the three branches is subdivided in various ways. Because it would lead us too far afield to mention them all, we will restrict ourselves to a few.

Philosophy of Nature. Bacon subdivides the philosophy of nature into a speculative part (*speculativa*) which investigates causes, and an operative part (*operativa*) which is concerned with effects. The former ascends from experience to principles (*ascensoria: ab expe-*

rientia ad axiomata), the latter descends from principles to new discoveries *(descensoria: ab axiomatibus ad nova inventa)*. Speculative philosophy of nature is subdivided again into special physics *(physica specialis)*, which investigates efficient and material causes, and metaphysics, which searches for final and formal causes. (Bacon tries to justify this unusual meaning of the term 'metaphysics'). Physics itself is subdivided into the sciences of the concrete *(doctrina de concreto)* and of the abstract *(doctrina de abstracto* or *de natura)*. In a similar way the various parts of the philosophy of nature undergo numerous subdivisions.

Mathematics. In a special chapter Bacon considers the place of mathematics. He views it as an auxiliary science for both the speculative and operative parts of the philosophy of nature. Thus it could be placed as a third branch of the philosophy of nature alongside 'physics' and 'metaphysics'. Nevertheless, he prefers to treat mathematics as a part of metaphysics.

Philosophy of Man. The fourth book of Bacon's treatise is dedicated to the philosophy of man. He divides it into the philosophy of human nature *(philosophia humanitatis)* and the philosophy of man as a social being *(philosophia civilis)*. The first of these two is subdivided into the sciences of man's body and of his soul. To prevent losing sight of man's unity through these separate studies of soul and body, he proposes a new science which should be concerned with the nature or proper character of man[11] and consider him as a body-soul unit. As a subdivision of this science he proposes a branch concerning the undivided nature of man *(natura hominis indivisa)*, which he calls the science of man's person *(doctrina de persona hominis)*, and another whose object should be the bond between body and soul *(vinculum ipsum animae et corporis)* and which he describes as the science of the bond *(doctrina de foedere)*.

It would be beyond our scope to reproduce here Bacon's further numerous subdivisions of the philosophy of man. However, we want to mention one, because it shows the place he assigns to logic and ethics. Bacon considers them as two parts of the science that is concerned with the use and objects of the soul's powers, and this science itself he holds to be a branch of the science of man's soul.

---

[11]"Constituamus scientiam generalem de natura et statu hominis." *Op. cit.*, p. 283.

The Importance of Bacon.   Although incomplete, the above-mentioned divisions show sufficiently how much Bacon contributed to the philosophy of science. Very important, for instance, was his distinction between human and theological sciences, preluded by Gundisalvi, and his recognition of the sciences of man alongside the sciences of nature. The last-named division was destined to recur frequently in subsequent centuries, although in modified forms. For the first time all kinds of sciences and branches of learning that in the course of time had gradually become more or less autonomous received an orderly place in the totality of the sciences. The way in which Bacon arranged the divisions and numerous subdivisions—sometimes equipped with appendices—showed unambiguously the penetrating mind and the broad knowledge which this scholar possessed with respect to all the sciences of his time. Many of his divisions have managed to maintain themselves as valuable even in our times.

Nevertheless, Bacon's division is not fully satisfactory in all respects, because it is often inadequate and not sufficiently sharp. Even his main division according to the three fundamental functions of memory, imagination, and reason is open to objection. Since these three powers do not at all operate separately but only in close union, a division that is based on these functions can never become sharp and adequate. Moreover, this criterion here and there results in patent anomalies. Thus, for instance, the 'history of nature', which belongs more properly among the sciences of nature, becomes a partner of the 'history of man', and this history of man itself should have been located under the sciences of man. Occasionally Bacon became the victim of exaggerated hairsplitting, and this resulted in divisions that are too artificial and consequently valueless.

Bacon's distinction of the sciences exercised great influence on those who after him studied the philosophy of science. It may be sufficient to point to the great eighteenth century French *Encyclopédie* edited by d'Alembert and Diderot. In his *Discours préliminaire* d'Alembert (1717-1783) based himself on Bacon's division, although he modified it somewhat and added new divisions, especially for the fine arts. He gave to art, as the product of our imagination, more autonomy with respect to history and philosophy and made these two the main branches of the sciences. In addition, d'Alembert placed both applied and abstract mathematics with the physical sciences because the number and extension considered by mathematics are general properties of bodies.

IV. Some Divisions of the Eighteenth and Nineteenth Centuries

Generally speaking, the preceding divisions were all divisions of philosophy or at least divisions of the sciences in which philosophy, in a proper or in a modified sense, occupied a privileged position. The divisions that follow, on the other hand, are more clearly divisions of the special sciences in the modern sense of the term. Strictly philosophical considerations remain in the background or become a secluded area of study, while the special sciences grow in scope and number, acquire more and more autonomy, and give rise to specialists who devote themselves totally to their development. The term 'science' becomes reserved for these sciences in separation from, and even in opposition to theology and philosophy in the modern more restricted sense of the word. These two are no longer even assigned a place in the scheme of the sciences.

Jeremy Bentham (1748-1832)

Despite the fame of Jeremy Bentham as a jurist and moral philosopher, we may omit the division he proposed in 1829. It is too artificial, because it uses all the time a forced dichotomy. Moreover, it could not exercise much influence, because Bentham's new and strange terminology, which exiled even such terms as mathematics, physics, and chemistry, made it ill-suited for holding the attention of the learned world.

André Marie Ampère (1775-1836)

The French philosopher-scientist André Marie Ampère in his *Essai sur la philosophie des sciences* (1834) offered a division of the sciences into two main groups: 'cosmological' or 'natural sciences' (*sciences cosmologiques ou sciences de la nature*) and 'noological' or 'moral sciences' Bentham (*sciences noologiques ou sciences morales*). In his subdivisions he followed Bentham by stubbornly adhering to dichotomy. By repeating his two-part divisions six times, Ampère arrived at a total of one hundred and twenty-eight special sciences.

However, his main division, which refers only to the sciences of experience, is very reasonable. Roughly speaking, the two main groups coincide with Bacon's sciences of nature and of man—although for Bacon these two were parts of his tripartition of philosophy. We will speak extensively about these two groups in a later chapter. Ampère's subdivisions, on the other hand, are of little value, because his desire to obtain symmetry by means of repeated dichotomies makes them too artificial. As Jolivet remarks: "For the sake of symmetry he opened too many false windows".[12]

Auguste Comte (1798-1857)

Of more influence than the considerations of Bentham and Ampère were the theories of Auguste Comte, the founder of French positivism. His views on the 'positive sciences' may be found in his six volume work entitled *Cours de philosophie positive*.[13]

Before undertaking the division of the sciences, Comte imposes two restrictions on himself. First, he wants to abstain from considering the practical sciences, for they are concerned with the various kinds of human activities and consist *de facto* in the applications of the theoretical, speculative or proper sciences. In these theoretical sciences he then makes a new distinction.

There are two kinds of natural sciences (*sciences naturalles*): abstract and general sciences (*sciences abstraites, générales*), whose object is the discovery of the laws which govern the various kinds of phenomena by considering all conceivable cases; and concrete, particular or descriptive sciences (*sciences concrètes, particulières, descriptives*), sometimes also called natural sciences in the strict sense of the term (*sciences naturelles proprement dites*), which consist in the application of these laws to the actual history of the various existing beings.[14] The first group, therefore, contains the 'fundamental sciences' (*sciences fondamentales*). The other sciences, no matter how valuable they may be, are only of secondary importance in comparison with the first, for they presuppose the study of the first group and, in addition, that of the general laws are valid for every order of phenomena. As examples of the second group Comte cites zoology and botany, which are concerned with the particular kinds of living being and have to rely on the abstract science of general physiology. Another example is mineralogy, which presupposes knowledge of chemistry.

Principle of Division. In his subsequent considerations Comte limits himself to the first group of 'natural philosophy' (*philosophie naturelle*),—viz., 'the abstract, general, fundamental sciences', and

[12]*Traité de philosophie*, vol. I, Lyon-Paris, 1945, p. 175.
[13]Paris, 1830-1842. We quote here the sixth edition, "*identique à la première*", Paris, 1934, vol. I, leçon II.
[14]*Op. cit.*, p. 39.

proceeds to arrange them in an orderly fashion. For his principle of division he does not want to follow Bacon and make use of the distinction flowing from the functions of man's different mental capacities, because these capacities never function separately but only in conjunction. Here Comte agrees with Bentham and Ampère, but he parts company with them when he considers it impossible to arrive at a division by the essential differences of the objects. According to Comte, all these objects are parts of nature—bodies, which agree in their fundamental properties and at most differ accidentally. Moreover, for 'positive philosophy' the essence (*la nature intime*) of things is beyond the reach of man.

Thus Comte has recourse to other criteria in his division of the abstract sciences. His purpose is to arrange the sciences in the order of their natural sequence, according to their mutual dependence, in such a way that one can explain one after the other without being ever forced into the slightest vicious circle. Of course Comte realizes that it will be impossible rigorously to adhere to the ideal of such a linear arrangement. Nevertheless, he thinks that for the six main sciences which are to be ordered it is possible to find among the seven hundred and twenty possible arrangements one that can withstand all critique. This one order must be the order of real dependence of the different sciences and flow from the difference in character of the investigated phenomena. These phenomena can be arranged in groups in such a way that a rational study of one category will be based on the knowledge of the general laws applying in the preceding category, and at the same time itself serve as the foundation for the study of the subsequent group. This order is determined by the degree of simplicity of the phenomena or, and this amounts to the same, by their degree of universality, for it is from this universality that flows the successive dependence of the phenomena and their greater or lesser accessibility to study.

According to this principle, 'inorganic physics' (*physique inorganique*), i.e., the science of lifeless objects, must be placed before 'organic physics' (*physique organique*), which studies the phenomena of living beings, for these phenomena are much more complex and particularized than those of lifeless objects. The same principle of universality and dependence forces us to divide 'inorganic physics' into 'celestial physics' (*physique céleste*) or astronomy, which studies the general phenomena of the universe, and 'terrestrial physics,' (*physique terrestre*), which considers the more particularized terrestrial bodies. The latter are subdivided by the same principle into physics proper and chemistry. Physics necessarily precedes chemistry.

'Organic physics' is concerned with living beings, and these give rise to two essentially different orders of phenomena—namely, those that refer to the individual and others that belong to the species, "especially when this species is sociable". With respect to man above all, this distinction is fundamental. The second category of phenomena is more complex and more particularized than the first. They depend on the first without themselves exercising influence on it. Thus there are two sections in organic physics: physiology, in the strict sense, and 'social physics' or 'sociology' (*physique sociale ou sociologie*). This division is based again on the above-mentioned principle of simplicity. According to Comte, one needs to have a profound knowledge of individual life before being able to make a serious study of social problems.

Comte was the first man to introduce sociology as a special science and he also gave this science its current name. Nevertheless, he seems to have preferred the term 'social physics'. This is easily understood if one keeps in mind that from his philosophical viewpoint every science is a kind of 'physics'. Comte's sociology is a very broad science which studies all phenomena of human society. Its scope extends to a large number of contemporary sciences, such as psychology, economics, history, law, ethics, etc.

The Hierarchy of the Sciences. Summarizing his thought, Comte concludes that 'positive' or 'natural philosophy' is divided into five sciences in the following order: astronomy, physics, chemistry, physiology, and social physics or sociology. This sequence, he says, is determined by a necessary and immutable subordination which, independently of any hypothetical views, is based on a simple comparison of the corresponding phenomena. It is a sequence of decreasing universality, simplicity, and abstraction and therefore of increasing particularization, complexity, and concreteness, but also of increasing interest for man. The excellence of this order is further revealed by several other characteristics:

1. It is the sequence that is spontaneously followed by men of learning who study the various sciences.

2. It is in agreement with the actual order in which these sciences developed.

3. It is the order in which the various sciences decrease in relative perfection, i.e., in degree of precision and greater or lesser interconnection.

4. It is the order to be followed didactically when one aims at a completely rational scientific education.

Mathematics. Till this point Comte's explanations do not mention the most important science—mathematics, but at this juncture he devotes a special study to it. For Comte, mathematics is not so much a constituent part as the fundamental basis of 'natural philosophy'. Yet, it is both at the same time. Mathematics is the most powerful instrument of the human mind in its investigation of the laws that govern the phenomena of nature. Mathematics must be divided into an abstract part, called arithmetic, and a concrete part that itself consists of general geometry and rational mechanics. The concrete part is dependent on abstract arithmetic and itself serves as the foundation of the 'natural philosophy', insofar as it considers all phenomena of the universe according to their geometrical and mechanical properties. In contrast with arithmetic, which is nothing but an extension of logic in a special category of deduction, geometry and mechanics should be considered as true sciences of nature, for just as these sciences they are based on observation. However, because of the extreme simplicity of the phenomena studied by them, geometry and mechanics possess a far greater perfection than the other sciences of nature. Moreover, both are used as a method rather than as a doctrine of direct interest in itself.

According to the principle enunciated above, mathematics should precede the other positive sciences, for the mathematical and mechanical phenomena are the most general, most simple, and most irreducible of all. They are also the most independent and constitute the basis of the others. Thus mathematics is to be given precedence over all other sciences, and therefore the final hierarchy is as follows: mathematics, astronomy, physics, chemistry, physiology, sociology. Later, in 1848, in his *Politique positive,* Comte added anthropology or ethics to the series.

Importance. We have reproduced Comte's ideas about the order of the sciences in a fairly extensive way, because for decades and even at present his views were leading for all who felt attracted to his positivistic philosophy. An additional reason was that many histories of philosophy summarize his ideas so much that they represent them inadequately or incorrectly.

The main criticism against Comte's philosophy of science is its positivistic foundation and especially its total disregard of the essential

difference between man and non-human things. However, his hier-
archization of the sciences itself is open also to many objections from
a purely scientific viewpoint. Their order of mutual dependence
certainly is not as simple as Comte would have us believe. Every
science is a fairly heterogeneous system, and what applies to one
part of a science cannot unqualifiedly be transferred to another part
or to the whole of science. To give only one example, it simply is
not true that the study of physics and chemistry depends on that
of astronomy. Rather the opposite is true, for one cannot be an
astronomer without a sound knowledge of physics. However, in
Comte's days this was not yet as clearly the case as it is now.
Finally, it certainly is not correct to call mathematics a natural
science.

Herbert Spencer (1820-1903)

In his work *The Classification of the Sciences*[15] Herbert Spencer
attempted to correct and complete Comte's division. In a previous
essay, *The Genesis of Science* (1854), Spencer had already tried
to show that the sciences cannot be hierarchized in the way Comte
had done it. In this new work he reproached the founder of French
positivism for using the terms *abstract* and *general* as synonyms,
although "abstractness means *detachment from* the incidents of particular cases", and "generality means *manifestation in* numerous
cases".[16]

Spencer begins his own explanations with a division into two main
groups: "The broadest natural division among the Sciences, is the
division between those which deal with the abstract relations under
which phenomena are presented to us, and those which deal with
the phenomena themselves". The first group contains the abstract
sciences, i.e., those "which deal exclusively with Space and Time".
By space he means "the abstract of all relations of co-existence", and
"Time is the abstract of all relations of sequence". As belonging to
this group he names logic and mathematics, "dealing as they do entirely with relations of co-existence and sequence, in their general or
special forms".

---

[15]The first edition appeared in London, 1864. We quote here the third
edition of 1871, which contains, in addition to the text of the first, a twenty-
four page *Postscript Replying to Criticisms* and a long appendix entitled,
Reasons for Dissenting from the Philosophy of M. Comte.

[16]*The Classification of the Sciences,* p. 7. Italics of the author.

These sciences "treat of the empty forms in which phenomena are known to us". As to the object dealt with by them, "The conditions under which we may predicate a relation of coincidence or proximity in Space and Time (or non-coincidence or non-proximity) form the subject-matter of Logic"; mathematics, on the other hand, "has for its subject-matter the relations between terms which are specified quantitatively but not qualitatively . . . . Mathematics is a statement of the laws of quantity considered apart from reality".[17]

The second group, which considers the phenomena themselves, is divided into two classes "having quite different aspects, aims, and methods".

The first class extends to the sciences "which treat of the phenomena themselves in their elements". It is the class of the *abstract-concrete sciences*, such as mechanics, physics, and chemistry. The second class, that of the *concrete sciences*, contains those "which treat of the phenomena themselves in their totalities"; for instance, astronomy, geology, biology, psychology, sociology, etc.

The abstract-concrete sciences "deal with Being under its universal mode, and its several non-universal modes regarded as independent" and "treat the terms of its relations as simple and homogeneous, which they never are in Nature". The concrete sciences, on the other hand, have as their object "the real, as contrasted with the wholly or partially ideal. It is their aim, not to separate and generalize apart from the components of all phenomena; but to explain each phenomenon as a product of these components". In the case of the abstract-concrete sciences we have *analytical interpretation;* synthesis is used merely to verify analysis. In the case of the concrete sciences we have *synthetical interpretation;* analysis is here used only to aid synthesis.[18]

At the end of his treatise Spencer summarily characterizes the three groups of sciences—abstract, abstract-concrete, and concrete—in the following way: "The three groups of Sciences may be briefly defined as—laws of the *forms;* laws of the *factors;* laws of the *products*". These three groups are fundamentally and irreducibly different, as appears also from a consideration of their functions.

> [For] the first, or abstract group, is *instrumental* with respect to both the others; and the second, or abstract-concrete group, is *instrumental* with respect to the third, or concrete group. An endeavour to invert these functions will at once show how essen-

[17]*Op. cit.,* pp. 4-12.
[18]Cf. *op. cit.,* pp. 18 ff.

tial is the difference of character. The second and third groups supply subject-matter to the first, and the third supplies subject-matter to the second; but none of the truths which constitute the third group are of any use as solvents of the problems presented by the second group; and none of the truths which the second group formulates can act as solvents of problems contained in the first group.[19]

Spencer subdivides the three groups resulting from his main division by means of certain criteria which, in his view, make a sharp partition possible. Mathematics, for example, is divided somewhat strangely in such a way as to give rise to the following mathematical sciences: geometry of position, indefinite calculus, definite calculus (which includes arithmetic, algebra, and calculus of operation), geo-metry, kinematics, and geometry of motion. The subdivisions of the other two groups are strongly influenced by Spencer's philosophical views about matter and the world as he conceived them in his work, *First Principles,* and therefore share in the general weakness of his system.

Importance. Without entering into great detail regarding the difficulties that can be made against Spencer's proposed divisions of the sciences, we may make a few remarks here. Although it is certainly correct to classify mathematics separately from the natural sciences and other sciences of experience, the arguments he adduces for uniting mathematics and logic as related sciences in one and the same group are not convincing. The difference between the groups of abstract-concrete and concrete sciences would be very sharp, of course, if the characteristics mentioned by Spencer really existed as clearly as he wants us to believe. Unfortunately, in general this is not the case. As far as the subdivisions of the three groups are concerned, although at first sight they appear very rational as they are proposed by Spencer in his schemata, a closer consideration shows that they are too artificial and cannot be maintained in practice.

Psychology, for instance, appears as a division of biology, which itself, alongside geology, meteorology, and mineralogy, is a branch of 'geogony'. It is concerned with the "organic phenomena of function in their external relations". Sociology is considered as a branch of psychology.[20] Although psychology, in contrast with what happened in Comte, obtains a special place, it is treated as a physical science.

[19]*Op. cit.,* p. 25. Italics of the author.
[20]Cf. the schema opposite p. 24 in *op. cit.*

Thus again no justice is done to the typically human object of this science. The fact that the many sciences about human culture and human relations which existed already at the time of Spencer are not mentioned as special sciences, but simply labeled as 'sociology' actually means that he misjudged them and thus points to a serious defect in his philosophy of science. The cause of it lies primarily in his positivistic philosophy which fails to take the typically human element into consideration. For this and other reasons his division of the sciences is rather unsatisfactory.

Although this historical survey is far from complete, we may terminate it here, because we wanted to present only those divisions which, in our view, are most important or exercised more influence than others on the development of the philosophy of science. In one way or another, most of them will again become the object of our discussion in the remainder of this book.

A few important divisions of the sciences of experience that arose in the second half of the nineteenth century, such as those of Dilthey, Windelband, and Rickert, have been left out here. The reason is that they will find a more suitable place in the chapter concerned with the division of the experiential sciences, for there the views developed by these authors will have to be critically examined before we can make use of them.

CHAPTER THREE

NORMS AND CRITERIA FOR THE DIVISION OF THE SCIENCES

I. Introductory Consideration of Division in General

In the preceding section we considered a number of historical divisions to obtain an idea of the way in which the solution of this problem was attempted in the past. Perhaps it will be possible for us to derive some benefit from the views upon which these divisions were based. Even the less fortunate attempts may be useful, at least insofar as they show us the difficulties that have to be overcome and the pitfalls which must be avoided. However, we will not investigate here the pros and cons of the above-mentioned divisions, but dedicate this chapter to the formulation of general norms and criteria for a good division of the sciences and investigate the demands which must be met by a satisfactory division.

Three points especially have to be kept in mind if one wants to arrive at a good division:

1. The nature of the whole that is to be divided;

2. The principle of division;

3. The parts resulting from the division.

Each of these needs to be considered somewhat more in detail.

1. *The Nature of the Whole that is to be Divided*

In general, any division is the separation of a whole into parts. The nature of the whole in question will give special characteristics to the division. For instance, it obviously makes a big difference whether one deals with a real whole or a logical totality which exists only in our mind. With respect to a real whole the meaning of the division again is different in the case of a substantially unified being, such as an organism, or that of a whole which possesses only a purely external unity, such as a library. Again, it makes a difference whether a real whole is divided by real means into real parts or merely mentally considered according to its essential or integral parts. Because we are concerned here with the division of the sciences, our attention has to be devoted especially to the logical whole, although many of our assertions will apply also to totalities of a different nature.

In a logical whole, which as such exists only in our thought, the division will have to be made according to criteria that are known only to the intellect. This is the case with the division of a totality which is seized in an intellectual concept; e.g., the logical whole indicated by the term 'animal' (sentient living being) is divisible into two parts defined as 'rational animal' (sentient living being, endowed with reason) and 'irrational animal' (sentient living being without reason). If there is question of concepts which are obtained from reality through abstraction, such a division of a logical whole may possess an obvious value for the reality in question. The same applies to the division of the sciences. Their division has first of all a logical value, but it may possess also some practical application if only because it offers a suitable principle for the systematization of an encyclopedia, the organization of an institute of learning, or the arrangement of a library.

As a rule, a single whole will permit several divisions, although its own characteristic nature may limit the number of possible divisions. For this reason one will have to be on guard not to make any division which conflicts with the proper nature of the whole or leads to results that do not contribute anything to a better understanding of the totality in question.

2. *The Principle of Division*

Every division has to be guided by a definite principle which allows the entire whole to be divided. The reason is that the distinction of the parts has to be made from a fixed point of view, i.e., by a definite criterion which, if possible, should be clear to all. Therefore, whenever feasible, the parts should be distinguished by clear characteristics. Frequently one and the same whole can be divided according to different viewpoints. Thus, e.g., the human race allows divisions into male and female by sex, endomorphic, mesomorphic and ectomorphic by body type, viscerotonic, somatonic and cerebrotonic by temperamental structure, brachycephalic, dolichocephalic by form of skull, etc. The students of a university can be divided according to sex, year of admission, age, religion, social or financial status, type of study, etc. In every division, however, care has to be taken to proceed logically according to one and the same principle of division. Thus it would be wrong to divide the human race into brachycephalics and pyknics.

To determine the suitability of a principle of division, it may be important to see also whether or not the principle in question is *natural,* i.e., concerned with essential characteristics, or purely arbitrary and artificial because it is based on distinguishing marks that have only an incidental or secondary importance. For instance, it would be artificial to divide a group of people by the alphabetical order of their names or of their places of residence, for these points do not indicate any characteristic differences. Although such an arbitrary division may sometimes have a practical value, it is useless in a theoretical treatise whose purpose it is to reach a natural division, determined by the very essence of the object to be divided, for only a natural division can give us a more profound understanding of the object in question.

Often it is only *a posteriori,* in the division itself, that one can determine whether a certain principle of division is suitable with respect to a given whole. For this reason attention must be paid to the parts resulting from the division.

3. *The Result of the Division*

A principle of division will be fully satisfactory only if it can lead to a complete and sharp division.

A division is *complete* if by the application of the principle the entire whole is divided so that nothing remains which does not belong to any of the parts and the sum total of the parts equals the original whole. For instance, a division of mankind into leptosomes and pyknics is not complete, for there are many men who do not belong to either group.

A division is *sharp* or *adequate* if the resultant parts do not overlap. It should not happen that some individuals of the whole belong to more than one group. Thus, e.g., the division of the sciences into deductive and inductive is not sharp, for most sciences work both deductively and inductively. For the same reason Comte's proposed division of science into abstract and concrete is not adequate and therefore not acceptable.

Summarizing we may say that a division will be fully satisfactory only if it satisfies these conditions:

    1. It is suitable for the nature of the whole that is to be divided;

2. It uses a single principle which leads to a natural division;

3. It is complete and sharp or adequate.

In the succeeding sections of this chapter we will use these considerations to search for suitable criteria in the division of the sciences. It will become apparent that it is difficult to satisfy the condition which demands sharpness of distinction.

II. Possible Criteria for a Good Division of the Sciences

In attempting to divide the sciences one can make use of different criteria. It will not always be possible to determine *a priori* whether these criteria will result in a division that satisfies all the conditions laid down in the preceding section. This is a point that will have to be mentioned again and again in the succeeding chapters.

In investigating the suitability of a criterion for the division of the sciences we must pay attention only to those characteristics which have a primordial importance for the nature or structure of the sciences, i.e., the essential aspects or constituent elements that were revealed by the analysis of science which was performed in Chapter II, Volume I. All these aspects and characteristics may perhaps be capable of serving as criteria for the division of the sciences. Thus one could attempt to use as a criterion the degree of abstraction, the universality, the mode of necessity proper to the statements of the sciences, the material object, the formal object, the foundation of the sciences, the nature of their methods, etc. In addition, one could consider their inner tendency or objective purpose, their mode of consideration, etc.

Several of these constituent elements have already been considered extensively in Part One, where they were discussed with respect to their value for science itself. In speaking about the material and formal objects we drew attention to their usefulness for dividing science and especially for subdividing one and the same science or for the distinction of new sciences through progressive specialization. It was pointed out also that the differentiation according to total and formal abstraction offers possibilities for division. Later this division by degree of abstraction will have to be considered once more. Not every constituent element or aspect of a science is a suitable criterion for a division of the sciences. Thus, for instance, a difference in mode of consideration, say, historic, physical, or philosophic, generally does not imply a distinction into different sciences, for it is often merely a difference in subjective attitude of the man of science and different modes of consideration can be handled within the same science. It is only insofar as the difference in consideration is connected with other differences, e.g., in formal object, that it has objective value. Likewise, the use of a certain scientific method does not as a rule characterize one science or group of sciences, and therefore in general cannot serve as a suitable criterion to distinguish the sciences. For instance, as was mentioned above, a division of science into deductive and inductive is not sharp because no science or group of sciences is exclusively deductive or inductive. It is true, of course, that there can be differences with respect to the relative prevalence of either deduction or induction in sciences which are distinct for other reasons and that these differences may be pointed out as secondary distinguishing characteristics. For example, mathematics and the physical sciences, which are distinct by other criteria, may be characterized also by means of the difference in the relative frequency of the use they make of deduction and induction.

Obviously, two groups of sciences which are distinct by a valid criterion may reveal also differences with respect to other elements or aspects that are connected with the accepted criterion and with one another, so that their differences occur in combinations. In general, this phenomenon will even be a sign that one is not dealing with an artificial or secondary distinction, but with a profound difference in nature or structure. We shall illustrate this point in the chapters where we will deal with the distinction of the experiential sciences and the difference of mathematics and physical science.

Remark. Because the complexity of structure proper to all sciences implies that all kinds of aspects are to a greater or lesser extent present in all sciences, there can hardly be a single criterion for making an absolutely adequate distinction of the sciences in such a way that a given characteristic occurs in all members of one group and is wholly absent in another. Any division of science is always somewhat artificial, for all scientific activity, no matter how varied and diversified it be, finds its one and only center and origin, and therefore also its source of unity, in man (cf. Ch. X.). The result is that objections can be raised against any proposed division. Nevertheless, the succeeding pages will show that it is possible to make divisions which are based on solid grounds and justifiable if one is

willing to follow the main line and to abstain from criticizing incidental defects. Usually it will even be possible to predict these
defects on the very basis which serves as the principle of the division
and this fact shows how these objections can be dealt with. We
may quote here a sentence from Spencer's book *The Classification of
the Sciences*. He too appears to have struggled with the difficulty
of finding a clear-cut criterion for division and therefore paid attention to complexes of characteristics:

> A true classification includes in each class those objects which have
> more characteristics in common with one another, than any of them
> have in common with any objects excluded from the class. Further,
> the charactersitics possessed in common by the colligated objects,
> and not possessed by other objects, are more radical than any
> characteristics possessed in common with other objects—involve
> more numerous dependent characteristics.[1]

III. Divisions Which Will be Considered

In this section we will indicate a few schematic divisions of the
sciences together with the main criteria upon which they are based.
It will be done in a very concise way, because the subsequent chapters
are destined for a more extensive investigation of these divisions and
of the nature of the criteria in question. Inevitably, we will have to
anticipate somewhat the names to be proposed for the various
groups of sciences and the justification of these proposals. Nevertheless, these preliminary considerations are intended only to indicate in
a schematic way the various groups and thus to give a provisional
explanation of the order and interconnection of the succeeding
chapters.

To prevent misunderstandings we would like to recall that the
term 'science' is used neither here nor in the first part of this book in
the restricted sense of specialized science and even less in the still
narrower sense of exact science, but in its broadest meaning, so that
it includes also theology and philosophy.

Theoretical (Speculative) and Practical (Operative) Sciences. As
our first criterion for a division of the whole of science we will take
the inner tendency or objective purpose of the sciences and the nature
of the knowledge involved in them. This criterion leads to the division

---

[1] H. Spencer, *The Classification of the Sciences*, London, 3rd ed., 1871,
p. 3.

into theoretical (speculative) and practical (operative or normative) sciences. As will be explained in the following chapter, the terms 'speculative' and 'operative' are to be preferred. The speculative sciences aim at knowing for the sake of knowing, the operative want to know for the sake of doing or making. This division will be extensively considered in Chapter IV.

Supernatural and Natural Sciences. Another criterion which allows a division of the totality of science is that of the foundations on which the sciences rest. As was indicated in Part One, every science has to build on a definite foundation, definite principles or data. But the fundamental data of the sciences may arise from two sources—namely, a supernatural source (divine Revelation) or a natural and purely human source, i.e., first principles and data that are obtained by means of intellectual insight and sense experience. This difference in ultimate foundation gives rise to the division of the sciences into supernatural (theological) and natural (non-theological) sciences.

These Two Divisions Cross Each Other. The division of science as a whole into speculative and operative runs across that into supernatural and natural, because they refer to the same whole. On the one hand, among both speculative and operative sciences there are some which arise from a supernatural foundation and, on the other hand, both supernatural and natural sciences can be divided into speculative and operative. In the supernatural sciences the distinction gives rise to the subdivision into dogmatic and moral theology, while in the natural sciences it results in natural speculative and natural operative sciences.

The theological sciences will be considered in Chapter V and the natural sciences will demand our attention in Chapters VI-IX.

Putting these two divisions into a schematic form we get the following:

TOTALITY OF THE SCIENCES

division by inner purpose and nature of knowledge	division by origin of principles and data on which the sciences are based	
	supernatural origin	natural origin
	supernatural or theological sciences	natural or non-theological sciences
speculative or theoretical sciences	speculative, theoretical or dogmatic theology	natural speculative or theoretical sciences
operative, practical or normative sciences	operative, practical or moral theology	natural operative or practical sciences

Philosophical and Non-Philosophical Sciences. The group of 'natural' sciences is divisible by another criterion into philosophical and non-philosophical sciences. The first group is collectively indicated by the term 'philosophy' and the second may be called 'special sciences'. This division also runs across that into speculative and operative sciences, for both speculative and operative sciences may be divided into philosophical and non-philosophical, while on the other hand both the philosophical and non-philosophical 'natural' sciences can be either speculative or operative. Metaphysics, for instance, may be considered as representing speculative philosophy, while ethics is a part of operative philosophy.

Accordingly, the group of 'natural' sciences allows two main divisions, as is indicated in the following schema:

'NATURAL' SCIENCE

	philosophical sciences or philosophy	non-philosophical or special sciences
speculative or theoretical sciences	speculative or theoretical philosophy	speculative or theoretical special sciences
operative, practical, or normative sciences	operative, practical, or normative philosophy	operative, practical, or normative special sciences

In Chapter IX we will devote some attention to philosophy and a few of its subdivisions, limiting ourselves strictly to those parts of philosophy that are closely connected with the non-philosophical or special sciences. Chapters VI-VIII will consider these speculative and operative special sciences.

Natural Speculative Sciences. The group of natural speculative sciences, including philosophy, may be divided by the level of abstraction on which most of their knowledge occurs, by the relative role played by man's different cognitive functions, which is connected with the level of abstraction, or by the character of knowability proper to the general object of the sciences.[2] By means of these criteria we find, first of all, the above-mentioned division into philosophical and non-philosophical sciences, but also the important division of the last-named group into *ideal* or *formal sciences,* such as mathematics, and *experiential sciences.* This division may be illustrated by a simplified version of the schema given in Part One (p. 31).

---

[2]Cf. Part One, Ch. III, sect. iv, pp. 26-33.

NATURAL SPECULATIVE SCIENCES

level of abstraction	cognitive functions which grasp the object		
first level	senses imagination intellect	experiential or factual sciences	speculative or theoretical special sciences
second level	imagination intellect	ideal or formal sciences	
third level	intellect		speculative or theoretical philosophy

The *experiential sciences,* which in the preceding paragraphs were named as a subdivision of the speculative sciences, are concerned with everything that is open to human experience in any way whatsoever, i.e., with all real beings under all their aspects. They can be subdivided according to their general object into sciences of nature, cultural sciences, and the sciences of man. The experiential sciences will hold our attention in Chapter VI.

The proper character of the *ideal* or *formal sciences* and their distinction from the experiential sciences will be considered in Chapter VIII.

Natural Operative Sciences. As was mentioned above, the natural operative, or normative sciences may be divided into operative philosophical and operative special sciences. The first will be treated in Chapter IX, together with speculative philosophy, and the operative special sciences are reserved for Chapter VII.

Unity of the Sciences. Finally, it would seem advisable to add a concluding chapter which will be devoted to a study of the unity of the sciences.

Schema of these Divisions of the Sciences. To summarize the preceding considerations we will insert here a schema in which all the above-mentioned divisions are put together in their interconnections. It surveys the totality of the sciences and the place which in our view belongs to each group within the whole. It exhibits the basic plan that will be worked out in the following chapters. Because it is impractical constantly to refer to the interconnection of the different groups, this schema should be useful in aiding the reader not to lose sight of the whole of science while he is studying the various groups.

DIVISION OF THE SCIENCES

according to inner finality and character of knowing (Chapter IV)	according to the origin of principles and data upon which the science is based			
	supernatural origin (revelation)	natural origin (sense experience and intellectual insight)		
	theological sciences (Chapter V)	non-theological or 'natural' sciences		
		philosophical sciences (Chapter IX)	special sciences	
			ideal or formal sciences (Chapter VIII)	experiential or factual sciences, viz., physical sc., cultural sc., sc. of man (Chapter VI)
speculative or theoretical or ontological sciences (to know for the sake of knowing)	speculative or dogmatic theology (Chapter V, II)	speculative philosophy (Chapter IX, I)	ideal or formal sciences (Chapter VIII)	experiential or factual sciences, viz., physical sc., cultural sc., sc. of man (Chapter VI)
operative or practical or deontological sciences (to know for the sake of doing or making)	operative or moral theology (Chapter V, III)	operative philosophy (Chapter IX, II)	operative special sciences (Chapter VII)	

CHAPTER FOUR

SPECULATIVE OR THEORETICAL AND OPERATIVE OR PRACTICAL SCIENCES

INTRODUCTION

As was explained in Chapter II, the dichotomy of the sciences into theoretical and practical or its trichotomy into theoretical, practical, and poietic goes back as far as Aristotle. The foundation he assigned to it remains acceptable as such even in the present times. For, as Aristotle pointed out, one can distinguish different inner tendencies according to the various purposes man wants to attain through his rational thinking: "All thought is either practical or productive or theoretical" and, in a different sequence, knowledge "speculates upon something, and produces something, and does something."[1] This difference in tendency corresponds to a difference in the character itself of the knowing in question.

These points will be further investigated in the first section of this Chapter. First, we will pay attention to the character of intellectual knowledge and then we will consider other aspects of it. The insights gained in this way will be used in the second section to justify and illustrate the division of the whole of the sciences into theoretical and practical. Section Three will be concerned with a study of the interaction of 'theory' and 'practice' and the importance attached to them.

I. THEORETICAL (SPECULATIVE) AND PRACTICAL (OPERATIVE) THINKING OR KNOWING

1. *The Different Types of Intellectual Activity: Theoretical, Practical and Poietic Thinking or Knowing*

Intellectual activity always has an object which is its content and to which the cognitive action is directed. This directedness or intention of the intellect differs according as the intellect considers its object as a being that is already there or as a being to be made. Let us consider both types of intellectual intentions.

---

[1]Cf. above, Ch. II, Sect. I, p. 15.

Theoretical Thinking. The intellect is capable of considering a definite object that is presented to it as a being that is already there, as an *ordo existens,* whose nature and properties have to be investigated. One may speak here with Aristotle of *theoretical* thinking or knowing or follow Thomas Aquinas and other medievals who called it *speculative* thinking (the Greek *theōrein* corresponds to the Latin *speculari,* to consider). The intellect engaged in this activity is often indicated by the term 'theoretical intellect'.

The nature of the being presented to the intellect may differ in the following ways.

a. It can be a concrete or abstract concept which was formed on the occasion of a certain sense experience and thus represents intentionally a real being that exists independently of our thought in the extramental world.

b. It can be a being that in one way or another is produced by thinking and exists only in dependence on thought, a so-called 'being of reason' or 'ideal being', e.g., a mathematical object such as a number, circle or perfect cube. Such a being of reason may be considered as something that is already there insofar as speculative inquiry is concerned.

c. Finally, the intellect can view every real or ideal being as 'being', under the aspect of being.

Accordingly, the object of theoretical knowing may be three-fold: real being, ideal being, or being as such. This tripartite distinction will later give rise to a subdivision of the natural theoretical or speculative sciences.

Practical Thinking. The intellect is capable also of considering a thought content as a being-to-be-made. Such a being is studied as a goal to be reached, as an end of human activity which is not yet present but has to be attained by suitable means and methods and perhaps only by progressive steps. The complete object of this way of thinking, therefore, is not only the being-to-be-made but also the order of man's activity by which the being in question has to be realized. Hence this object of thought is an *ordo efficiendus.*

Regarding this attitude of the intellect one may follow Aristotle and many scholastic philosophers who speak here of *practical* thinking and knowing or also and preferably of *operative* thinking and knowing —the term 'operative' being derived from the Latin verb *operari,* to work, to act, and from *opus, operis,* work, action. Such thinking results in the establishment of norms in the various realms of human activities. For this reason one may also call it *normative* thinking, for the Latin *norma* means rule or standard.

The possibility of practical thinking, with its typical tendency to the realization of a purpose is based on the twofold character of man's spiritual nature, i.e., the fact that man has not only the power of knowing intellectually but also that of striving freely for an intellectually known purpose. This striving power offers two possibilities.

First of all, it may happen that the realization of the tendency can be attained in its essential elements through pure acts of will. In this case the tendency will give rise to bodily manifestations only insofar as they are conditioned by the psychosomatic structure of man and reveal corporeally the activities of his spirit. As examples we may adduce here certain somatic symptoms accompanying internal acts of love or hatred, acts of prayer, etc.

However, it may happen also that the corporeal activity is the natural continuation and complement of the acts of will, as for instance almsgiving naturally brings to completion the will to aid one's neighbor. The essential, moral or human element lies contained in the act of will and this value is saved even if through circumstances beyond the control of the will the external corporeal act has to be omitted.

In both cases we are dealing with *practical* thinking, in the narrow sense of the term, for the thought is directed to regulating or stimulating mainly imminent human acts of *doing* (Greek *prattein,* Latin *agere,* to do).

Poietic Thinking. In other cases the realization of the purpose intended is possible only through corporeal action on matter with or without the aid of tools or machines. This will always be the case when there is question of expressing in matter an idea about making or building something, e.g., a painting, a poem, a financial, legal or social organization, a bridge, airplane, factory, an agricultural or forestry project, etc. We are dealing here with poietic thinking, with thought that is directed to a making (Greek *poiein*), the organizing or guiding of mainly transient human actions whose purpose usually is the production of something that is to be realized in matter.

Dichotomy or Trichotomy? In this way one who is desirous of preserving the foregoing subdivision of practical thought, in the broad sense of the term, arrives at the Aristotelian trichotomy of theoretical, practical, and poietic thought which leads to a corresponding tripartite division of the sciences. Although such a division is meaningful and provides us occasionally with a suitable terminology, we do not think that the distinction of practical (in the narrow sense) and poietic thought is always adequate. In both cases the intellectual attitude is the same, inasmuch as it is directed to something that somehow is to be realized.

On the other hand, the basis for the distinction is clear only in extreme cases and may often be even wholly absent as, for instance, in theological and philosophical thought. For this reason we think that there should be no objection against the simple dichotomy of intellectual thought into theoretical and practical, using the last named term in the broad sense. Hence we will divide the sciences only into the two groups of theoretical or speculative and practical or operative. (See Section II).

Remark. To prevent misunderstanding, let us state explicitly that in speaking of theoretical, practical, and poietic thought or of a theoretical and practical intellect, we do not at all want to suggest distinct intellectual powers for these types of cognitive functions. There is question only of distinctly typical ways in which one and the same intellect approaches its object.

2. *Other Differences Between Theoretical and Practical Thinking*

The distinction between theoretical and practical knowing will become still clearer if we pay attention to other aspects of difference—namely, 1. the inner tendency of thinking, 2. the truth character of the statements in which it is expressed, and 3. the type of necessity proper to these statements.

a. DIFFERENCE IN INNER TENDENCY

The Tendency of Theoretical Thinking. By its very nature theoretical thinking aims at obtaining an insight into existing being which is presented to the intellect as the content of a cognitive act. The theoretical or speculative intellect investigates the object with respect to its nature and properties. It seeks an answer, in the broadest sense of the term, to the question: what kind of being is it? This question contains others such as: what is its essence? What are its properties? How did it come to exist? How does it function? What is its purpose? Accordingly, the inner tendency of theoretical thought is to investigate the foundation and causes of the cognitive object. In the Aristotelian view, these causes embrace the material and formal causes whose union constitutes the essence of the object, the efficient cause which determines its coming to be, its 'to be', and its mode of being, and the final cause or intrinsic finality which belongs to the object by its very nature.

Theoretical thought is 'thinking in order to know', it leads to knowledge which satisfies in its self-containedness and has no other purpose outside itself, but is knowledge which of itself makes the thinking man happy because he is made richer and more perfect in his intellectual capacities.

The Tendency of Practical Thinking. Practical thought by its very nature aims at obtaining an insight into something which must be reached or realized and therefore also into the means and methods through which the purpose in question can or must be reached. Because of this inner tendency, practical thinking seeks an answer to the questions: what has to be done? How should human activity be regulated to attain the desired purpose, to realize a certain intention, or express it in a material form? For this reason practical thought always tends to organize or direct free human activities with respect to a certain purpose that is to be reached or realized.

Briefly put, the difference between theoretical and practical knowing may be characterized in this way: theoretical knowing is knowing for the sake of knowing, and practical knowing is knowing for the sake of doing or making.

b. Difference in Truth Character

'Truth' always indicates a relationship between a being and the knowing intellect, *habitudo inter rem et intellectum.* This general definition contains several meanings whose discussion is beyond the scope of this book. Only logical truth is important for us here, i.e., truth as a property of the act of understanding which presents to the intellect a certain object or a certain objective state of affairs. According to the classical definition, logical truth indicates the agreement of intellectual insight with the object known as it really is *(adequatio intellectus et rei).*

The intellect expresses its insight into a proposed complex content of thought by an affirmation or negation: "it is this or that" or "it is not this or that". Nevertheless, there exists in this respect a clear difference between the statements of the theoretical intellect and those of the practical intellect.

Truth in Theoretical Thought. In theoretical thinking the result of the intellect's understanding is expressed in the form of a judgment which connect a predicate affirmatively or negatively with a subject: *S* is *P* or *S* is not *P*. Such a statement is true if, e.g., the essence, properties, and relations of the being in question, whether it be real or ideal, considered by the intellect are *de facto* as they are seen by the intellect.

Accordingly, with respect to extramental reality that is intentionally present in the intellect, the judgment has to be an exact representation of this reality, even though it may be true that this representation will always leave the reality somewhat 'veiled' and incompletely represented. Examples of such theoretical statements are: the extended is divisible, Socrates is a man, an animal has no intellect.

In an ideal being, say, a mathematical object, whose reality exists only as a 'thought reality', the predicate attributed to the subject by the intellectual judgment will have to belong to the being in question as it is conceived and constructed by the intellect, for instance, as a circle, a parallelogram, a cube, or a number. Examples of such statements are the following: in a parallelogram (which is conceived and defined as a quadrilateral whose opposite sides are pairs of parallel lines) the diagonally opposite angles are equal and the diagonal lines divide each other into equal parts; in a triangle the perpendiculars intersect in one point and the length of one side is never equal to but always smaller than the sum of the other two sides.

Truth in Practical Thought. In practical thinking the intellect's statements always refer to human activities that are to be regulated, have or have not to be performed, may or may not be performed if a certain purpose is to be reached. Examples of the resulting statements are: one must give everyone his due; one may not kill; reasoning should follow the laws of logic; to preserve or restore health one should do this or that or omit this or that; in building a bridge the demands of strains and stresses should be fulfilled. Such statements or norms are 'true' if they present correctly the required direction of activity or forbid its opposite.

c. DIFFERENCE IN TYPE OF NECESSITY AND IN TYPE OF 'LAWS'

In statements which express an intellectual insight into an extra-mental reality or into a mere 'reality of thought' the asserted relation between the connected parts, say, subject and predicate, may be qualified in certain ways, e.g., as necessary, contingent, or probable. We will restrict ourselves here to the type of necessity and try to indicate the difference in this respect between statements of the theoretical and of the practical intellect.[2]

Necessity in Theoretical Thought. In theoretical thinking the intellect makes a statement regarding a necessary or actually existing connection in a certain being. The ideal will be reached here if one does not only understand that the connection is really as it is asserted to be but also that it is necessarily so and cannot be different.

The necessity of the relation between subject and predicate differs according to the proper nature of the object considered. It is absolute or metaphysical in statements referring to a relation that cannot be different under any conditions. In all other cases there is question only of a hypothetical necessity. This hypothetical necessity has a very special character in relations that belong to the domain of ideal or formal sciences and especially mathematics—whence the term 'mathematical necessity'. In the experiential sciences the necessity of the relation between subject and predicate differs according as the relation in the object is uniformly determined or not. The former is the case in purely material things, the latter in free human activities. In this way we arrive respectively at 'physical' and 'moral' necessity.[3]

Necessity in Practical Thought. In practical thinking which aims at formulating the norms human activities should follow if a certain purpose is to be reached, there is always a causal connection between this purpose and the required regulation of man's actions. In general this connection may be formulated in the following kind of conditional proposition: "if one has to or wants to reach a certain goal, one has to regulate one's activities in accord with this goal". It should be clear that such a conditional connection allows two kinds of necessity—namely, with respect to the purpose to be reached, and with respect to the choice of means.

---

[2]Cf. what has been said in Part I, Ch. IV about necessity in science.

[3]Part One of this book referred to this type of moral necessity as "moral necessity in the broadest sense" to distinguish it from another kind which will be considered presently.

Regarding the *purpose,* first of all, it may be necessary to reach it either for all men—the so-called ultimate end of man—or for a group of men or even a single individual. However, it may also happen that there is individual freedom with respect to the choice of the purpose to be reached. In the second case the norm of action can be expressed only in the following conditional sentence: "if one *wants* to reach the purpose in question, one will have to regulate one's actions in accord with this purpose".

Regarding the *means,* there is a necessity which flows from the relation between means and purpose. If the necessary or freely chosen purpose can be realized in only one way, the norm of action is determined in a uniform way. In this case the existing necessity may be expressed as follows: "if one *has to* or *wants* to reach this purpose, one *has to* regulate one's activities in this particular way". On the other hand, it may happen that there are several possibilities for reaching the desired goal and in this case there will be a certain amount of freedom with respect to the means to be used.

Only if the purpose is necessary and the activities towards this purpose are determined in a uniform way, so that there is no freedom of choice with respect to the means, the practical intellect can reach statements which do not have to be formulated in a conditional proposition but may be expressed categorically in this form: "man, this group of men, or this individual must necessarily act in this way". Such cases occur in the general moral laws, because the purpose in question is the ultimate end man must strive for, at least if he does not want to jeopardize his eternal happiness. However, the norms in question have a very general character, such as: man must do good and avoid evil, or somewhat less general: he must adore God, he may not steal, he should honor his parents, love his neighbor, and make his contribution to human society. These general norms may be specified somewhat and assume the form of a statement like: in these or those circumstances man must act in this or that way. Nevertheless, even from the viewpoint of ethics, an individual's life can run its course in a multiplicity of concrete ways, so that it is not possible to provide general ready-made norms for all.

Outside the realm of ethics also there can be purposes which have to be reached of necessity, although this necessity is not of the same type as that in the domain of ethics. We may think here, e.g., of the necessary organization in the realms of legal, social, and economic life. Frequently, the norms or laws regulating these domains will be specifications of general ethical rules for a definite culture and time. However, it may happen also that ethics intervenes merely indirectly, e.g., insofar as all authority finds support on ethical grounds when it establishes norms and expects that they be followed.

Moreover, there are numerous statements of the practical and poietic intellect in reference to affairs in which there is no general necessity to reach a certain goal here and now. They have necessity only in the conditional connection expressed by the proposition: "if one wants to realize this or that project, one has to act in this or that way". Such norms direct man's activity in daily life with respect to technical, social, economic, medical and other areas. They are based on experience or derived from the practical sciences.

From these brief considerations of the type of necessity which characterizes the statements of the practical intellect it becomes apparent that one has to proceed with due caution and take care to differentiate the necessity sufficiently. In particular—and this is the main point here—it should be clear that the type of necessity proper to the statements of the practical intellect differs from that belonging to the theoretical intellect. In the latter the necessity refers to a statement of the form "it is this or that", or "*S* is *P*". In the former, however, it refers to a mode of acting: "one must act in this or that way" and usually contains an implicit or explicit condition, 'if one wants to reach this or that goal". Thus we see that in this point also there is a clear difference between the statements of theoretical and practical thought.

Difference in Type of 'Laws'. Statements of the theoretical or practical intellect which have a general application are sometimes indicated by the term 'law'. As should be evident from the preceding explanations, the value of such 'laws' is quite different in the two cases and corresponds to the proper character of the necessity expressed by statements. In the first case the 'law', 'rule' or 'theorem' assumes the form: "*S* is *P*" or "it is this or that"; in the second case the form is: "this or that has to be done" or "this or that may, or may not, be done". (The second case allows the use also of the term 'norm' instead of 'law'.) Moreover, within each group the conformity with the 'law' allows further differentiations with respect to the character of the expressed necessity, such as absolute, physical, and moral necessity.

3. *Supplementary Considerations of Theoretical and Practical Thought*

Although at first sight the above-mentioned differences appear clear, many remain reluctant to accept a sharp distinction between theoretical and practical thought or the theoretical and practical intellect. This reluctance seems to arise from a misunderstanding of the exact meaning attributed to these terms. For this reason we consider it desirable to enter somewhat more profoundly into this matter by making use of an article in which Thomas Aquinas investigates whether God can have speculative knowledge of things.[4] He points out that intellectual knowledge may be purely theoretical (speculative), purely practical, or speculative in one respect and practical in another.[5]

Some objects allow only theoretical knowledge—namely, those beings which cannot be produced by human activity, e.g., the things of nature and God. In this case *because of the object known itself (ex parte rerum scitarum),* there is only a possibility of theoretical or speculative knowledge.

On the other hand, there can be theoretical or speculative knowledge regarding things which can be realized through man's imminent or transient activities *(operabilia)* and, as such, are the object of practical knowledge. A twofold possibility may thus be distinguished as consequent on the mode of knowing and the subjective intention of the knower.

The Mode of Knowing (quantum ad modum sciendi). It is possible to study in a speculative way something that is or can be the product of man's activity and, as such, is the object of practical or operative knowledge, such as a machine, a factory, a painting or a poem. This theoretical knowledge will analyze the object's structure in its component parts and explain the properties of the whole by means of these parts. It does not consider the object as something which is to be produced, but as a being that already is, a reality whose nature and properties it wants to understand. This intellectual attitude differs from that of the practical intellect, for it pays attention to aspects which are irrelevant for the practical way of knowing, and *vice versa.*

---

[4] *Summa Theologica,* p. I, q.14, a.16 c.

[5] "Aliqua scientia est speculativa tantum, aliqua practica tantum, aliqua vero secundum quid speculativa, et secundum quid practica". *Ibid.*

The same applies also to ideal beings, which exist and can exist only as products of our thoughts. For instance, one can consider a conic section operatively as the result of a certain construction, i.e., as a figure whose every point must satisfy a given condition, but also theoretically or speculatively as an already existing figure of which one wants to investigate the shape and properties. Likewise, man's immanent and transient activities may be considered as something that has to be directed and regulated, but also as psychological and physiological entities whose proper nature one wants to study.

The Subjective Intention (quantum ad finem). This intention (*finis*) determines also the inner subjective tendency of thought. For one and the same entity can be the object of thinking both for the sake of doing or making and for the sake of knowing the structure and properties of the entity in question. In this way, the intention gives rise, on the one hand, to practical or operative knowing and, on the other, to theoretical or speculative knowing.[6] Thus one may study aeroplanes for purpose of constructing a new type, or pedagogy for the sake of applying this knowledge to the education of youth. Such knowledge is directed towards doing or making. However, study may also be directed solely to the acquisition of knowledge, e.g., out of pure interest or to give a lecture about the subject matter in question. In such a case the study is theoretical or speculative. It is possible also to study or learn by heart the norms established by the practical intellect in a given realm of human activities in order to know them, without there being any question or need of putting them into practice. It is to be noted that the subjective intention which directs the cognitive activity will influence also the mode of knowing, so that these two are not wholly independent.

Conclusion. From these considerations it should be clear that the theoretical or practical character of thinking is not exclusively determined by the nature of the object known, but also by the mode of knowing and the subjective intention of the knower. With respect to things that cannot be produced by man's activities, only theoretical thinking is possible. Regarding objects which man can produce or perfect, thought will be purely practical if it tends to the production or perfection of these objects. However, as soon as such an object is considered as an already existing being and the subjective intention

---

[6]"Nam intellectus practicus differt fine a speculativo. Intellectus enim practicus ordinatur ad finem operationis; finis autem intellectus speculativi est consideratio veritatis". *Ibid.*

aims merely at knowledge about this object, the resulting thinking is
theoretical or speculative. Accordingly, one and the same object which
can be produced may give rise to knowledge which in one respect is
practical and in another is theoretical.

It is true also that all practical knowledge about such an object
presupposes theoretical knowledge regarding its producibility, i.e.,
its nature, structure, and properties, and therefore also about everything that is needed for its production, such as raw materials and tools.
Thus theoretical knowledge is more fundamental than practical
knowledge.[7]

Despite the fact that theoretical and practical knowledge, as we
have defined them here, often go hand in hand, the essential differences indicated above (Nos. 1 and 2) persist. Clearly understood,
these differences should not cause any misconceptions. For this reason
one is fully justified in distinguishing the theoretical from the practical
sciences on the basis of these differences. This point will constitute
the object of our consideration in the succeeding section.

II. Theoretical or Speculative and Practical or Operative Sciences

1. *Division and Terminology*

Theoretical (Speculative) and Practical (Operative) Sciences.
It will not always, or rather almost never, be possible to have direct
knowledge, whether in the theoretical or the practical meaning of the
term. For both types it will usually be necessary to begin with a
definite starting point, to make use of a variety of interconnected data,
to proceed step by step following the deductive, inductive, analytic,
synthetic or some other method, and thus by cogent reasoning to
arrive at logical conclusions. These conclusions may be classified as:
1. statements concerning the nature and properties of a given real
or ideal being; 2. statements regarding the organization of human
activities for a certain purpose. In this way we arrive at systems
which satisfy the definition of science formulated in Part One. And,
according to the two different modes of thinking explained in the preceding section, viz., theoretical or speculative and practical or operative thinking, we get two different groups of sciences which,

---

[7]Concerning the relative value of theoretical and practical knowledge, see
Section Three of this chapter.

consequently, may be called *theoretical* or *speculative* and *practical* or *operative sciences.*

Different Terminology. Because the theoretical sciences endeavor to give an understanding of existing being (an *ordo existens*), they may be called also *ontic* or *ontological sciences* (from the Greek *to on, ontos,* being).

The practical sciences, which attempt to give rules or norms for man's activities in different realms, could suitably be indicated by the term *normative sciences.* Custom, however, often reserves this term for sciences of the human mind, such as ethics, law, pedagogy, and aesthetics. Nevertheless, there should be no objection against a more liberal use of the term 'norm' and its application to the realms of medicine and technology, so that we could justifiably speak of medical and technical sciences as normative.

Practical sciences are by their very nature directed to the regulation of human activities, to that which is to be done (to an *ordo efficiendus*). For this reason they may be called *deontic* or *deontological sciences* (from the Greek *to deon, deontos,* it behooves). They sometimes go also by the name of *teleological sciences* (from the Greek *telos,* end), because they are always directed to a purpose. Often, however, the qualifier 'deontic' or 'deontological' is reserved for moral obligations, which would limit its use to the moral sciences. But in principle there is no reason why it could not be used more broadly to indicate all practical sciences.

Thus the two main groups or highest genera into which the totality of the sciences can be divided may be called by the following pairs of names:

theoretical sciences	practical sciences
speculative sciences	operative sciences *or* normative sciences
ontic sciences	deontic sciences
ontological sciences	deontological sciences *or* teleological sciences

The different pairs may be used according to each one's own preference to suit the needs and purpose of a particular context. Personally, we prefer the terms 'speculative' and 'operative' or 'normative' or one of the subsequent pairs, because their etymological meaning allows them to indicate the proper character of the groups in a very clear way and without great danger of being misunderstood. As a rule, we will make use of the terms 'speculative' and 'operative', but on occasion we will use also 'theoretical' and 'practical' or any other term because of the existing prevalence of these terms in the philosophy of science.

2. *Difference in Character of Both Groups of Sciences*

We may be satisfied with a brief consideration here because of the extensive way in which Section One of this chapter has treated the proper character of theoretical and practical thinking by which the nature of the corresponding sciences is determined. Our main task will be to apply to these sciences what has been said about the different characters our intellectual activity may assume.

a. FUNDAMENTAL DIFFERENCE

The most important basis for the distinction between theoretical and practical sciences lies in the *general object* on which the scientific activity is centered and consequently also in the characteristically different way of knowing this object. It is a genuine difference in formal object.[8]

Object of the Speculative Sciences. In these sciences the object is an already *existing being,* whether real or ideal, an *ordo existens,* whose nature, structure, properties, etc. we want to learn. Systematically and methodically, using all available data and means, one will try to investigate this existing being in its foundation and causes. The result of this search will be expressed in certain or at least probable statements attributing one or more predicates to a given subject. These statements will have to be based on arguments if they are to satisfy the requirements of truly scientific activity. Examples of theoretical or speculative sciences are the following: dogmatic theology, metaphysics, mathematics, physics, the sciences of history, language, and literature.

Object of the Operative Sciences. In the operative sciences the demands of system, method, argumentation, etc. are the same from the viewpoint of their general scientific character, but here scientific activity is directed toward an *ordo efficiendus,* a *being that has to be produced* by man's immanent or transient actions. These sciences, therefore, must first study in a theoretical way the producible object

---

[8]Cf. Part One, Ch. V.

(objectum operabile) or purpose of man's activity and then on the basis of this knowledge proceed to the formulation of directives and norms which have to be followed if the proposed goal is to be reached.[9] Examples of such practical, operative, or normative sciences are moral theology, ethics, pedagogy, hygiene, medicine, practical economy, also technical sciences such as mining, hydraulics, aeronautics, agriculture, and forestry.

A Distinction in Formal Object. The preceding considerations show that the basis for the distinction between speculative and operative sciences does not lie in a difference of their material object, i.e., in a concentration of their attention on different things. It is quite possible that scientific activities of a speculative nature are directed to the same material object as those of an operative nature. Whether the object be the same or not is irrelevant for the distinction in question. It is a difference in the type of thinking, based on a different scientific attitude regarding the object, which leads to the distinction between the two groups of sciences. A speculative and an operative science may consider the same material object, but they do not study it in the same way. The distinction is in the formal object. For instance, the human body is considered differently when it serves as the object of a speculative science, such as anatomy or physiology, and when it constitutes the object of an operative science, e.g. practical medicine.

This fundamental difference between the two genera of science gives rise to other differences corrsponding to the distinction between theoretical and practical thinking indicated in Section One. We will not speak of them again in an extensive way, but merely propose a few considerations to apply them to the distinction of the sciences and to render this distinction more precise.

b. Difference in Character of Truth and Necessity

The qualifiers 'true', 'false', and 'necessary' in their various meanings pertain to the statements expressing a speculative or practical insight. It does not matter whether this understanding is immediate or obtained through a progressive and complex scientific argument. If one wants to attribute to the sciences themselves, considered as systems, a typical character of truth or necessity, it will have to be done in such a way that this character corresponds to that of the statements in which the results of these sciences are expressed.

---

[9] Cf. above, Section I, 3, pp. 52 ff.

It should be noted that by the character of necessity proper to a science we do not mean the necessity of logical consequence pertaining to the scientific process which leads to the statements of this science, but only the kind of necessity that is the property of these scientific statements themselves.

c. DIFFERENCE IN OBJECTIVE PURPOSE

Objective Purpose and Subjective Intention. The difference of which there is question here did not have a counterpart in the preceding section, so that it has to be explained more fully.

By objective purpose we mean here the inner tendency or inner finality (*finis operis*) proper to a science considered as an existing scientific system. This objective purpose should be clearly distinguished from the subjective intention (*finis operantis*) of the man who studies science or wants to apply scientific knowledge in some way or other. Let us clarify this distinction.

Everything produced by an intelligent maker for a definite purpose possesses, by virtue of the purposive activity of its maker, a certain intrinsic finality or objective purpose. If the productive activity is exercised correctly, the intrinsic finality of the object will correspond exactly to the purpose which was in the mind of its maker and directed his activity. This objective purpose remains proper to the object—at least as long as it does not undergo a modification not intended by its maker—regardless of the subjective purpose or intention which moves another to make use of the object. Thus, for instance, a clock will retain its original purpose of indicating time as long as its structure remains unchanged, even if one acquires it merely as an ornament or as an investment.

Application to Science. Similar considerations can be applied to a science, considered as a systematic whole which was produced by intelligent beings and now serves again as the object of a study. A science which has resulted from a systematic investigation concerning the nature and properties of an already existing being or state of affairs will always retain the structure determined by this investigation. The same applies to a science which, by virtue of the intention of its inventors, must produce the norms regulating man's activities in a given realm or with respect to an order of things that still has to be established. This objective purpose or intrinsic finality will always persist, even if someone were to use this science with a subjective intention that deviates from its inner purpose. Thus, for instance, geometry, by its inherent objective purpose (*finis operis*), is a speculative or theoretical science which tends to give an understanding of the nature and properties of extended figures and bodies, without being immediately directed to practical applications. This speculative character is retained even if one studies geometry with the subjective intention (*finis operantis*) of using his knowledge practically to organize his technical operations or to pass it on to others against payment and thus to make a living. On the other hand, an operative science retains its inner purpose of making or doing things even if one studies it theoretically, i.e., in a subjectively speculative attitude, e.g. only for the sake of knowing.[10]

d. DIFFERENCE IN FOUNDATION

This difference also remained unmentioned in the preceding section, for it does not appear before there is a structured scientific system. Every science, considered as a system, has a definite foundation, and this foundation reveals a twofold character insofar as it implies both the starting point and the presuppositions on which the scientific edifice is constructed by means of certain methods. As we will see, both foundation and methods are strikingly different in the speculative and the operative sciences. Reserving the differences in method for the succeeding number, we will consider here only the difference in foundation which, as was mentioned, is reducible to differences in starting point and presuppositions.[11]

Difference in Starting Point. In the *speculative* sciences the starting point of the process lies in the initial knowledge of the beings that are to be studied. If this being is a datum of experience, as is the case in the sciences of nature, man, and culture, the starting point will lie in the experiential knowledge of nature, man, and culture. If, on the other hand, there is question of an ideal being, which exists only in and through our thought, as e.g., in mathematics, then the starting point will be constituted by a few general concepts derived from experience, such as plurality (number), extension, line, surface or solid; by a number of axioms or postulates, which are chosen somewhat arbitrarily; and finally by representations of the imagination,

---

[10]Cf. what has been said in the preceding section under No. 3. Most of it applies also to the present subject matter.

[11]Cf. Part One, Ch. VI.

which may be clarified and fixed by means of drawings or constructs. Speculative philosophy begins all its considerations with an intellectual reflection on the general data of experience and especially on man's own mode of being, while speculative theology starts from the data of divine Revelation, as they are laid down in Scripture and tradition.

In the practical or *operative* sciences the purpose intended will always be the directing principle and therefore in a true sense the starting point of the entire scientific activity. This purpose is the starting point in the same way and even to a greater extent than the first principles and initial knowledge are the starting point of the speculative sciences. As Thomas Aquinas expresses it: "The end plays the same role in operative sciences as the principle in the speculative sciences."[12] This point should be evident if one keeps in mind that in every purposive activity the end to be reached is present in the mind of the intelligent agent and directs his whole activity even in its details until this activity produces a terminus which adequately corresponds to the idea in the mind of the agent. The same object, therefore, in the order of intention stands at the beginning of the activity as the purpose to be reached, and in the order of execution at the terminus of the activity as the end that is realized. Thus purpose and terminus of activity somehow are identical. This identity is nicely expressed by the twofold meaning of the Greek *telos,* the Latin, *finis,* and the English *end.*[13]

Because the operative sciences always presuppose ontic knowledge of what has to be reached or made and of suitable means for attaining this purpose, they will have to be based on theoretical or speculative knowledge that is acquired either directly or through the speculative sciences. Technical sciences, for instance, presuppose a theoretical knowledge of materials, which is obtained from physics, chemistry, technology, etc., and also of physical, chemical, and mechanical laws. Pedagogy makes extensive use of theoretical knowledge concerning the successive stages of child development and borrows it largely from the theoretical science of psychology. In a similar way all operative sciences derive their initial data mainly from the speculative sciences.

---

[12]*Summa Theol.* p. I-IIæ, q. 72, a. 5c and *passim.*

[13]St. Thomas expresses this truth repeatedly and in different ways in such well-known axioms as: "Although the end is last in execution, it is first in the intention of the agent and in this way it is a cause" (*Summa theol.,* I-IIæ, q. 1, a. 1, *ad* 1); "The end is first in intention, but last in execution" (*op. cit.,* I-IIæ, q. 20, a 1, *ad* 2).

If it happens that the necessary data are not yet available, the man of practical science will first have to lay down the necessary theoretical foundation. Thus it is not surprising that the authors of books about the operative sciences usually take care to include the required theoretical sections in which they enumerate the indispensable positive data borrowed from the speculative sciences or, if need be, pioneer in setting them forth for the first time.

Frequently the theoretical part of a practical science occupies the last place in the historical development of this science. Temporally speaking, the sequence is often as follows. First comes the formulation of empirical rules whose efficacy was discovered accidentally; then these rules give rise to a certain technical ability and know-how; finally, there develops a truly scientific insight into the subject matter in question and especially into the relationship of means and purpose.[14] The old rules continue to be followed, but now they are understood. There are numerous examples of such an historical development in medicine, pharmacology, agriculture, technology, etc.

Difference in Presuppositions. Among the presuppositions of the *speculative* sciences belong, first of all, general principles of a metaphysical or epistemological nature which are presupposed by most sciences; for instance, the principles of identity, of contradiction, causality, and intelligibility. Secondly, there are presuppositions that pertain to certain groups of sciences, e.g., to all physical or all theological sciences. The common element of all these presuppositions is that they are concerned with ontic knowledge. They are statements about being in general or about certain types of beings, e.g., material beings, or they express a relationship between our intellect and being in general or a special kind of being.

In the *operative* sciences such general principles of being obviously also are presuppositions, for these sciences are concerned with beings, although only under the aspect of their production or modification through man's activities. However, it is precisely because of their viewpoint of purposive activity that the operative sciences presuppose, in addition to the above-mentioned principles of being, certain other implicit insights regarding man's free activity which can be regulated by an intellectual idea of something that does not yet exist in reality. Moreover, there are other implicit or explicit principles regarding man's natural ends, such as survival, eternal happiness, reproduction and foundation of a family, social organization, etc.

---

[14]In this sense one may understand the well-known expression of Goethe's *Faust*: "Im Anfang war die Tat".

e. DIFFERENCE IN METHOD

The *speculative* sciences start with a consideration of all the available data pertinent to their subject matter and endeavor to enrich our knowledge of these data and to render it more profound. For this reason these data have to be treated synthetically or analytically as is required by the science in question or by one's personal preference. These sciences use also general scientific methods, such as deduction and induction.

Experiential sciences will usually start in an inductive way so as to arrive at general insights. However, they make also constantly a deductive use of whatever general knowledge they have gathered by applying it to particular cases. It is especially in the more 'theoretical' part of a science that this happens, e.g., more in theoretical physics than in experimental physics.[15] In the *ideal* sciences, such as mathematics, the procedure is generally deductive, except when a concrete datum of experience or imagination is utilized for the invention of new propositions (cf. Ch. VIII Sect. III, No. 4).

With respect to the *operative* sciences, as we have seen, it is always the purpose to be reached which determines the entire character of a science. For, it is the task of these sciences to proceed from our knowledge of this purpose and of the subject matter on which man's activity will have to be exercised to a correct understanding of the means that are suitable for this purpose, and to formulate, in the order of execution, the directives which have to guide man's activities in the correct use of these means. Consequently, this procedure largely determines the method of the operative sciences. They proceed mostly analytically in the derivation of the means from the purpose, and mostly synthetically in determining the norms proper to the order of execution. The application of acquired general operative principles to less general cases is deductive in nature. On the other hand, if concrete experiences about the suitability of a procedure are utilized to arrive at logical generalizations, the thought process will be inductive.

Accordingly, the difference in methods of the speculative and operative sciences does not lie in an exclusive use of one method in preference to another, or in a significant prevalence of deduction, induction, synthetis, or analysis, but rather in this that the general procedure is determined and differentiated by the diversity of purpose proper to these two groups of sciences.

---

[15]Cf. below, pp. 65 ff.

3. *The Interconnection of Theoretical or Speculative and Practical or Operative Sciences*

After the extensive consideration of the differences between speculative and practical sciences, it appears desirable to draw attention also to their essential interconnection, lest misconceptions arise. Moreover, an understanding of their connection is necessary for a good insight into the subsequent chapters.

Speculative Science is More Autonomous. Without any further explanation, it should be apparent that the theoretical sciences enjoy a greater self-sufficiency or independence than the practical sciences. In studying existing being, one may be motivated by a pure desire to know for the sake of knowing, without any preconceived intention or plan to use the acquired knowledge for the organization of human activities in a definite realm. Historically speaking, there always have been and there still are sciences which developed and were studied as purely speculative sciences, e.g., astronomy and mathematics. Although it remains true that important sections of the speculative sciences developed and reached a greater perfection only under the impulse of needs arising from daily life or from the practical sciences, nevertheless it is true also that this same development could have taken place without such an external pressure and solely as the result of an inner desire for speculative knowledge.

On the other hand, it should be evident also that any speculative science, precisely because of the ontic knowledge it offers in certain areas, is capable of serving as the foundation of an operative science which uses this knowledge in deducing norms for the correct regulation of man's activities in these areas.

Practical Science Depends on Speculative Science. In the operative sciences the situation is significantly different, for the speculative role of man's intellect fulfills an essential function. To arrive at well-founded norms for man's activities in a given realm, one needs broad and profound ontic knowledge, first of all, regarding man himself and his active powers in general; secondly, concerning the special realm of activities which constitutes the object of the operative science in question; thirdly, about the purpose to be reached by these activities and the available means and methods. Consequently, an operative science, as such, does not have the same amount of self-sufficiency and independence as a speculative discipline. No norms can be proposed without ontic knowledge of the realm to which they are to be applied; hence there is no deontology without ontology. Accordingly, every operative science will have to seek support in a speculative science that considers the same objects.

As we will see more extensively in the succeeding chapters, speculative sciences often have a counterpart among the operative disciplines. But every operative science presupposes one or more speculative sciences. This rule applies to all groups into which the operative sciences can be divided, such as theological, philosophical, and special operative sciences.[16] For instance, moral theology presupposes dogmatic theology, ethics philosophical anthropology, theodicy and various special theoretical sciences; the technical sciences could not be developed without the speculative sciences of mathematics, mechanics, physics, chemistry, etc.

Speculativo-Operative Sciences. Obviously, the theoretical foundation of a practical science may be laid by the adepts of this science themselves. For this reason the required ontic knowledge is sometimes in an apparently inseparable way connected with the normative considerations that are based upon it. In such a case, the result is a unified scientific system possessing a twofold speculativo-operative character. As examples of such a science we may name legal science. It first considers existing laws (*ius constitutum*) and a given state of affairs, but at the same time it endeavors to arrive at norms for the desirable legal organization (*ius constituendum*), and as such it is an operative science. Another example is offered by pedagogy. On the one hand, it studies in a speculative way the child and his various stages of development and, on the other, it gives well-founded directives, based on this study, for correct education. Books about operative sciences often intermingle speculative and operative elements to such an extent that it becomes difficult to separate them. Nevertheless, the experts in such speculativo-operative or theoretico-practical sciences often make a clear distinction between these two complementary parts and speak of theoretical and practical law, theoretical and practical pedagogy, psychology, economics, etc.

This frequent and intimate connection between speculative and operative aspects, especially in the practical sciences, flows logically from the very nature of these mental disciplines. Therefore, it does not at all blur the profound differences between speculative and operative thought which were considered in this chapter. Hence the division of the totality of the sciences into these two groups is not jeopardized by it.

---

[16] Cf. the schema on page 42.

4. Supplementary Considerations About the Use of the Terms 'Theoretical' and 'Practical' or 'Theory' and 'Practice'

The preceding pages viewed the theoretical and practical sciences as two genera which are fundamentally distinguished by the difference in the character of their knowledge and their formal objects. In addition, they reveal other important differences that are connected with this fundamental diversity. Alhough this division of the sciences may be considered adequately justified, nevertheless objections against it are raised from various view points. These criticisms would probably cease or at least diminish if ordinary speech did not attribute to the terms 'theoretical' and 'practical' many additional meanings which easily obscure the technical sense of these terms described above. Although a few of them have been mentioned before in an incidental way, it will be useful to put them together here and to add a few remarks to clarify any obscurity which may be left.

a. Theoretical Character of a Practical Science. A practical or operative science, as a science, may be called theoretical if this term is supposed to mean that the science supplies certain or at least probable knowledge accompanied by an insight into its reasons and proceeds in a strictly scientific way in the deduction of its statements. For both genera of sciences the scientific criterion is the same. However, it is rather unfortunate that in order to emphasize this 'theoretical' character of practical science, the term 'theory' is often used.[17]

b. Role of Theoretical Understanding in Practical Science. As was mentioned before, the theoretical intellect plays an important role in the practical sciences, for it acquires the ontic knowledge of the purpose that is to be reached and the means which are to be used, as the necessary foundation of the practical sciences. For this reason books about the practical sciences usually reserve considerable space for a theoretical part which either simply explains already existing ontic knowledge or pioneers in proposing and developing it.

c. 'Theory' as Philosophical Investigation. Sometimes the term 'theory' is even reserved for the more philosophical investigation of the foundations on which a science rests, and 'practice' is used for the actual pursuit of the science itself. Such a usage of the terms, however, is hardly to be recommended.

---

[17]Cf. below, p. 67.

d. Theoretical Study of a Practical Science. The object of a practical science and the practical science itself may be studied theoretically or with a theoretical intention.[18] However, this approach does not change the proper nature, the objective presence of the operative purpose in a practical science. On the other hand, a science which in itself is theoretical does not become practical by being studied for a practical purpose, such as the organization of human activities on the basis of the acquired speculative knowledge and *a fortiori* not by being subordinated to a purpose that is wholly outside science, such as making a living by teaching it.

e. Applicability and Practical Science. In connection with the preceding paragraph, the remark must be made that the possibility of applying a science does not make it a practical science. For such total or partial applicability of a science, taken as a scientific system, does not at all change its proper nature or objective purpose. An important part of the theoretical sciences, such as mathematics and the sciences of nature, man, and culture, quite naturally has many applications in the regulation of human activities. Usually this applicability reveals itself only later and therefore cannot have influenced the proper nature of the science in question. However, even if a part of a science which in itself is speculative, e.g., mathematics, is especially developed to satisfy a practical need, such as aiding another science or solving technological problems, it does not *ipso facto* become practical or operative. For, if there is question of an incidental development of a theoretical science, the immediate purpose still remains the acquisition of ontic knowledge and is not changed into that of formulating norms of human activities.

We will speak somewhat more extensively of so-called 'applied science' in no. 5 of this section, where we will see that it is sometimes incorrectly identified with practical science.

f. Practical and Experimental Science. In ordinary speech and also in scientific language 'theoretical' and 'practical' are sometimes used as equivalent to 'theoretical' and 'experimental', e.g., in distinguishing two complementary sciences, such as theoretical and experimental or practical physics, astronomy, or psychology. 'Theory' and 'practice' are used in the same way, especially to mark a certain contrast, as in: "Practice (i.e., experience) has shown that this theory is false".

---

[18]Cf. Section I, No. 3, pp. 52 f.

This usage of speech can easily give rise to misunderstanding, because these meanings of the terms do not coincide with their significations in the philosophy of science which were explained in this chapter. In the philosophy of science 'theoretical science' is synonymous with 'speculative' or 'ontic science' and contains both the 'theoretical' and the 'practical' sciences or 'theory' and 'practice' taken as equivalent to 'theoretical' and 'experimental' sciences. For an experimental science, precisely because it endeavors to acquire knowledge of existing being through observation and experiments, is a true ontic or theoretical science. Thus, for example, experimental or practical physics together with theoretical physics constitutes the one speculative science of physics. The same applies to the other cases. Experiential sciences, i.e., all sciences which study nature, man, and culture, are *per se* theoretical sciences in the sense of being ontic or speculative sciences. It is irrelevant in this respect whether they pay more attention to the experimental aspect or to the construction of theories in which the data of experience are incorporated, as is done by 'theoretical' physics, astronomy, etc.

g. 'Practice' as Actual Behavior. Finally, there is a meaning of 'theory' and 'practice' which is somewhat connected with the sense indicated under *a* (p. 65), but deserves to be mentioned separately not only for the sake of completeness, but also because it can be readily misunderstood. In ordinary speech, 'practice' often refers to the actual way men behave, and 'theory' is used to indicate the abstract, scientific reflections of a practical, operative, or normative nature upon this behavior and also the corresponding section of a practical science. These meanings may be further differentiated according as the terms refer to man's ethical behavior or to his aesthetic and technical way of acting.

Such significations show themselves when, for instance, one says that 'practice' (man's actual behavior) does not agree with the 'theory' (the intellectual norm governing this behavior), that a theory has to give way to practice or is overtaken by practice. Other examples are statements expressing an axiological judgment. This meaning of 'theory' and 'practice' is found especially when there is question of human activities in their ethical aspect. Because of the difficulties inherent to the subject matter and man's frailty, 'practice' will often deviate from the 'theory' e.g. in sexual matters.[19]

---

[19]For the relative value of both see Section III, No. 3, pp. 76 ff.

Ambiguity of the terms. The preceding reflections show very clearly how easily there can be misunderstandings if the terms 'theoretical' and 'practical' or 'theory' and 'practice' are used without further specifications. At the same time we may conclude that it is advisable to substitute, if necessary, other terms for these misleading expressions, as we have done throughout this chapter.[20]

5. *The Meaning of the Term 'Applied Science'*

In modern times especially, the term 'applied science' is frequently used not only to indicate a third group of sciences alongside the theoretical and practical sciences, but also as a substitute for practical science. In the last-mentioned case it is often opposed to 'pure science'. The opposites 'pure' and 'applied' science, however, do not usually coincide entirely with 'theoretical' and 'practical' science in the sense which we have given to these terms.[21]

In general, the term 'applied' indicates that which is put to practical use or at least is made suitable for such use. There are, however, also somewhat different meanings. On the other hand, 'science' itself can have various meanings. Hence the expression 'applied science' is open to diverse interpretations. It is desirable to consider these meanings briefly insofar as this is demanded by the scope of this book.

a. APPLIED SCIENTIFIC KNOWLEDGE

According to the grammatical meaning of the past participle 'applied', the term 'applied science' is equivalent to 'science which is applied'. In this way the term is meaningful only if science is used in the objective sense, as scientific knowledge *(scientia quae scitur)* or a complex whole of scientific data and propositions which are applied to a concrete case. For example, we have to do with applied science when an engineer uses his mathematical knowledge in solving a quantitative problem (applied mathematics), his physical and chemical knowledge in handling a technical job (applied physics and chemistry), or when a physician utilizes his medical knowledge to cure a patient (applied medicine). In these cases, therefore, 'applied science' is synonymous with 'applied scientific knowledge'. This synonymity holds not only for applied theoretical or specu-

[20]Cf. No. 1 of this section, p. 54.
[21]Cf. here below under *b*, p. 69.

lative knowledge, such as applied knowledge of mathematics, physics, chemistry, or mechanics, but also for applied practical or operative sciences, e.g., applied knowledge of the medical sciences.

b. APPLIED SCIENTIFIC SYSTEM

Generally, however, 'applied science' is used in such a way that 'science' means 'scientific system', i.e., a logically ordered whole of statements regarding the nature, purpose, etc. of a certain realm of objects. Nevertheless, even in this case the expression is not without ambiguity and allows various interpretations according as it is used in connection with theoretical (speculative) or practical (operative) sciences.

Applied Speculative Science. It is, first of all, possible to adapt and arrange a purely speculative science in whole or in part in such a way that this theoretical system is now suitable for application to concrete problems. For instance, in the many books of applied mathematics the authors usually limit themselves to those parts of mathematics that lend themselves easily to practical applications and treat these parts in such a way that they are as much as possible adapted to practical use, e.g., by analyzing and solving problems borrowed from concrete cases in daily life or in technical work. In a similar way many speculative sciences may be made suitable for practical applications and thus lead to 'applied' physics, chemistry, geology, economics, etc. Sciences or the parts of them whose statements have a more abstract and general nature are then called 'pure' sciences, or sometimes also 'theoretical' sciences in a more restricted sense of this term than was used in this chapter.

In such applied sciences the scientific character remains theoretical, speculative or ontic, but by means of the special way they are presented they have become more suitable for application to practical problems.

Secondly, one could even go further and use the term 'applied science', as some authors do, to indicate the contents of a book which contains only a collection of formulas and tables e.g., the physical and chemical constants of solids, liquids, and gases, that are useful for practical purposes. Nevertheless, even here the content remains of a theoretical nature, for it consists only of the results of theoretical or speculative sciences. It is to be noted, however, that one could hardly speak of science in this context unless the term is used in an extremely broad sense.

Applied Operative Science. It is in reference to the operative sciences that the expression 'applied science' occurs most frequently. It then indicates a scientific system which is considered as the result of a particularization and concretization of a practical or operative science. Such a development makes the abstract and general results of the practical sciences more suitable for application to man's concrete activities. To understand the necessity of this particularization and concretization, the following points may be useful.

A practical or normative science establishes directives for man's actions with respect to a purpose to be reached. These norms, however, are of an abstract and general nature and still too far removed from concrete activities. For instance, the practical science of ethics formulates such norms as: the good is to be done and evil to be avoided, or one should not kill, steal, or lie. Hence these general norms have to be particularized and rendered more specific for cases of less scope which more closely approach concrete acts.

This particularization is the task of the corresponding 'applied science'. For instance, ethics is supplemented by the applied science of casuistry, which formulates more detailed directives for ethical behavior in particular circumstances. For example, the general ethical rule which condemns stealing as immoral will be specified for certain categories of actions, such as over charging during a famine, taking food while starving, wasting time sold to one's employer. The rules drawn up for such cases remain somewhat general, but less so than the laws of ethics, and they are further illustrated by means of real or fictitious examples.

Another instance of applied science is provided by the operative science of architecture. It has a corresponding applied science which particularizes the general aesthetic and practical construction norms by taking into consideration conditions and specifications that more closely approach concrete reality.

In a similar way it should be possible to add to every practical science an applied branch whose function it is to prolongate this science in the direction of actual application and concrete realization. As should be clear from the examples, such an applied science is not always easily distinguishable from the practical or operative science whose complement and continuation it is. One passes almost imperceptibly from one into the other, and often it will be mostly a question of personal preference whether a certain part of the treatise should be classified as operative or as applied.

Applied Science and Prudence or Art. Not even applied science itself brings us completely to the concrete individual action which at a given moment has to be performed by a definite person in a concretely given situation and upon which the norms established by practical and applied science have to be brought to bear. A correct application requires not only knowledge of the most general and more specific norms of activity but also an understanding of the concrete situation. It demands, therefore, that the intellect possess a measure of adeptness, based on personal ability and developed by practice, which enables man to judge the concrete situation correctly and act accordingly. This adeptness was known to Aristotle as *phronêsis* in the case of immanent action or doing (*prattein, agere,* to do), especially in that of moral acts, and as *technê* in the case of transient actions which make something (*poiein, facere,* to make). The corresponding medieval terms were *prudentia* and *ars,* whose English equivalents are prudence and technique or art.

c. A THIRD KIND OF APPLIED SCIENCE

The expression 'applied science' may be used in still another sense, which is somewhat related with the preceding one (applied scientific system). It differs from it insofar as the strictly scientific character is present only in such a reduced way that some people are reluctant even to use the terms 'science' and 'scientific' for it. What we mean are so-called 'sciences' which mainly collect all kinds of data and results from various realms of science, coordinate and adapt them systematically for certain applications. As an example of such a science one may name, it seems, criminalistics, for it may be considered as a collection and adaptation of data derived from various sciences because they can be useful in the investigation of a crime and the tracking down of the criminal. It studies, e.g., the methods for identifying fingerprints, footprints and tire tracks, for discovering traces of blood and other substances, for analyzing microscopically small quantities of poison, alcohol, or ink. It considers the symptoms and effects of alcoholic intoxication, studies criminal psychology, the falsification of paintings, etc. This hodge-podge of heterogeneous subject matters is then richly illustrated with all kinds of examples taken from practical life.

As other examples of such applied 'sciences' we may name those of advertising, journalism and library science. They and other similar 'sciences' borrow the most heterogeneous data from all kinds of specu-

lative and operative sciences in order to throw light on a limited but
complex area of daily life in all its aspects. Hence they are not natural
complements of any such science, as was the case with the categories
named under applied scientific system, but they take as the object of
their study certain complex situations, phenomena, or institutions
existing in concrete reality, collect and arrange all data which somehow may be useful for the practical handling of their object. They
may be called sciences only if this term is given a very broad meaning.

III. INTERACTION OF THEORY AND PRACTICE AND THEIR RELATIVE APPRECIATION

The preceding sections considered theoretical and practical thinking and the two genera of theoretical or speculative and practical or
operative sciences. They were viewed with respect to their proper
nature and, as a rule, without any explicit study of their general interconnection. Likewise, no value judgment was presented to compare
theory and practice. We will investigate these two points here and
at the same time refer to certain views of the past which can serve as
useful illustrations. However, lack of space forces us to abstain from
developing these questions in any extensive way.[22]

1. *Historical Consideration of the Relationship of Theory and Practice*

Primitive Man. In his behavior towards his fellow-men and his
work on material objects primitive man must have been led, first of all,
by the experience previously acquired by himself or his fellow tribes-
men or passed on from his ancestors. His activity was regulated by
norms which to a large extent had been discovered accidentally or at
least without much understanding. These norms were accepted because they had proved their usefulness in daily life. Because of the
prevailing defective knowledge regarding the nature and structure of
matter, it would even have been impossible to arrive at a true insight,
for such an insight implies an understanding of the reasons behind
these norms. Only very gradually could such an insight be obtained

---

[22]The terms 'theory' and 'practice' are used here in a general sense. Our
reflections will apply sometimes to the relationship between theoretical and practical thinking, sometimes to that between theoretical and practical sciences,
sometimes also to both. It will not be necessary to specify constantly to which
relationship we are referring.

and developed according as observation and systematic research revealed more about the nature of matter. Even today it is still defective, so that many human activities continue to be governed by experience. We may refer, for instance, to various natural medicines whose working is not or only partially understood, and also to numerous procedures commonly used in daily life whose causality escapes us.

Thus centuries of experience show that practice can lead to good results even when there is no theoretical basis. On the other hand, it must always have been apparent that man could work more successfully and accurately if his labor would be directed by an intellectual insight into the foundation and causes of the various properties and activities proper to matter.

Ancient Greece and the Middle Ages. Historically speaking, the origin of scientific study, at first of course in a very rudimentary way, must be sought in the practical need to arrive at a more successful mastery over matter by means of a better understanding of it. We may refer here, e.g., to the working of metals, waterworks for irrigation, and the surveying of land. In general, the demands of practical life must have preceded theoretical study.

On the other hand, the ancient Greeks deserve credit for having developed a few sciences for science's sake, because of their own value, without any direct reference to an extrinsic purpose. As examples we may name mathematics and astronomy. Philosophy, too, had a purely speculative or theoretical meaning for them if we abstract from some branches such as logic, ethics, and politics. For, as is generally admitted, wonder (*thaumazein*) lies at the origin of philosophical thought. But wonder or surprise is possible only about what *is,* about the existence, nature, and properties of a *being,* about what shows and reveals itself to the observer. Thus the ancient Greek philosophers strove for knowledge for its own sake and not for its possible applications. Generally speaking, there was a higher regard for theory than for practice in Antiquity, except perhaps in the ethical schools of philosophy such as that of the Stoa and also of Plato. This preference prevailed even when in the same person speculation was accompanied by the application of the acquired insight to the organization of human activities or the production of useful and aesthetic objects. In the Middle Ages the same relatively higher regard for theory than for practice was, as a rule, predominant.

Since the Sixteenth Century. When the development of the physical sciences in the sixteenth and seventeenth centuries increased the possibilities of practical application, it obviously became easier to study and develop these sciences also for the sake of their usefulness. Thus in the last few centuries there were many who studied theoretical sciences but at the same time thought about the practical application of their findings. Kepler, for instance, utilized his astronomical observations and calculations to compose nautical tables. Huygens, Stevin, and others looked for understanding, but also for opportunities to apply their scientific results to practice. *A priori* speaking, such a dualistic attitude regarding theory and practice is something that should be expected, for it flows from the plurality of man's powers, each of which demands to be realized in its own way. Intellectually man strives to understand everything that pertains to himself and his surroundings or enters into a relationship with him, but at the same time he is inclined to make his surroundings serve him by becoming the useful or aesthetical expression of his ideas.

In periods, such as that after the sixteenth century, during which the development of the physical sciences offered hitherto unknown possibilities of new applications, it was inevitable that practice gained great esteem and was even often valued higher than theory. Nevertheless, even in such times there were always some who attributed a priority in rank to purely theoretical science which is studied for the sake of knowing. By way of illustration we may refer to Niels Stensen (1638-1686). After studying medicine, Stensen devoted the greatest part of his scientific career to such speculative sciences as anatomy, physiology, crystallography, paleontology, and geology. He is even rightly regarded as one of the founders of the three last-named sciences. Stensen criticized the conception of contemporary physicians who were of an exclusively practical orientation and without sufficient theoretical understanding of their professional field. In his inaugural address delivered in 1673, on the occasion of his appointment as 'Royal Anatomist', he said: "Whoever attributes to anatomy only a utilitarian function in the healing and prevention of disease errs and does not do justice to anatomy. . . . The study of anatomy is right when it gives us knowledge of the body and through this knowledge knowledge of God."[23]

---

[23] Nicolai Stenonis, *Opera Philosophica,* Copenhagen, 1910, vol. II, p. 255.

2. *Interaction of Theory and Practice*

As was pointed out in Section II, no. 3, of this chapter, there is an intimate relationship between the theoretical and the practical sciences. We will consider here now how theory and practice interact, taking the term 'practice' in the sense of practical application.

The existence of such an interaction appears clearly when attention is paid to their interdependence and the mutual influence of the theoretical physical sciences and the development of technology. No one will doubt that the evolution of technology is greatly dependent on the progress and results of the physical sciences, for nearly every theoretical discovery contains a possible technical application. Reversely, technique gives an indispensable support to the physical sciences—namely, insofar as it produces the instruments and installations needed by the research scientist. Moreover, the demands of practice and technique stimulate new theoretical investigations, and the results of these in turn make new and better applications of science possible. For instance, the speculative studies of light gave rise to the creation of all kinds of optical instruments and, reversely, the imperfection of the existing instruments and the growing need for more exact and more powerful optic tools strongly influenced the reconsideration of the theoretical foundations.

In former centuries it frequently happened that the theorists themselves took care to apply the results of their speculations to practice and found inspiration for the rethinking of their theories in practical needs. The two above-mentioned scientists, Huygens and Stevin, may be referred to as examples. In modern times, however, the development of a theory and its practical application are usually taken care of by different persons. The reason is that both functions entail so many difficulties that very few scientists are capable of fulfilling both.

Sometimes the possibility of practical applications appears only after long and profound work of purely theoretical research. We may cite here the speculative investigations concerning the nature of elementary material particles, whose results have led to the development of all kinds of electronic equipment and the utilization of atomic energy.

In modern times the conviction that purely theoretical research often has unpredictable practical applications has induced large industrial corporations to found expensive laboratories in which well-paid scientists are offered an opportunity to engage in purely scientific research that at first sight has nothing to do with the present situation and needs of the industry.

It is true that our age is characterized by triumphs of technique in all kinds of ways, so that a superficial observer could easily be brought to an overestimation of practice above theory. Nevertheless, it remains true also that the scientific world continues to have a very high regard for purely theoretical research, although this esteem may be based more on a realization that speculative work is indispensable than on an understanding of its intrinsic value.

3. *Influence of World View on the Appreciation of Theory and Practice*

The relatively higher esteem accorded to either theory or practice depends to a large extent on man's world view and philosophical attitude. It, therefore, varies in accord with one's philosophical background. Whoever appreciates the mind more than the body will, *abstractly* speaking, attribute a higher value to theoretical insight than to bodily activity and to the mastery of matter. At the same time, however, for one who recognizes the unity of man's spiritual-corporeal being it will be quite natural that in one and the same person theoretical reflection goes hand in hand with the practical regulation of human activity and that their interaction is mutually fruitful. It will depend on the personal mentality of the man of science and on the character of his scientific activity whether knowledge for the sake of knowing or knowledge for the sake of doing or making *de facto* predominates. One who studies mathematics, astronomy, or general linguistics will more easily retain a purely theoretical attitude than a man who does research in the physical sciences, which offer more possibilities of practical applications.

a. Periods of time in which a pragmatic or materialistic mentality prevails attach more importance to practice than to theory. They have more regard for knowledge of man's active potentialities in the realm of matter than for an understanding of the essence of things, because the former can aid man to dominate matter and thus to improve his situation in the world. It means real progress. Purely theoretical knowledge, on the other hand, taken in itself or abstracting from possible practical applications, may perhaps provide satisfaction for a few individual minds, but remains sterile for humanity as a whole. For proponents of such a view theoretical reflection and pure science possess value only if they can be of service to practice. They have no right to exist save insofar as they are capable of solving practical problems and indicating new norms for man's action on matter. It is possible even, as the past few decades prove, that the Government will determine the direction theoretical research must take because of economic, agrarian, or military needs. When there is such an overevaluation of practice, obviously pure science will be hard pressed. It becomes officially and intentionally degraded to the rank of being an *ancilla praxis,* a handmaid of practice, and some may go so far as to simply deny pure science the right to exist.

Such an extreme position obviously militates against any sound view of man in his world. Therefore, it should not surprise us that in recent times resistance against it has arisen on all sides and that the rights of pure science have been repeatedly and emphatically defended. Since World War II the governments of several countries have created organizations and institutes to stimulate pure scientific research and supplied them with the necessary financial resources for the execution of their plans.

Even in Subservience Theoretical Science Retains its Proper Nature. After this brief and obviously superficial consideration whose sole purpose was to draw the reader's attention to this point, we want to make the following remark. Even when there exists such an overestimation of practice at the expense of theory, even when theoretical research is performed solely for the sake of practical applications, this research retains the theoretical or speculative character, proper to it, which was described in the preceding pages, although the domain of theory or pure science is severely restricted under such conditions. Therefore, despite all objections which can be raised against the proposed division of science into theoretical and practical, and despite the existing pragmatic or materialistic attitude which seems to militate against the division, a more profound reflection shows that it remains meaningful to maintain the distinction between theoretical or speculative and practical or operative sciences. On the other hand, in some cases it becomes necessary to differentiate the distinction between theoretical and practical more accurately and to pay attention to the context in which the distinction is used. We hope that the content of this chapter[24] will make it possible for the reader to do so when the need arises.

b. As was pointed out in Sect. II, the terms 'theory' and 'practice' are sometimes used to indicate the relationship between

---

[24]Cf. especially Sect. II, Nos. 4 and 5.

actual (practical) behavior and normative reflection on it. Thus practice may or may not be in opposition to theory. With respect to activities in the technical or aesthetic realms, the success of practice or its lack of it is correctly valued as a suitable criterion for the truth or falsity of theoretically established norms, i.e., theory in the sense explained above. Hence if a theory does not agree with practice, man will easily correct or revise it, regardless of his personal philosophical or religious world view.

In Ethical Matters. The situation is different, however, when there is question of the ethical character of human activities. Here two attitudes are possible with respect to the appreciation of theory versus practice.

1. It is reasonable that actual behavior agree with the results of the theoretical reflection which, after considering the divinely revealed moral norms and the demands of human nature with due regard for all its relationships and aspects in man's concrete situation, comes to the conclusion that a certain way of acting is ethically justified, desirable, or even necessary. In this case the theory is valued as the stable foundation to which practice has to be conformed. Every deviation from the theoretical norms is considered as an evil deed that is to be disapproved of and perhaps even deserves punishment. This attitude will be assumed especially in christian cultures which can rely on stable norms guaranteed by divine revelation and, for Catholics, by the teaching authority of the Church.

2. Often, however, the existing pattern of behavior which evolved gradually and became generally accepted in a certain culture will speak more strongly than what is prescribed by intellectual reflection and ethical or religious tradition. Such an adaptation to existing practice will be easily accepted and even promoted by the adherents of an ethical positivism or empiricism for whom the conceptions generally accepted in a given culture constitute the highest ethical norms. Such a view attaches more value to the actual practice than to hitherto accepted theory. It seeks to formulate and defend a new theory that is more adapted to the existing practices.

Note. Thus, it follows that, even if theory and practice are understood in the just-mentioned sense, the value attached to theory versus practice can vary. However, this meaning of the terms is only remotely connected with the one that was explained in this chapter and will be used throughout this book. For this reason we will not dwell upon it.

CHAPTER FIVE

THE THEOLOGICAL SCIENCES

I. Supernatural or Theological and Natural or Non-Theological Sciences

1. *Introduction*

"God who at sundry times and in divers manners spoke in times past to the Fathers by the prophets, last of all in these days has spoken to us by His Son, whom He appointed heir of all things, by whom also He made the world." Heb. 1:1-2.

A New Source of Knowledge. In these words addressed to the Hebrews the Apostle Paul proclaims the fact of divine revelation— that God has spoken to man, first through the mouth of the prophets to the Fathers of the Old Testament, and then in the fullness of time, when the many centuries of messianic expectation had been fulfilled, through his Son Jesus Christ in the New Testament.

God's speaking to man in a language that is open to human understanding gave rise to a new source of knowledge. This source placed at man's disposal certain data which were not accessible to him in a natural way through the use of his senses and intellect. At least, in the case of data which he could perhaps reach through his natural powers, it made these data known to him in a new way, on the authority of the revealing God and consequently with infallible certainty and without any danger of error. In principle, this new source of knowledge provides the foundation and starting point of a new type of sciences. They are labeled 'supernatural sciences' by reason of their supernatural origin, and 'theological sciences' or 'theology'[1] because of their object, which is God and anything pertaining to God. Provisionally, then, we will mean by supernatural or theological sciences systematically arranged and coherent systems of statements concerning God and things pertaining to God insofar as these objects are known to us through divine revelation.

---

[1]From the Greek *theologia* (from *Theos* = God and *logia* = doctrine). It is to be noted, however, that the Greek term does not always indicate what we mean by theology. Aristotle, for instance, uses the term as synonymous with *philosophia theologikê* or *prôtê philosophia* to indicate the philosophical science of the first principles, i.e., the part of philosophy which was later called metaphysics or ontology.

Speculative and Operative Theology. The data of revelation possess a twofold character. On the one hand, they provide us with some knowledge about God Himself, creation, etc. and especially about man and his relations to God. This ontological knowledge supplies the foundation for a *theoretical* or *speculative* theology. On the other hand, God's revelation teaches us about man's special vocation and indicates the norms according to which man must respond to this vocation and reach his final destiny. In this way it opens up the possibility of a *practical, operative,* or *normative* theology. Speculative theology is also called *dogmatic* theology, and operative theology is usually indicated by the term *moral* theology.

2. *The Place of the Theological Sciences in the Whole of the Sciences*

By reason of their foundation, i.e., the way in which they obtain their fundamental data, the 'supernatural' sciences are opposed to the 'natural' sciences. The latter do not use any other insights or data than those that are obtained through man's cognitive powers of intellect and senses. In this sense, therefore, the 'natural' sciences extend to all non-theological sciences, whether they be philosophical or non-philosophical or special sciences.

The division, then, of the sciences into supernatural and natural is a clear-cut division, so that every science can be assigned to one or the other of the two groups. This division of the whole of the sciences runs across that into theoretical or speculative and practical or operative sciences for, as we have said, a part of the supernatural sciences—namely, dogmatic theology—is speculative, and another part—namely, moral theology—is operative or practical. The same is true for the natural sciences, as appears from the schematic divisions of Chapter III (pp. 39 and 42). The mutual relationships of theological and non-theological sciences will be considered in Section V of this chapter.

3. *The Theological Sciences Have to be Considered in the Philosophy of Science*

Divergent Views. As a rule, books about the philosophy of science pay little attention to the theological sciences. If they are mentioned at all, it is usually to assert that, strictly speaking, they should not be honored with the title 'science', because they do not satisfy the scientific criterium. Likewise, it is sometimes claimed that the absence of a theological faculty in a university does not jeopardize the universality of scientific knowledge which such an institute of higher learning is supposed to represent.

Occasionally a different attitude is adopted. We find an example of it in the 1876 Dutch Law on Higher Education. It consists in this that a theological faculty is maintained or at least tolerated in universities, but only in such a way that its supernatural character, its foundation in divine revelation, is negated. This goal is reached by prescribing that the theological sciences be studied in a so-called 'scientific' way—this term being considered as equivalent to 'profane'. It means that religion is treated merely as a cultural phenomenon presented to man's experience, that the Bible and the history of the Church and religion are studied exclusively according to philological and historical principles. It was especially against such views that Newman directed some of the lectures which were published later collectively under the title, *The Idea of a University*.[2] According to Newman, such a procedure as the one outlined above is an "intellectual absurdity".

The reluctance of certain circles to recognize theology as a science is usually based either on an absolute denial of divine revelation or, if the existence of such a revelation is admitted, on a refusal to accept that relevation is a suitable foundation of science. In the subsequent pages we will have an opportunity to revert to this point.

Why Theology Should be Considered Here. For these reasons it should be evident that as a Christian the author of this book is abundantly justified in dedicating a chapter to the theological sciences. The purpose will be to investigate their proper nature and to reassert their scientific character, despite the supernatural nature of their foundation and object against the claims arising from divergent and non-Christian conceptions.

Because theology escapes the control of natural reason by virtue of its object and foundation, it may surprise certain quarters that we want to consider this science in a book that purports to be purely philosophical. Nevertheless, this procedure is fully justified for, as will become clear in the subsequent section, man's natural cognitive powers play a role in the theological sciences. The act of faith by which divine revelation is accepted is an act of the intellect, the object of this act is truth, and the result of it is intellectual knowledge. On these foundations even an unbeliever who rejects the basis and starting point of theology can recognize that, once this basis is accepted at least hypothetically, it is possible to

---

[2]J. H. Newman, *The Idea of a University*. We have made frequent use of this work in this chapter and especially in Section V. We will quote from the 1947 edition published by Longmans, Green and Co., New York, London, and Toronto.

construct on it a scientific system whose proper character and place in the whole of science is open to philosophical investigation.

Division of this Chapter. For brevity's sake, we will limit ourselves here to aspects and problems whose consideration in one way or another enters into the scope of this book. More specifically, we do not think that it is our task here to establish divine revelation in the Old and the New Testament as an historical fact. The scientific investigation of this question pertains to the so-called *praeambula fidei* and is considered in apologetic writings. Even when divine revelation is accepted as a fact or at least as an hypothesis, there remain enough problems that deserve attention in a philosophy of science. Moreover, in explaining the proper nature of the theological sciences, we will have to restrict ourselves to what fits into the framework of this book and is connected with the other problems considered in it. For a more detailed study of these points we will have to refer the reader to the technical literature published by theologians.

In Sections II and III we will devote our attention successively to speculative or dogmatic theology and operative or moral theology. Section IV will consider the theological sciences in the broad sense of the term. The final section will study the relationship of theological and non-theological sciences.

Remark. It is difficult to speak of the theological sciences in such a way that one's own religious standpoint and view of life does not repeatedly show itself. Thus it will soon become evident to the reader that the author speaks here as a Christian and even as a Catholic. Nevertheless, we think that the non-Catholic and non-Christian will be able to read this chapter profitably without being disturbed by the Christian and Catholic views expressed in it. It is our conviction that most of the chapter has value not only for anyone who accepts a revealed religion, whether he be a Christian, a Jew, or a Mohammedan, but also for the unbeliever who rejects all revelation if, by way of hypothesis, he places himself on the standpoint of those who accept such a revelation.

II. Speculative or Dogmatic Theology

In this section we will devote our attention to speculative, theoretical, or dogmatic theology. However, much of what will be said here applies not only to dogmatic but also to operative or moral theology. For this reason we may use here most of the time the term 'theology' without any qualification.[3]

1. *Introductory Considerations*

As has been said in Section I, theology is the science of God and of created things in their relation to God insofar as they are known through divine revelation. What God reveals about Himself, precisely because it cannot be grasped by man's finite intellect, can be accepted by man only in a supernatural *act of faith*. For the ordinary faithful this act of faith is a terminus. However, it is possible also to take the content of faith as the starting point and foundation of a systematic intellectual investigation, and in this sense there can be question of a theological science. Theology systematically searches for the 'knowable' element in the content of faith, it seeks to discover mutual connections between the various truths of faith, and endeavors to deduce new truths from them. Nevertheless, even in his scientific labor the theologian must always preserve the correct attitude of faith; his mind, illuminated and guided by grace, must always remain in an attitude of respectful listening to what God Himself makes known to him even in the scientifically deduced results of his work. For the object of theological knowledge is always a 'divine mystery' which can be known in all its riches only through a faith that obtains its true character through charity or love of God (*caritas forma fidei*). To remain in the proper supernatural attitude, the theologian must always remain open in all humility to the divine light and prepare himself through meditation and prayer for his task, which by far surpasses the natural powers of man.

How can there be question of a theological 'science' if the basis and means of such knowledge are supernatural acts of faith, and the object known is a 'divine mystery'? To solve this difficulty, it will be necessary to digress somewhat extensively concerning the proper character of supernatural faith and the content of this faith. In this digression we will, on the one hand, have to safeguard absolutely the supernatural aspects of the act of faith but, on the other hand, we

---

[3]In this section we have made a greatful use of the works published by Prof. G. Kreling, S.T.D., the well-known professor of dogmatic theology at the Catholic University of Nijmegen, and especially of the following titles: "De aard der H. Godgeleerdheid", Inaugural address, *Jaarboek der R. K. Universiteit* 1928-29, Nijmegen-Utrecht, 1929; "Het Goddelijke geheim in de theologie", *Rectorial address*, 1939, Nijmegen-Utrecht, 1939; "Beschouwingen rond de theologie", *Ned. Kath. Stemmen*, vol. 54 (1958), pp. 1-9.

will be able to show that despite this supernatural character it is not irrational and below man's dignity to make such a 'blind' act of faith. Next, we will demonstrate that speculative theology is possible and that it can justly lay claim to the title of 'science', although its scientific character differs from that of other sciences.

2. *Faith as the Foundation of Theology*

According to the common usage of the term, 'to believe' means to accept a truth on the authority of someone else, i.e., without having a personal insight into this truth.[4] Formally speaking, every act of faith is an act of the intellect, for there is question here of accepting a truth formulated in an intellectual judgment. Since, however, there is no personal insight which moves the intellect to accept this truth, the acceptance can be rational only if it is based on the conviction that the one who communicates it possesses the necessary insight, and that neither he nor his intermediary is mistaken or wants to deceive us. Once this conviction is present, the intellect is causally moved by the will to admit the proposed truth as true, although the acceptance itself is an act of the intellect, an intellectual assent. The authority which substitutes here for the personal insight may be a human authority or the authority of God as communicating something to man. Only in the second case does one speak of 'supernatural faith' when a truth is admitted in this way. When in the subsequent pages we speak of faith without any qualification, we mean supernatural faith. However, it should be kept in mind that the above-mentioned characteristics of faith in general remain valid even for this supernatural faith which is unique in its kind.

a. THE SUPERNATURAL CHARACTER OF FAITH

Every Christian believer admits that the act by which the intellect admits something on the authority of the revealing God has a supernatural character and possesses as its object a 'divine mystery'. For Christians in general, this point is certain on the basis of unequivocal texts of the New Testament[5] and for Catholics in particular it is confirmed by definitions of ecclesiastical authority.[6]

---

[4]Cf. for what follows also Part One, Ch. X, Sect. VI, pp. 154-158.

[5]See, e.g., Heb. 10:23; 11:1; 12:2; Col. 1:12.

[6]Cf., e.g., Denziger, *Enchiridion Symbolorum*, nos. 1789, 1791, 1794, 1811. See also *Codex Juris Canonici*, no. 1323, paragraph 1.

Supernatural Character of the Act of Faith. The individual act of faith is an expression of a permanent disposition, called the 'habit of faith'. The Vatican Council defined this habit as follows: "A supernatural virtue through which, with the inspiration and help of God's grace, we believe that what He has revealed is true, not because its intrinsic truth is seen with the natural light of reason, but because of the authority of God who reveals it, of God who can neither deceive nor be deceived".[7] Every individual act of faith which at a particular time is made with respect to a particular truth emanates from this supernatural habit and consequently presupposes grace as its operative and formative element.

Supernatural Character of the Object of Faith. The object or content of faith and therefore also of theology is always a 'divine mystery'. God and His attributes, as such, can never be comprehended by man's limited intellect, not even when God himself speaks to man and reveals something about Himself.[8] A God who would be comprehended by man would be a limited being that can be understood in abstract concepts and consequently would not be God. The element of 'mystery', then, cannot be eliminated from faith or from the theological science to be built on it, so that there can be no question of a rationalistic study of God. St. Thomas Aquinas, who so often is accused of being too rationalistic, does not hesitate to write: "The summit of human knowledge about God is reached when man knows that he does not know God, i.e., when he knows that what God is transcends everything which we understand of Him".[9] No matter how much man endeavors to arrive at a more profound understanding of God by means of the methods proper to the theological sciences, he will never succeed in solving the 'mystery'. This 'mystery' faces him at the beginning of theology as the content of the fundamental acts of faith, and even when he arrives at the end of his studies, the 'mystery' is not yet solved.

Supernatural Faith and Theology are Not Below Man's Dignity. Despite the supernatural character of the act of faith and the mysterious nature proper to the object of faith, it can be shown that to make such an act is not unworthy of man but, to the contrary, is fully in accord with reason and man's dignity. We will endeavor to prove this point in the following pages, where it will become clear

---

[7] Cf. Denziger, no. 1789.
[8] Cf. Denziger no. 1796 (Vatican Council).
[9] *De potentia*, q. 7, a. 5, *ad* 14.

also that notwithstanding the limitations of man's intellect with respect to God and His attributes, there is a possibility of arriving at a certain intellectual knowledge of the divine and consequently a possibility of creating a theological science.[10]

On the one hand, therefore, we must vigorously reject epistemological *rationalism* in the doctrine of faith but, on the other, it is not necessary to adhere to *fideism,* which admits revelation but denies the possibility of any natural knowledge concerning the data of revelation. Still less is it necessary to follow the views of *agnosticism,* which rejects all problems transcending experience as *a priori* unknowable and insoluble. As we will see more in detail, the 'knowable' element in the content of faith can serve as the foundation for a theological science, and the mysterious character of the object does not take away or diminish the scientific nature of theology but ennobles it and raises it to a higher level.[11]

b. THE RATIONAL CHARACTER OF FAITH

The Supernatural Basis of Faith. In endeavoring to show that the act of faith is rational, one may not proceed superficially and claim, as is sometimes done, that rationability is present in this act because the motive leading us to surrender in faith is rational. Such an assertion merely expresses that with his natural intellect man can know these two points: 1) God has spoken to man about Himself, i.e., the fact of revelation is certain from the historical examination concerning the sources of revelation and the reliability of the witnesses and writers; 2) God is veracious, i.e., He is not deceived and neither can nor will deceive us. All this, of course, is true, but it would be erroneous to think that such an intellectual insight obtained in a natural way would be sufficient to lead man to the supernatural act of faith and consequently that apologetics would be an adequate basis for theology.

Modern theologians generally reject such a conception and defend again the Thomistic viewpoint that faith is supernatural in all its essential characteristics and therefore in its totality derives its origin from God. The motive of faith which leads us to the act of faith is not excluded from this totality. As Prof. Kreling expresses it, "Faith finds its motive solely in the divine revelation, as this revelation is given to the believer in the supernatural light of faith."[12]

---

[10]Cf. No. 3, *a,* p. 89.

[11]Cf. below, No. 3, *a* and *b,* pp. 89 ff.

[12]"De aard der H. Godgeleerdheid", *Jaarboek der R. K. Universiteit* 1928-29, p. 34.

The *certainty* of the knowledge given in faith does not have its basis in any intellectual insight but solely in divine truth, i.e., in God who in the act of faith communicates Himself in a supernatural way to the believer. In the act of faith the believer leaves the firm foundation of natural insight and, inspired and aided by grace, courageously leaps into the darkness of mystery. Consequently, it will never be possible to arrive at supernatural faith in God's revelation by way of profane inquiry or philosophical speculation. In all its essential elements the act of faith transcends the natural powers of man's reason. It is founded solely on God who communicates Himself to man.

Faith is a Rational Surrender. In spite of this irrational feature, it remains true that the act of faith is not an ill-considered adventure, a blind manifestation of a religious instinct,[13] but a rational submission (*rationale obsequium*) which man can justify by reason. To see this clearly, one should keep in mind the following points.

1. *God Does Not Go Against Man's Nature.* Even *a priori* speaking, it should be clear that man's surrender in faith must be rational, for as the Creator of human nature God can never demand something of man which would be non-rational, beneath man's dignity, i.e., something which would go against man's proper nature. On the other hand, God can make to man a gift which is beyond man's natural reach, provided that this gift does not militate against man's nature and, in addition, corresponds with a real possibility in man, an innate receptivity for the supernatural gift in question.

With respect to the first condition, there is no contradiction between human nature and faith but rather the opposite, inasmuch as the act of faith is adapted to man's character. For such an act is formally an act of the intellect, its object is truth, and the result of the surrender in faith is a type of knowledge.

As to the second condition, human religious experience shows that man possesses an innate capacity which renders it possible for him to accept supernatural faith. Although he is unable to actuate this capacity—which theologians call an 'obediential power'—by virtue of his own power, its actuation is brought about by an act of God when He infuses as a free gift the grace of faith.

2. *Man's Receptivity for the Supernatural.* A certain receptivity for a higher type of knowledge which is beyond the reach of his own

---

[13]Cf. Denziger, *op. cit.*, no. 2145.

powers may be said to be somewhat experienced by man when, reflecting on himself and the world, he is constantly confronted with mysteries that are impenetrable for him. In his search for the ultimate foundation of reality he is capable of arriving in a purely intellectual way at the conclusion that there exists an infinite self-existent Being. Proceeding very carefully, he manages to assign some attributes to this Being, but constantly he is forced to admit that he lacks the power to comprehend this Being, which he wants to call God, in human concepts. When in this way man endeavors to approach the bottomless mystery of the Godhead, he experiences, on the one hand, his own impotence but, on the other, he feels the desire to receive some light from this God, so that at least a tiny fragment of the veil may be lifted.[14] It is in this sense that the so-called philosophical proofs for the existence of God may produce a favorable disposition for the supernatural acceptance of faith.

3. *Intellectual Predisposition*. On the basis of signs that are knowable in a natural way, e.g., the fulfillment of prophecies, miracles, certain visible marks of the Church, and under the influence of grace, which is always available for anyone of good will, man can become convinced that what is proposed to him in faith is worthy of belief. In this case there arises a certain natural readiness to faith. Although in itself such readiness is not sufficient to bring man to the surrender demanded by supernatural faith, it can create a favorable disposition for God's action in man.

4. Once the supernatural virtue of faith is infused into someone, he will, inspired and illuminated by the Spirit of God, admit the proposed truth as certain and recognize the rationality of surrendering to God in faith. It is only then that the natural signs, enumerated in the preceding paragraph will be appreciated at their full value, i.e., as signs of God and as true motives of credibility.

5. *Analogy with Human Authority*. Man does not deem it unfitting or beneath his dignity to admit all kinds of facts and statements in the realm of profane science on the authority of a trustworthy person when he does not have a personal insight into the truth of the points in question. In the same way he should not consider it an affront to his dignity to give his intellectual assent to what is communicated to him by the authority of God and therefore

---

[14]Cf. Sect. V, No. 1 p. 105 f.

evidently true. Here too what leads him to assent is the 'evidence' for the proposed truth—namely the evidence of God's insight into it. As Thomas Aquinas expresses it, "In this science [theology] the immediate principle is faith, but the ultimate principle is the intellect of God in which we believe".[15]

6. *Faith Presupposes Natural Knowledge.* Although the object of faith is a mystery which man's intellect cannot fathom with its own power, nevertheless this mystery is something revealed to us in human language and consequently by means of human concepts. Thus there is a certain analogy between the divine Logos and human understanding. The collaboration of man's intellect is required in the act of faith, and therefore faith presupposes natural knowledge just as grace presupposes nature.[16] It is in this interconnection of knowledge through faith and natural knowledge that lies the possibility of the theological science which we will now consider.

3. *The Scientific Nature of Theology*

a. THE POSSIBILITY OF A THEOLOGICAL SCIENCE

Reflection on, and Synthesis of the Truths of Faith. As has been explained in the preceding pages, the act of faith through which man humbly makes himself receptive to the Self-revealing God is a function of reason, an intellectual assent, and consequently presupposes the natural operations of the human intellect. As required by the nature of this intellect, the truth of faith is seized in human concepts whose meaning man understands. Although such concepts are incapable of expressing the mystery fully, nevertheless despite their inadequacy they are sufficient to give us some human understanding of their object. The intellect is enabled to think about these concepts, analyze them as much as possible, explicate their contents, and clarify them by means of analogies. In this way a certain intellectual approximation of the mysteries of faith is possible and such an approximation in its turn can lead to an attempt to interconnect the various truths of faith. Thus it becomes possible to arrive at a certain synthesis of the revealed truths.

Derivation of New Truths. One may even go further and logically deduce new hitherto unknown truths from the truths accepted

---

[15]*In Boethium de Trinitate*, q. 2, a. 2, ad 7.
[16]Cf. Thomas Aquinas, *Summa Theol.*, p. I, q. 2, a. 2, ad 1.

through faith. Thus additional truths become known through the intermediary of a scientific process. It is in this way that "a believer may say that he has 'science' of all the conclusions derived from the articles of faith".[17] It is this intellectual reflection of the believer on the object of his faith which is meant by the classical dictum *"fides quaerens intellectum"*, i.e., faith that seeketh understanding.

Of course, in its reflection on the truths of faith the intellect makes use of purely human knowledge acquired from experience and resulting from the special sciences or philosophical considerations. However, in sacred theology one will always have to be on guard lest purely theological speculations, which are based on revelation, be mixed uncritically with mere human insights resulting from philosophical considerations. Too often such a confusion has obtained in the past to the great detriment of the authentic character proper to sacred theology.[18]

The Definition of Science Applies to Theology. The preceding remarks, then, mean that it is possible to study the object of faith intellectually in such a way that the conditions laid down by the definition of a scientific system[19] are largely met by theology. For the study described above terminates in a logically ordered whole of true, or sometimes merely probable, statements concerning the essence and properties of a certain object—namely, God and the relations of other things to God—in which due reference is made to the investigations, arguments and reasons on which the statements are based.

The statements of this science have a singular character insofar as they are directly concerned with God, but they are universal insofar as they pertain to man or more generally to created beings in their relationship to God. Universal in scope also are the norms for human activity which are deduced in the operative or moral part of theology.[20]

Although the preceding considerations could suffice for our purpose, it may be useful to mention and refute a few objections that are often raised against the scientific nature of theology, especially because the refutation will serve to clarify certain aspects of the theological sciences.

---

[17]Thomas Aquinas, *De veritate*, q. 14, a. 9, *ad* 3.
[18]Cf. Sect. V, No. 2, a, p. 110.
[19]Cf. Part One, Ch. II, no 8, p. 14.
[20]Cf. Sect. III, pp. 93 ff.

b. The Special Character and Dignity of Theology as a Science

Theology distinguishes itself from the other sciences especially in two respects—namely, 1) the mysterious nature of its object and 2) the supernatural origin of its foundation. These two aspects, obviously, are interconnected. For, if the first is accepted as a datum, it is evident that the statements concerning it have to be based on a source which is supernatural, i.e., transcends man. Reversely, the supernatural origin of the foundation implicitly contains that what is communicated must refer to something that is a mystery to man's intelligence, for God does not resort to revelation to teach man about profane things which he can discover and understand by means of his natural reason. God speaks to man about Himself, He reveals something of His mysterious nature to man in a language that man can understand. God, then, makes use of human concepts, but in such a way that what is communicated to man absolutely transcends human understanding. Because this aspect of revelation has already been spoken of when we considered faith as the foundation of theology,[21] we may restrict ourselves here to the refutation of a few objections.

Divine Revelation. The main reason why many philosophers of science do not want to recognize theology as a science lies in the peculiar character of its foundation—namely, divine revelation. First of all, the fact of revelation may be denied and, secondly, if the fact is admitted, one may reject that it can serve as the foundation of a system deserving to be called a science. This rejection is based on the supernatural character of revelation and its content. Let us make a few remarks about both.

The Fact of Revelation. Even for the believer the fact of revelation must be certain, because its content must be worthy of belief and the act of faith must be rational.[22] This fact and the exact verbal expression of what is contained in the revelation can be investigated and determined by means of the usual historical and philological methods, and this in such a way that any intellectual can be convinced unless he makes it a matter of principle not to consent. The task described here properly belongs to the historical sciences, exegesis, apologetics and so-called 'positive' theology.[23] When the fact of

---

[21]Cf. No 2, *a*, p. 84.
[22]Cf. No. 2, *b*, p. 86.
[23]Cf. Sect. IV, p. 97.

revelation and its literal content in this way have become no longer
subject to dispute, they can be admitted as the foundation of a scientific system. As to the content, meaning, and interpretation of
revelation, they can be seized to a certain extent only through a
supernatural act of faith, and this act is possible only for those to
whom God communicates Himself in a free gift.

The scientific nature of theology can be defended also against
those who for one reason or another do not wish to recognize the
fact of revelation. In this case theology is put on the same line as
various other sciences which likewise have a hypothetical and therefore disputable foundation but whose scientific character is not denied
by anyone. We are thinking here, for example, of a system built
on a number of axioms that have been chosen rather arbitrarily. To
illustrate our assertion, we may quote here a few lines from Prof. E.
de Bruyne: "Even theology should be respected by the non-believer
when it lays claim to being scientific. As soon as it is impossible
to demonstrate that its fundamentals are evidently absurd, so that
they have to be accepted at least as non-contradictory, although in
themselves unproved, postulates, one is forced to qualify as formally
scientific the system of deductions and analogies which, following
the rules of formal logic, remains faithful to its fundamental definitions."[24]

The Supernatural Character of Revelation. To refute objections
based on this character, one may fruitfully make use of what has
been said above about the rationality of the act of faith and about
the possibility of a theological science. In addition, one should keep
in mind that it is precisely the supernatural character of theology
which constitutes the basis for its exceptional dignity among the
sciences, despite the fact that this character is the reason why many
who are willing to accept theology as a science hold theology in less
esteem than the natural sciences. Let us explain our reasons for
saying this.

In theology it is impossible to arrive at a purely intellectual
insight into the fundamental truths. In surrendering in faith one
can rely only on the insight God has into these truths. Hence it is
easy to see why many are not inclined to put the value of theology
on a par with that of the non-theological sciences, even if they are
willing to recognize theology as a science. Against this view we

---

[24]*Ethica,* Antwerp-Brussels and Nijmegen-Utrecht, 1934, Part I, p. 35.

may maintain that theology as a science is the most eminent of all sciences inasmuch as it transcends the others in the certainty of its foundation and in the dignity of its object.[25] Its starting point is revealed truths which owe their intrinsic evidence to God's insight. Thus theology can boast of the greatest possible certainty, while the natural sciences, on the other hand, have to rely on human insight which in many ways can be deficient.

Moreover, theology has as its object God Himself, who infinitely transcends man's intellect, although He makes Himself known to man to some extent in the free gift of faith. The natural sciences, on the contrary, are concerned with created, finite and limited objects and with truths that are accessible to man's restricted intellectual powers. In applying himself to the natural sciences, man remains on the level which is adapted to his natural capacities, but in faith the theologian is raised through God's power to a level which he could never reach by means of his natural powers. Thus, even as viewed from man's state, theology demands to be valued as pertaining to a superior rank of science, for it gives man a higher and more certain knowledge than do the natural sciences.

Finally, the theological sciences have an eminently practical value for man insofar as the knowledge contained in them teaches him about his relationship to God and makes him understand the ultimate destiny for which he has to prepare himself actively through his earthly life. This point will be considered more extensively in the succeeding section.

III. OPERATIVE OR MORAL THEOLOGY

1. *Introduction*

As was pointed out in Section I, the data of revelation are partly of a speculative and partly of an operative nature. Data of the first kind, in which God to some extent makes himself known in His essence, may be taken as the foundation of the speculative or dogmatic theology considered in the preceding section. On the other hand, God has revealed Himself as the final end to which man, as raised to the supernatural order, should direct himself in his free activities. Moreover, He has come to man in a special way through Jesus-Christ, God Incarnate, whose living example serves to direct man and whose power enables man to conform himself

---

[25]Cf. Thomas Aquinas, *Summa Theol.*, p. I, q. 2, a. 5.

with God. Through faith man is orientated to God, through the supernatural disposition of hope he is able trustingly to surrender to God. But it is especially the supernatural virtue of charity or love of God and man that must determine man's moral life in all its aspects. As Saint Thomas expresses it very succinctly, "Charity is the form of all virtues" (*caritas est forma omnium virtutum*). Revelation has given man also various positive and negative norms governing his moral life. However, insofar as they are positive, these norms may all be viewed as further specifications of the general command of love with respect to different realms of life and, insofar as they are negative, they draw attention to certain deviations from the requirements imposed by the command of love. The virtue of charity, therefore, dominates so much that there is some justification for the claim of certain theologians who want to call moral theology the 'theological science of charity', at least if love is viewed in its operative aspect, i.e., as the principle of all moral activity.

These and other similar data of revelation constitute the fundamental principles on which an operative or moral theology can be built.

To prevent misunderstandings, let us remark at once that, as will become increasingly clear in the course of this section, speculative and operative theology cannot be rigorously separated. Only a distinction can be made on the basis of their general scope. Both are integral parts of one and the same supernatural theology. They need and complement each other in the sense that dogmatic theology is an ontological science and therefore purely speculative, while moral theology, like any operative science is both speculative and operative.[26]

What has been said in the preceding section concerning theology in general holds also for moral theology. This applies especially to the nature of its foundation in revelation and faith and to its supernatural character. For this reason we may limit ourselves here to a brief explanation of what is proper to moral theology.

2. *The Proper Character and Dignity of Moral Theology*

Object of Moral Theology. Like dogmatic theology, moral theology has God as its principal and primary object, but only under a certain respect—namely, God as the ultimate end of man, in other words, God insofar as, being infinite Truth and Goodness, He has to be the final goal of man's free activities of knowing and willing, and insofar as He can fully satisfy man's desire of happiness. Moral theology speaks also about man, but only as a secondary object, inso-

---

[26]Cf. Ch. IV, Sect. II, No. 3, p. 63.

far as divine revelation teaches us something concerning his mysterious elevation to the supernatural order, his ultimate goal in God, and his possible answer to the appeal of God Himself. As Thomas Aquinas expresses it, moral theology is concerned with the rational creature's ascent to God.

Speculative Aspect. Moral theology does not limit itself to a mere enumeration of divinely revealed norms which recommend, command, or forbid certain human activities. Otherwise it would not even deserve the name of science. Like any operative science, its task is to make the rules of human behavior which it formulates intelligible by means of speculative considerations. The theoretical foundation for these speculations may be derived from dogmatic theology or also developed within the domain of moral theology itself. With St. Thomas in his *Summa theologica* (Part II), modern moralists speak of God as the final end of man, man's elevation to the supernatural life of God, grace, the nature of supernatural human acts, good and evil in moral actions, divinely infused theological and moral virtues in general and in particular, the vices opposed to these virtues, the Gifts of the Holy Ghost and the Sacraments, active and contemplative life, the vision of God as the prolongation and terminus of faith, conscience, etc. A Christian moral theology obviously will have to speak also about Christ, who revealed Himself as the Way and the Life, whom every Christian must imitate in his supernatural life, as well as about the Church whose task it is to lead mankind on its pilgrimage to its final destiny and to fortify man supernaturally by means of its sacramental and non-sacramental fountains of grace as long as he is a wayfarer seeking his ultimate goal.

All these and many other points belong to the speculative or ontological foundation on which the more operative considerations have to be based. The revealed norms of morality are placed within the framework of these speculative positions and rendered intelligible in their mutual interconnection. New and more particularized norms— which still remain of a universal character—are deduced from them with respect to special states of life and situations. In this way the scientific character of the whole is safeguarded, for it remains a logically ordered system of true and universal statements which are recognized as built upon an ontological basis and understood in their interrelationship.

Operative Character. Briefly put, moral theology may be considered as the science of what God has revealed about His plan to save man. In the execution of this plan man must freely collaborate according to the lines formally laid down by God or discovered through the investigations of individual believers or the scientific research of moral theologians. Because the statements of moral theology are an expression of God's will with respect to man in the supernatural development of his being, and because these statements are consequently norms for man's activity in his striving for God as his ultimate end, it follows that we have to do here with a practical or operative science.

Accordingly, it should be clear that moral theology is not a purely theoretical science, as is sometimes claimed. On the other hand, it should not degenerate into an applied science which supplies priests and directors of souls with useful data for their pastoral duties and sermons and has no other meaning for human beings in general than to provide a collection of various special directives and counsels in the most diverse situations.

Casuistry. The norms of morality known from revelation or deduced by moral theology remain of a very general character and therefore do not provide more than general principles for man's orientation to God. For its practical applications moral theology needs to be extended in so-called casuistry. In our time many distrust or even despise casuistry. Although there is some justification for this attitude, casuistry cannot simply be set aside as wholly useless. On the other hand, it goes without saying that one should be careful not to proceed in a way that is too rationalistic and too objectivistic. The function of casuistry is to derive from general insights acquired in moral theology the specific directives for particular situations, which it usually illustrates by means of concrete examples. However, in his concrete actions man is always faced with a unique situation and consequently will have to be guided not only by general and specific norms of moral theology and casuistry but also and especially by his personal conscience and by the virtue of prudence.[27] For this reason moral theology has the task of considering *in extenso* the supernatural virtue of prudence and especially the value and function of the personal decision of conscience and its relationship to the general norms. All this should be done in such a way that there is no danger of lapsing in the onesidedness of situational morality.

Natural Elements in Moral Theology. After the preceding remarks it should not be necessary to repeat that moral theology as a whole possesses a supernatural character because of its foundation in revelation and its divine object. However, the secondary object of moral theology is man himself. Although man is considered pri-

---

[27]Cf. Ch. IV, Sect. II, No. 5, b, p. 70.

marily insofar as through God's favor he is raised to a higher order, this elevation does not destroy human nature but presupposes it. For this reason moral theology may and must prudently make use of the various insights into man and his relation to God that have been obtained through natural human means. Thus certain results reached by philosophy and the experiential sciences may be useful also for moral theology. We will revert to this point in Sections IV and V.

Dignity of Moral Theology. The character of an operative science is determined by the purpose of the human activity considered in that science. Therefore, an operative science will have to be valued more highly according as its object aims at a higher goal. Consequently, moral theology is the most worthy of all operative sciences, for it aims at the highest goal attainable by man—namely, his supreme happiness through knowing and loving God. All other operative sciences are subordinated to moral theology, because their scope extends only to a purpose to be realized here on earth in a limited realm of life.[28] For one who possesses a balanced and integral view of man there can be no doubt that the other, special, operative sciences in the derivation and formulation of their norms of action must always take into account the ultimate destiny of man and consequently the statements of moral theology insofar as they affect the realms of human activity in question. Accordingly, moral theology possesses a unique and predominant significance for human culture in general. We will say more about this point in Chapter VII when we will consider the special operative sciences.

IV. THEOLOGICAL SCIENCES IN THE BROADER SENSE

1. *General Consideration*

After paying attention to the theological sciences in the strict sense of the term, i.e., speculative or dogmatic theology and operative or moral theology, one should keep in mind that there are a number of sciences which, on the one hand, are distinct from the above-mentioned theological sciences but, on the other hand, do not belong to the purely profane or natural sciences. We are referring to the sciences which, because of their connection with purely theological science, are usually attached to the theological department of universities and seminaries.

---

[28]Cf. Thomas Aquinas, *Summa Theol.*, p. I, q. 1, a. 5, and also Sect. V, No. 2, *b*, p. 111 of this chapter.

Speculative Sciences. This group contains first of all a group of speculative sciences, such as hermeneutics and scriptural exegesis, the history of revelation, Church history, general history of religion, science of liturgy, philosophy of religion, etc. A few of these will be considered more in detail in this section.

This group contains also so-called 'positive' theology, at least if this term is taken to mean the science which studies the sources of theology. Because the primary object of theology is God Himself, the first and most fundamental source of theology is, of course, divine revelation, as it is contained in Scripture and Tradition, interpreted under God's guidance by the teaching authority of the Church, and proposed to the believer in the articles of faith. The domain in question pertains mostly to exegesis. However, in his scientific labors the theologian will make a fruitful use also of the work and ideas of his Christian predecessors, especially those of the first centuries of Christianity, among whom, of course, most useful are the considerations of those who because of their holiness and doctrine are honored with the titles of Father or Doctor of the Church.

Operative Sciences. There exists also a group of operative sciences which have a certain theological bearing without, however, simply belonging to moral theology as we have considered it in the preceding section. In the first place, we may name so-called 'pastoral' theology, which seeks the norms according to which the minister of religion has to exercise his triple functions of priest, teacher, and director of souls. Next, homiletics, which teaches the best way of preaching the Gospel in sermons and addresses, and catechetics or the study of the teaching of religion. Sometimes homiletics and catechetics are considered as parts of pastoral theology. To this group one may add practical liturgy or the teaching of rubrics, although it is difficult to apply here the honored title of 'science' if the teaching is limited to a mere enumeration of liturgical or rubrical rules.

Some of these sciences could easily be incorporated into dogmatic or moral theology. However, in practice they are usually given a separate status and taught by specialized teachers, because they contain so many data of auxiliary sciences that a special study is required. This is an *a posteriori* sign that these sciences have a character of their own. They are always sciences which have unmistakable profane aspects because in many ways they rely on the data of profane sciences but, on the other hand, they also have an unmistakable non-profane aspect insofar as they are all concerned with faith and consequently with the divine mystery.

Missiology. Special mention should be made here of missiology. Strictly speaking, missiology is not a single science, but a complex of many speculative and practical sciences. It studies, first of all, in a fundamental way the essence and history of the mission insofar as it is the mission of the Church to preach the Gospel. Next, it extends itself to operative sciences which can indicate directives that should be followed in the enormous realm of missionary activity if the task imposed by the Church's mission is to be accomplished as effectively as possible.

This brief mention of some sciences which in our view possess a theological character without, however, belonging to the purely theological sciences is perhaps sufficient to illustrate the proper nature of these groups of sciences. Nevertheless, it may not be amiss to clarify our view by means of two examples—namely, scriptural exegesis and Church history.

2. *Scriptural Exegesis*[29]

By *exegesis,* which comes from the Greek verb *exêgeisthai,* to explain, in general is meant the explanation of a certain religious or profane text. In this sense exegesis is an application of the so-called '*hermeneutics*', the science which establishes the general and particular norms for investigating and determining the meaning of a text. In what follows we will limit ourselves to the hermeneutics and exegesis of the Bible.

General Rules of Hermeneutics. Because Scripture is a text written by human beings, one can apply to it the general rules of hermeneutics which apply to every explanation of a text. For the divine inspiration of Scripture does not prevent its sacred human author from using his own initiative and working according to his own capabilities. Consequently, in this respect the method of procedure can be the same for both believer and unbeliever. This method implies several phases:

1. To establish the correct text by studying and comparing the relevant manuscripts and old translations;

---

[29] For this part we have made use of the article "Bijbelverklaring" in *Bijbels Woordenboek*, Roermond-Maaseik, 2nd ed., 1954-57.

2. To study its context, coherence, parallel places, commentaries, etc. in order to arrive at the exact meaning of the words and expressions intended by the author;

3. To determine the literary nature of the text, the character of its author, the circumstances of place and time of composition, the occasion, and the purpose intended by the author, for they influence the exegesis of the text.

The same hermeneutic rules and the same requisites of learning are demanded for profane and for sacred writings if a correct interpretation is to be made; consequently, believers and unbelievers can make equal contributions in this respect.

Scriptural Hermeneutics. However, the exegesis of the books of the Bible, like that of typically religious writings in general, require more than the above-mentioned general rules of text interpretation. The special character of these books demands a peculiar attitude and openness on the part of the interpreter, without which it is impossible to find the exact meaning and intention of such texts. Many things, persons, and events mentioned in the Bible have a special figurative meaning, intended by God, which does not reveal itself from the context alone, but becomes clear only from other scriptural texts or the general consent of Tradition. Such a sense, of course, is convincing only for one who recognizes God as the ultimate author of the whole Bible and is willing to hear the Holy Spirit speaking in Tradition.

Especially in the exegesis of Scripture the exegete must allow himself to be guided by specifically 'Christian' rules of hermeneutics, as they have been laid down for Catholics in the encyclicals *Providentissimus Deus* (1893) of Pope Leo XIII and *Divino Afflante Spiritu* (1943) of Pope Pius XII and further explained and clarified by the Pontifical Biblical Commission. A few rules of a Christian hermeneutics are the following:

1. The specifically proper religious and moral character of the Bible must be recognized;

2. As the word of God, the Bible cannot contain any formal errors;

3. The interpretation of learned and holy Fathers of the Church and ecclesiastical writers must be taken into account, especially when they are unanimous in their interpretation;

4. Catholic exegetes especially should not go counter to the interpretation given by the teaching authority of the Church if such an
interpretation has been proposed as definite.

These rules of a Christian hermeneutics are clear and do not need
any further explanation for anyone who admits what has been said
in Section II regarding the supernatural character of faith, which
ultimately obtains its content from these sources of revelation. If
God uses human language to speak about Himself, then His words
are, of course, to some extent intelligible for man, but at the same
time they are of an analogous nature and consequently their ultimate
meaning cannot be fully grasped by purely human means. One can
learn by heart entire sections of the Bible and still be blind to their
proper content as intended by God. The 'divine mystery' contained
in the sacred books is accessible only to those to whom God reveals
Himself in a personal encounter and only to the extent in which in
this encounter He wishes to reveal Himself. Accordingly, a genuine
biblical exegesis is possible only if the interpreter approaches the
sacred text in an attitude of faith and humility, in a constant readiness
to listen to what the Spirit of God says, even if it be by means of
the human voices of authoritative believing interpreters and especially
the authentic statements of the teaching authority of the Church which
God has established specifically for this purpose.

3. *Church History*

Among the theological sciences in the broader sense of the term
we should classify also the history of revelation and especially that of
the Church. For such history evidently contains a profane or natural
aspect in addition to its non-profane, religious, or supernatural aspect.
For brevity's sake we will limit ourselves here to the history of the
Church founded by Christ.

Similarity with Profane History. First of all, we find in Church
history an abundance of sense perceptible data, such as Church institutions, authorities and other ecclesiastical persons with their activities, manifold manifestations of the Church, publications for or
against the Church, events of importance for its development, etc.
Briefly put, there are all kinds of facts, in the broad sense of this
term, which can be described and recorded for posterity just like
the facts pertaining to other histories.

However, when the work of the historiographer, who records the
facts, is finished, the task of the historian begins: he has to interpret

the facts, place them in the framework of place and time, of surroundings and persons, to find in this way the connection between
the various facts and explain the actual course of history. It is in
this stage that every historical science experiences great difficulties
because of the danger of subjectivity, inasmuch as in the interpretation
of the facts the psychological attitude toward personalities proper to
the interpreter and his views of life and the world threaten to play
too great a role. We will say more about this point in the next
chapter when we will have to consider the so-called *Geisteswissenschaften* or cultural sciences. At present we will restrict ourselves
to the peculiarities and difficulties that occur in the study of Church
history.

Supernatural Aspect. Just as the innermost nature of the person
and work of Jesus Christ is and remains a mystery for us, so also
will there always be for us something of this divine mystery in the
Church He has founded to continue His Incarnation and work
among man. Although we must try to penetrate as deeply as possible
into this mystery, there will always remain a veiled core. In Church
history one should always keep in mind St. Augustine's famous saying: *"factum audivimus, mysterium inquiramus",* now that we know
the fact, let us search for the mystery (contained in it). Because
there is question here of a divine mystery, the search will have to be
conducted with the proper 'theological' attitude mentioned in Section II.

Accordingly, it follows that only a convinced Christian is capable
of approaching as much as possible the essence of the Church and
its development through the course of centuries. Because he is
aware of the divine element in the Church, he will allow the facts
to speak while as a believer he listens in an attitude of respect. He
will see Church dignitaries, in spite of their human faults and
defects, as representatives of Christ on earth who, although they
are often unaware of it, undergo in their activities the directing
influence of God's Spirit. To say it in a few words, the Christian
historian will pay attention to the 'miracle' that the Church itself
is and at the same time he will distinguish the divine from the human
element.

A Genuine Science. Again, the question arises whether the history of revelation and the Church deserves to be called a science. Is
it not true that such an attitude does violence to the truth for the

sake of faith and Christian piety? The reply here also lies in a reference to the proper character of Church history as a theological science in the broader sense. Truth in this realm is not a purely natural truth, which can be reached by means of purely human abilities. There is a mixture here of natural and supernatural truth which in its totality can be seized to some extent only by a human mind that is illuminated through divine grace.

A conflict between truth and reverence is not possible in the Christian historian in the sense that out of reverence for the Church he would be inclined to camouflage or omit the less flattering part of the truth and to confer in this way more splendor on the attractive aspects of Church history. In this domain the sole truth is a respectful truth. For this reason the Christian historian will consider it his duty to let the facts speak and only the facts, without concealing or adding anything. In his interpretation and explanation of the facts, however, he will proceed in another way than a non-Christian or unbeliever. The believing historian possesses a great advantage over his non-Christian colleague, insofar as because of his faith he disposes, as it were, of a sixth sense and has an added dimension which is lacking in the unbeliever who does not perceive the supernatural.

If it were necessary to remove the supernatural aspect from Church history in order to study this history 'objectively', consistency would demand that more confidence be shown to unbelieving historians than to believers. Von Harnack and Renan would be more reliable guides than Pastor or Newman. This is a consequence which even the opponent of the above-explained conception of Church history would hesitate to admit.

4. *Summary and Concluding Remark*

The preceding considerations should suffice to justify the view that there is a group of theological sciences in the broad sense of the term. They clearly possess definite profane aspects insofar as in many respects they are based on the data of the profane sciences or use their methods. On the other hand, they also have an unmistakably non-profane character because they are concerned with supernatural faith, with the divine mystery. As such, they themselves are of a supernatural or theological nature, so that purely natural means are not sufficient to develop them.

If one wants to proceed in a profane or 'positive' fashion, relying solely on modern philological and historical methods in investing the origin of dogmata from the sources of revelation or their development in the course of time, one can undoubtedly do useful work of incalculable advantage to genuine theology. However, such a procedure does not go beyond the boundaries of purely human science, so that it would be a grave mistake to think that there is question here of theology in the sense of a 'science of God'. Historico-philological methods may help a scholar to approach the divine, so to speak, on the surface, but they are powerless to seize it in its inner core. Only God's Spirit provides the necessary light and insight in this matter to those who are open for Him when He communicates Himself as a free gift.

There is no need to fear that the admission of natural and supernatural elements in the theological sciences may put the unity of thought into jeopardy. For there are no two distinct thinking subjects here, but one and the same human mind, illuminated by grace, seizes both aspects at the same time, so that this mind is the principle of unity.

V. Relations of Theological and Non-Theological Sciences

As was pointed out in the first section, the theological sciences, because of their supernatural foundation and object, are opposed to the non-theological sciences, in which man restricts himself to data and insights that are obtainable through purely natural cognitive powers. For this reason we called the non-theological sciences 'natural' or 'profane' sciences. This group contains not only philosophy but also non-philosophical or specialized sciences.

In this section we will devote some attention to the manifold reciprocal relations existing between the theological and non-theological sciences. Limiting ourselves to certain aspects which are within the scope of this study, we will first consider the relationship of theological and philosophical sciences[30] and next that between theological and specialized sciences.

---

[30]We are presupposing here two points that will be considered only in Chapter IX—namely, the existence of a philosophical science and the way in which, in our view, philosophy should be conceived. This anticipation is sufficiently motivated by the legitimate desire to group the relationships of all other sciences with theology under a single heading.

1. *Relationship of Theological and Philosophical Sciences*

Material and Formal Objects. The division of the sciences into supernatural and natural sciences is not necessarily a division according to their material object. Even *a priori* it is not excluded that the same material object may be known by means of man's natural sources of knowledge as well as through revelation. Although *de facto* divine revelation is concerned with God Himself and the relations of world and man to God, there are some fundamental truths concerning God and these relations which man is capable of learning by means of his natural powers. Hence alongside statements or dogmata based on divine revelation there may be human assertions which in part express the same truths, but only insofar as these truths flow from man's intellect as proceeding and reasoning in a natural way. For this reason in principle there is a possibility that alongside the supernatural sciences other sciences will develop which have the same material object, but differ from them in the nature of their foundation, the origin of their fundamental data, the view point adopted by them, and consequently, their formal object.[31]

Briefly put, we may say this—the theological sciences have as their formal object (*objectum formale quod*) God and created things with respect to God as manifested in revelation, but the natural sciences in question have as their formal object God and created things with respect to God as knowable to man's intellect by virtue of its own power and without revelation. The means and methods (*objectum formale quo*) for studying this object are, in the case of the theological sciences, the God-given grace of faith, the light of revelation, and devout meditation; in the case of the natural sciences of God, rational consideration of, and reflection on the nature of man and the world.

These 'natural' speculations about God and things pertaining to God lie beyond the realm of the specialized sciences. First of all, because of their profound nature, they do not belong to the domain of the experiential sciences, for the latter are concerned with nature, man, and culture insofar as through the senses these things can become the object of intellectual knowledge. Secondly, they are not interested in ideal beings, such as mathematical objects. Finally, they do not belong to the group of profane operative sciences, for these

---

[31]Cf. Part One, Ch. V, pp. 43 ff.

study the different realms of human activities concerned with profane endeavors and attempt to arrive at the correct norms of human actions by studying the nature of these activities and the purpose to which they are directed.[32]

It may be admitted that a 'natural' scientific study of God can take its starting point in certain data supplied by specialized sciences, but such a study transcends the realms of these sciences by virtue of its distinctly proper character. This scientific study of God is of a philosophical nature. It pertains partly to the speculative part of philosophy and partly to the operative part according as the considerations in question refer to the material object of speculative theology or to that of operative theology.

a. DOGMATIC THEOLOGY AND THE PHILOSOPHY OF GOD

Existence of God. Speculative or dogmatic theology is concerned with God as He can be known from the sources of revelation, i.e., Scripture and Tradition. However, a number of truths about God can be discovered by man's natural intellect in considerations and arguments of a philosophical nature. Reflecting on the world and on himself, and especially on the aspects of mutability, dependency, contingency, limitation, and inner finality in the parts as well as the whole of the world, man is capable of arriving with certainty at the conclusion that there exists a Being which is immutable, independent, necessary and therefore eternal, a Being that is the fullness of 'to be', infinite in its perfection of being, and the groundless ground of all particular beings. This Being, which transcends the world, is called God.[33] This God of the philosophers has to be identified with the God of revelation, the God of Abraham, Isaac, and Jacob.

God's existence may be discovered also, as it was done by Newman, by reflecting on the existence of moral categories or man's conscience. In this way He becomes known as the Supreme Lawgiver and the ultimate ground for the existence of an absolute moral order to which all men are subject. Still other approaches to God are possible.

Philosophy of God and Metaphysics. These and other similar considerations lie, as was mentioned, outside the realm of the special sciences and consequently are of a philosophical nature. They constitute that part of philosophy which sometimes is indicated by the

---

[32]Cf. the schematic division of the science in Ch. III, p. 42.
[33]Cf. Thomas Aquinas, *Contra Gentes,* bk. I, ch. 13.

Leibnitzian term 'theodicy'. However, we prefer to speak of it as 'natural' or 'philosophical' science of God or also as 'natural theology' and consider it as the crowning point of metaphysics, inasmuch as the study of the 'to be' of particular beings would remain incomplete if it did not culminate in statements concerning the absolute 'to be' itself, i.e., the personal God.[34]

Accordingly, philosophical theology is more a study of being than of God. It makes Him known to us from His creatures in the way a cause is known from its effects. From limited beings known by the human intellect it reasons to the infinite and transcendent absolute Being itself. Natural theology does not speak of the divine as such, but of the absolute cause of being, the groundless ground of all that is, the being which is the fullness of ontological perfection, the infinite and absolute being, which man calls God.

Dogmatic theology, on the other hand, speaks about God and the divine as such, according as He has freely manifested Himself in revelation. From this knowledge of God as Creator and Governor of all, and Father of mankind, it deduces conclusions concerning creatures as God's handiwork and concerning man as a child of His heavenly Father, an image and partaker of divine nature. Its purpose is not to acquire knowledge about creatures in themselves, i.e., according to their specific nature, but its object is always God and God alone.

b. MORAL THEOLOGY AND MORAL PHILOSOPHY

Analogously to the twofold study of God in dogmatic theology and the philosophy of God there is also a twofold way in which the principles can be considered which lead man's life to its ultimate destiny. In operative or moral theology the final end of man and the supernatural life leading to it are known to us from revelation. The same is true of certain norms which man has to observe in his life and in realizing his potentialities. We may name, for instance, the Decalogue and the commandment of love for God and man which Christ gave us.

The branch of philosophy called moral philosophy or ethics also speaks of the way in which man must direct his life to his ultimate

---

[34]Less fortunate is the conception of Christian von Wolff (1679-1754), which subsequently was taken over by many scholastic handbooks, who considers the philosophical study of God as a special metaphysics alongside the special metaphysical studies of man and cosmos.

goal. It also deduces certain norms which ought to rule his actions. However, the intellectual process is different. In ethics one starts from man's position as a creature and his relation of dependence to God as they are known from the philosophy of God or are arrived at in the theoretical part of ethics. In this way one can obtain knowledge of man's natural ultimate end. Next, one relies on philosophical and non-philosophical insights into man's nature, taken in its broad sense, i.e., specifically and individually, socially, abstractly and concretely, in all its relations to God, fellow human beings and other creatures. From this starting point and on this basis the moral philosopher proceeds to derive norms man has to follow in order to unfold his vital capacities in the correct way with due regard for God, himself, his fellow-men, both in their individuality and in the manifold social relationships in which he encounters them, and also with respect to non-human creatures.

c. DIFFERENCES AND RELATIONS BETWEEN THEOLOGICAL AND PHILOSOPHICAL CONSIDERATIONS

Differences. Although the considerations of dogmatic and moral theology on the one hand and those of the philosophy of God and ethics on the other largely refer to the same object, nevertheless there exist between the two also great differences. First of all, as has already been pointed out, there is a difference in formal object. Next, and as a result of this difference, the procedures do not at all run parallel. With respect to the fundamental truths, the paths are even opposite: what in theology is a revealed truth functioning as a starting point, e.g., the existence of God, the final end of man, and norms of human actions, in philosophy usually is the terminus resulting from a difficult and involved argumentation.

Mutual Relations. Although in principle theological and philosophical speculations may take an independent course, in practice many mutual relations are possible. A philosopher who believes in God and divine revelation knows already the fundamental truths which will result from his philosophical considerations. Thus he is *a priori* willing to accept these results and is safeguarded from essential errors.

On the other hand, philosophical thinking is capable of aiding theology, insofar as it is able to clarify somewhat or interconnect revealed truths or deduce new truths from those known through revelation.[35] For instance, the philosophical analyses of such concepts as substance, nature, essence, and person may provide some light in the study of the purely theological problems of the Holy Trinity and the Son of God, insofar as they lead us to speak of one God in three Persons or of the hypostatical union of the divine nature and the human nature in one Person. On the other hand, these truths of faith may prove fertile and enriching when the above-mentioned concepts are studied in a Christian philosophy. Moreover, the knowledge of God obtained through metaphysical speculations as the self-subsistent being, the first cause, and the ultimate end, if compared with knowledge gathered from faith or theological deductions, will safeguard the theologian from too anthropomorphistic statements about God and keep alive in him a holy fear for the mysterious object of his study.

A Twofold Way to God. Accordingly, there is a twofold way to God: first, a direct way through faith by surrender to the self-revealing God; secondly, a philosophical way which from the creatures leads to God as the first cause and ultimate ground of everything, insofar as it teaches us to see the things of this world as pointers to God. The difficulties of this second way flowing from the limitations of our mind and the lack of a guaranteed certainty may induce the philosopher to see the advantages of the first way and consequently to admit the reasonableness of surrendering to God in faith. In such fashion a philosophical consideration of God may gradually render someone who does not yet believe susceptible of supernatural faith. On the other hand, when the believer engages in a philosophical study of God, he will be greatly comforted to see how nature and supernature, philosophical insight and infused knowledge aid and complement each other and find their synthesis in a single act of the intellect.

2. *Relations of Theological and Non-Philosophical Sciences*

The relations of the theological sciences with other disciplines are not limited to philosophy but extend also to the non-philosophical sciences, with which they can have manifold contacts. On the one hand, the theological sciences depend in many ways on the specialized sciences with respect to their foundation and development and, on the other, the special non-philosophical sciences may be comple-

---

[35]Cf. Sect. II, No. 3, a, pp. 89 ff.

mented and supported in a variety of ways by the theological sciences. Let us devote some attention to these two points.

a. The Theological Sciences Need the Special Sciences

After what has been said in the preceding sections this assertion hardly needs to be proved. The theological sciences do not merely speak about God and the attributes which in terms of human concepts pertain to Him, but also about created beings and especially man in their relationship to God. Hence it should be evident that naturally-acquired knowledge about human and non-human objects may often be useful and even necessary for a more perfect understanding of theological problems, at least insofar as such an understanding is possible for man's limited intellect. This point is valid for the purely theological sciences and especially for moral theology, but it applies more strikingly still to the theological sciences in the broader sense of the term. Christian thinkers and men of science, therefore, have an important role to play in this respect insofar as they develop the profane sciences in question in such a way that the theological sciences can derive full profit from them.

Examples. Let us illustrate the point by means of a few examples. As was pointed out in Section III, moral theology has to pay attention to many natural elements because its function is to prescribe directives for man's actions in all kinds of real-life situations. This is true especially of casuistry. Obviously, therefore, to proceed scientifically, it needs the aid of various natural sciences, such as cultural anthropology, psychology, law, sociology, and the history of morality.

Pastoral theology, in the broad sense indicated in Section IV, will have to take into consideration various data of medical sciences, e.g., pastoral medicine and psychiatry; likewise, the findings of psychology, sociology, pedagogy, anthropology, etc.

Scriptural exegesis makes use of many auxiliary sciences, such as archeology, philology, comparative linguistics, history in the broadest sense and especially the history of religion, geography, ethnology, paleontology, papyrology, etc.

Remark. It may be useful to remark that the data of the profane sciences, as such, can never become integral parts of the purely theological sciences. They are used in them only as building blocks and supplementary materials which are ennobled by the supernatural whole in whose construction they take part.[36]

b. The Special Sciences Need the Theological Sciences

For this part we should be satisfied with referring the reader to Newman's THE IDEA OF A UNIVERSITY and urging him to read Discourse III, "Bearing of Theology on Other Branches of Knowledge".[37] In this discourse Newman indicates better than we ourselves could do it the manifold implications theology has for other sciences and in all kinds of areas of human life. "I only say, if there be Religious Truth at all, we cannot shut our eyes to it without prejudice to truth of every kind, physical, metaphysical, historical and moral; for it bears upon all truth."[38] Newman begins by remarking that everything considered by the profane sciences is something created by God: "The laws of the universe, the principles of truth, the relation of one thing to another, their qualities and virtues, the order and harmony of the whole, all that exists, is from Him."[39] The same applies to the intellectual, moral, social, and political world: "Man, with his motives and works, his languages, his propagation, his diffusion, is from him. Agriculture, medicine, and the arts of life, are His gifts. Society, laws, government, He is their sanction."[40] Accordingly, the profane sciences are always concerned with God's creatures in the broad sense of the term. For this reason the man who studies these sciences will receive a reference to God from the object of his study, at least if he is receptive of such a sign. In God alone lies the ultimate explanation of all that is and of the laws that rule everything.

Philosophy and the Sciences of Man. In particular, the theological sciences have to exercise influence on philosophy and the sciences of man and civilization, for such sciences are concerned with the truth or falsity of things which interest man as man. As Newman says, "What results of philosophic speculation are unquestionable, if they have been gained without inquiry as to what

---

[36]Cf. Thomas Aquinas, *Summa Theol.*, p. I, q. 1, a. 5, *ad* 2: "[Theology] does not borrow anything from the other sciences as from superior [disciplines], but uses them as subordinate and auxiliary [sciences]."

[37]Longmans, Green and Co. ed. of 1947 pp. 39-62. The quotations which follow are taken from this edition.

[38]*Op. cit.,* p. 47.

[39]*Op. cit.,* p. 57.

[40]*Ibid.*

Theology has to say of them? Does it cast no light on history?
Has it no influence upon the principles of Ethics? Is it without
any sort of bearing on physics, metaphysics, and political science?
Can we drop it out of the circle of knowledge, without allowing,
either that that circle is thereby mutilated, or on the other hand,
that Theology is really no science?"[41] Theology "has *prima facie*
claims upon us, so imposing, that it can only be rejected on the
ground of those claims being nothing more than imposing, that is,
being false. As to our own countries, it occupies our language,
it meets us at every turn in our literature, it is the secret assumption,
too axiomatic to be distinctly professed, of all our writers; nor can
we help assuming it ourselves, except by the most unnatural vigilance.
Whoever philosophizes, starts with it, and introduces it, when he
will, without any apology."[42]

Examples. A few examples may serve to clarify all this. It
depends, for instance, on the extent to which faith or the data of
the theological sciences influence a person how he will view the
meaning of his own existence, what attitude he will adopt toward
human culture, whether he will give a pessimistic or optimistic reply
to the question concerning the present value of mankind, its future
development, etc.

In their most profound meaning the life and death of man are
sacred values. True, philosophical speculations may give us some
insight into the origin, duration, and end of human life; biological
and medical sciences may teach us much about the biological significance of life and about death as the natural terminus of man's life.
But, as R. Schwartz expresses it eloquently, "Who really wants to
die a 'scientific death'? Who wants his life to have value and his
death to have meaning only with respect to the God of scientists
or 'the first unmoved Mover' of philosophical speculation?"[43] In
these matters man, as a rule, is possessed by a desire for a kind of
knowledge which transcends natural means and provides him with
the necessary certainty in this point that is of such primordial importance for his personal life.

In studying human behavior one is constantly confronted with the
fact that human beings often do not act as to the best of their
knowledge they ought to act and that often they do things which

---

[41]*Op. cit.,* p. 59.
[42]*Op. cit.,* p. 60.
[43]R. Schwartz, *Wissenschaft und Bildung,* Freiburg-München, 1957, p. 29.

they ought not to do. As St. Paul said, "I do not understand what I do, for it is not what I wish that I do, but what I hate, that I do" (Rom. 7:15). Man discovers in himself an inner tendency to evil and a resistance to doing good. This is the problem of original sin. Although this sin itself is a mystery, man without original sin would be an even greater mystery. But only revelation and, consequently, theological science can give us some understanding knowledge of the mystery of original sin.

Man realizes that if his activities are to lead to results they must be in accord with certain immutable or changeable norms established by the operative sciences, e.g., practical law, practical economics, or practical medicine. The norms of these sciences have to take into consideration the laws of ethics. But in many cases these laws can be certain only if they are directly supported by Revelation or the teaching authority of the Church or if they are well-founded conclusions of the operative theological science.

What applies to man as an individual with due changes is valid also for human societies. In studying what these activities are or ought to be, one is constantly faced with situations that raise theological questions or can be viewed in full only in the light of theological knowledge. For instance, the science of history, taken in its broadest sense, continually encounters religious phenomena, ecclesiastical activities, and conflicts of Church and State. For an historian who has no knowledge of theology it will be impossible to give a correct interpretation to such facts.

The sciences which study the fine arts may be mentioned also in this connection. Painting, sculpture, music and especially church music, architecture, and literature owe an important part of their inspiration to religious motives. Without this theological inspiration, they would not at all have arisen or at least not in the same form. Hence it should be obvious that the sciences of fine arts cannot fulfill their functions adequately without a decent theological background.

Many other examples illustrating how the profane is influenced by the sacred could be enumerated. However, the few which we have adduced here should suffice to make clear that in many ways the natural sciences are aided and enriched by the theological sciences.

3. *Conclusion*

The manifold relations between theological and non-theological sciences contribute to the determination of the place and value to be assigned to theology in the totality of the sciences. To summarize and clarify this chapter, we may propose here a schema in which the place of the theological sciences in the whole of science is indicated. The mutual relations between the theological sciences and non-theological sciences are marked by means of arrows.

	supernatural sciences	natural sciences	
		philosophical sciences	non-philosophical sciences
speculative or theoretical sciences	speculative or dogmatic ← theology ←	philosophy ←→ of God —————→	other speculative philosophical sciences	1. ideal or formal sciences 2. experiential → sciences of man, culture, and nature
operative or practical sciences	operative or moral ← theology ←	moral ←·→ philosophy —————→	other operative philosophical sciences	operative special → sciences

We now arrive at the end of our task with respect to the theological sciences. Despite our efforts to remain concise, the chapter has become rather long. Our purpose throughout this chapter has been all the time to show that theology cannot be left out of the whole of the sciences and consequently deserves to be included in a philosophy of science. If theology is not given a place in the structure of a university or in the realm of science, the resulting damage will affect not only theology but even more so the profane sciences and especially philosophy. As Newman says, "It is not only the loss of theology, it is the perversion of other sciences".[44] It is man's task to search for truth. A particular truth, however, is never isolated but always connected with all truth and, consequently, mankind cannot be satisfied with applying itself to some sciences only but has to study the totality of all science. To quote Newman again, ". . . in order to have possession of the truth at all, we must have the whole truth; and no one science, no two sciences, no one family of sciences, nay, not even all secular sciences, is the whole truth; that revealed truth enters to

---

[44] *Op. cit.*, p. 69.

a very great extent into the province of science, philosophy and literature, and that to put it on one side, in compliment to secular science
is simply, under colour of a compliment, to do science a great
damage".[45]

   If one or the other science is deliberately neglected, the other
sciences will usurp the domain and deform it. "If you drop any
science out of the circle of knowledge, you cannot keep its place vacant
for it; that science is forgotten; the other sciences close up, or, in
other words, they exceed their proper bounds, and intrude where
they have no right".[46]

   From all these considerations, therefore, we may correctly conclude that theology may not be neglected in the totality of the sciences.
And, as follows from what we have seen in Sections II and III, it
should occupy a place of honor among them.

---

[45]*Op. cit.*, p. 64.
[46]*Op. cit.*, p. 65.

CHAPTER SIX

EXPERIENTIAL SCIENCES

INTRODUCTION

After considering the theological or 'supernatural' sciences in the preceding chapter, we will devote the remainder of this book to the so-called 'natural' sciences. By this term we mean those sciences in which man relies exclusively on the cognitive powers that pertain to his nature, such as the senses, imagination, and intellect. In other words, no positive appeal is made to knowledge obtained by Revelation, for this knowledge is accessible only through supernatural faith.

The Intellect and the Senses. In any science man's natural knowledge ultimately has to be intellectual knowledge. Our intellect, however, does not have any innate knowledge but enters the world as a *tabula rasa,* a writing tablet on which nothing is written yet; hence in one way or another we have to acquire the contents of our acts of cognition. Since man is not a pure spirit but a spirit-in-matter, an incarnated or embodied spirit, he acquires his primary cognitive contents by way of material reality, i.e., by way of his corporeal powers of contact with matter. This first cognitive contact takes place through the *sense powers* by means of certain parts of the body, called *sense organs.* The contents of sense cognition can be retained in sense *memory,* so that even when actual sense cognition ceases man can still make use of the cognitive contents which he has acquired in this way.

The second natural cognitive power which plays an important role in man's knowledge is the *imagination.* This power enables man actively to reproduce what he directly perceives or retains in his sense memory. At the same time it makes it possible for him actively to modify the retained data of the senses in a fairly arbitrary way and to combine them in various ways. The activities of the imagination prepare and accompany man's intellectual acts. Without phantasms there are no ideas, and without the accompanying activity of the imagination, there are no intellectual judgments or reasonings. The function of the imagination supplies the body's material contribution to intellectual thinking and, therefore, is present as a necessary condition in every intellectual activity.

Intellectual knowledge itself is mainly a knowing by means of abstract concepts, i.e., concepts formed through the abstractive operation of the intellect, which in this sense is called 'abstractive power' or 'agent intellect.'[1]

The Division of the Sciences. It may be useful to repeat here briefly what we mentioned in Chapter III (Sect. III, pp. 40 ff.) and treated extensively in Volume I, Chapter III (Sect. IV, pp. 29 ff.) regarding the possibility of dividing 'natural' theoretical sciences into experiential or factual sciences, ideal or formal sciences, and philosophical sciences. This division distinguishes these sciences according to grades of formal abstraction and at the same time according to the different role played by the senses, the imagination, and the intellect.

The character of the object proposed to the speculative intellect differs in the above-mentioned groups of sciences in the following way:

a. In the *experiential* or factual sciences we are dealing with concepts which have been formed on the occasion of a certain sense experience. Thus these concepts intentionally represent a really existing being, i.e., a being which exists independently of our thinking in an extramental world. According as the intellect progresses further in its abstractive operation, the character of the proposed object will be different: for instance, concrete, individual, specific, generic, e.g., Socrates in these concrete conditions, Socrates as an individual, and then through progressive abstraction, the concepts of man, sensitive living being, material substance, etc.

b. In the *ideal* or formal sciences we are always dealing with beings which in one way or another have been produced by our thinking and to which nothing has to correspond in reality. Such a being exists only as a 'thought being', as an 'ideal being'; for instance, a mathematical object (a number, a circle). Such a thought being also may be considered as 'given', as a datum, in speculative research. Its nature and properties can be investigated.

c. Finally, every real or thought being can be considered by the intellect as 'being', from the viewpoint of 'to be' or with respect to the proper nature of its 'to be'; e.g., as material being, living being, human being. In such a case we have to do with the *philosophical* sciences.

---

[1]Concerning the proper nature of abstraction and its various kinds see Part I, Ch. III, pp. 16 ff.

If this brief summary needs further clarification, we may refer the reader to the schemata on p. 31 of Vol. I, and pp. 41 and 42 of this volume. Moreover, much of what is merely pointed out here in a provisional way will be clarified and considered more extensively in the subsequent pages of this book.

Content of this Chapter. This chapter is devoted to the group of those 'natural' theoretical sciences which we called 'experiential' or 'factual' sciences. The first section will speak of experience and reality. The second surveys a few historical divisions of these sciences. The third is dedicated to the division of the experiential sciences, according to their object, into sciences of man, of nature, and of culture. The subsequent sections deal with the differences existing between these groups of experiential sciences with respect to their use of different methods and with respect to the character of their knowledge.

I. Experience and Reality

As a rule, an author or lecturer likes to begin his work by indicating exactly, and preferably by means of a clear-cut definition, what he wants to speak about. If no such definition is available, he desires at least to clarify the point by means of a description which expresses the matter in different words that are clearer to his audience because they refer to ideas already known to them. Unfortunately, the effort to satisfy this desire very frequently encounters invincible difficulties. This happens especially with respect to many 'ordinary' concepts. Nearly everyone is in possession of them and constantly makes use of them, as daily practice shows, to clarify other concepts. Apparently we have to do here with very fundamental ideas which man acquires very easily. Precisely because of their natural priority they cannot be reduced to others and, consequently, they cannot be rendered explicit in a definition or description without re-introducing the original idea in one way or another. This situation does not particularly embarrass anyone who, like the author, adheres to a realistic epistemology which he considers the only philosophy of knowledge that can successfully overcome any form of critical examination. The realistic epistemologist will have no objection against the admission of such fundamental ideas which cannot be defined or can be defined only with great difficulty. In describing them, he will not hesitate to appeal to the pre-scientific knowledge of his readers or listeners. Examples of such fundamental ideas are being, existence, essence, activity, ground, cause, unity, plurality, extension, and many others.

The above-mentioned difficulty presents itself also with respect to the concepts indicated by the terms 'experience' and 'reality'. These ideas may be brought to bear upon each other, so that one clarifies the other, but it does not appear possible to give for each separately a definition which satisfies the demands of logic, viz., a definition which determines the object to be defined by genus and specific difference.

1. *The Meaning of the Term 'Experience'*

The term 'experience' is used mainly in two senses—namely subjectively and objectively.

Subjectively, i.e., as seen from the subject, 'experience' means a subject's activity mingled with passivity, through which the subject acquires some knowledge of itself and of the surrounding world in its concreteness. In this sense we may say that man has experience of his own existence, of his own corporeal and psychical states and activities, of the existence of other human beings, of plants, animals, and inanimate things in their concrete individuality. In this experience we learn something about these individual objects, we get to know something about their properties and activities.

In its subjective sense, experience may be considered to be largely identical with sense perception, at least if sense perception is taken in its broadest meaning as extending to every cognitive grasp of reality which originates in the inner and outer senses. Subjective experience, however, includes also intellectual intuition and reflection insofar as they make us conscious of our own existence and make the activities of intellect and will known to us as realities. It includes, moreover, also that intuition which makes us grasp being as being in a concrete experience.

Objectively, i.e., as viewed from the object, 'experience' means 'that which is experienced or perceived'; for instance, when we say that 'experience' teaches us that . . ., or that we must base ourselves on 'experience'. In this sense we may speak of 'data of experience', 'facts of experience' and 'observed facts'. In its objective sense, therefore, 'experience' applies primarily to events in the broadest sense. Usually the meaning of the term is restricted to this sense. However, in accordance with what has been said above in the preceding paragraph, the term extends to everything which in its concreteness is known through intellectual intuition or reflection.

2. *The Meaning of the Terms 'Real' and 'Reality'*

Extension of the Term 'Real'. Because experience, in the subjective sense, or perception presupposes receptivity or passivity in the subject, the experienced or perceived object must be somehow active, it must be capable of influencing the sense organs either directly or through a medium. Only the real can be experienced. Whatever is experienced, i.e., whatever falls under the objective sense of the term 'experience', must be said to be 'real'. This assertion, of course, does not mean that everything real *is* also an object of experience. On the other hand, however, anything real, as such, can be considered a potential object of experience. For this reason it is appropriate to investigate the extension of the term 'real' in a study about the object of the experiential sciences.

1. We must consider to be real, first of all, everything pertaining to man's body as well as everything that exists outside man's corporeal limits and can be perceived by his senses, i.e., seen, heard, touched, tasted, smelled, etc.

2. Secondly, the term applies also to one's own corporeal or psychical states, e.g., the feeling of being satiated, hungry, cold, warm, of pain, sadness, and joy, which are observed as real by an internal sense.

3. A person's own intellectual and volitional activities also are real, as are the concepts and their contents at the moment when they are conceived. Likewise, the phantasms which we form as long as they are actual.

4. The term 'real' applies also to everything which is not directly experienced in the above-described way but nevertheless has to be pre-supposed of necessity if the direct data of experience are to be real. If we experience activities and properties as realities, everything has to be real without which these realities cannot exist or at least not exist in the way in which they exist. Real properties presuppose a subsistent being as their support, and the activities which we experience as real presuppose an active principle that either exists in

itself or as a real power in a subsistent being. In this way we experience in and together with the perceived properties and activities also the subsistent being which is their support and active source. In the same way we experience also our own existence. Frequently, however, the reality and essence of a subsistent being as the bearer of properties and the source of activities will be known only through an intellectual process of thought. This is the case, for instance, of man's spiritual soul.

5. Everything also is real which is interconnected with the actual data of experience in space and time; for instance, the phases of the past which find their continuation in the present and in this way continue to exist, or the future which will develop out of the present condition. Thus the experience of the present condition of an object may reveal us something about its past and future development. Sometimes it is possible to make direct observations of conditions or situations of the past. We may refer here to astronomy which, through observing the light emitted by celestial bodies, can ascertain directly the conditions in which they were in a distant past. For a body which was *n* light-years away from us, is at present observed in the condition in which it was *n* years ago.

6. Real also are the potencies founded upon the properties of real beings. Although these potencies, as such, neither exist nor are known as data of experience, we conclude to their existence in the individual or the species on the basis of a perceived concrete and individual actualization. The term 'real' applies therefore to man's freedom, his power of thinking and his capacity of self-reflection. Likewise, to the power of the sensitive living body to learn from experience, although this power shows itself only after repeated confrontation with certain concrete situations. In a similar way we have to admit, on the basis of concrete realizations, that non-living materials have many real potencies, e.g., flexibility, elasticity, magnetizability, the power of fluorescence, etc.

7. Finally, everything also is real which cannot be known directly by our natural cognitive powers but whose existence and properties have become known to us through divine Revelation, i.e., the objects of the theological sciences. The objects in question, however, do not fall under experience in the usual sense of the term and cannot be considered to be subject matter of the experiential sciences.

The Real as Object of the Experiential Sciences. As should be clear from the preceding pages, not everything real is *per se* and directly an object of the experiential sciences. Only reality which can be reached by means of man's natural cognitive powers belongs to this object. Thus the object of the experiential sciences is mainly limited to 1) that which lies within the reach of the external and internal senses or can be brought within their reach through the use of instruments; 2) that which is presupposed by the data of sense experience and can be discovered through intellectual analysis and reasoning.

Description of the Concept 'Real'. After enumerating the various groups of entities which must be considered to be real and to be potential objects of the experiential sciences, we feel the need for a description of 'real' or 'reality' which in a single formula applies to all these groups. Of course, we are faced here again with the same difficulty which was mentioned at the beginning of this chapter. We cannot go beyond a formula which by means of other terms somewhat clarifies the concept 'reality'. There can be no question of a strict definition through more fundamental and more general terms. This inevitable limitation has to be kept in mind when we make an attempt here to describe what is meant by 'reality'.

In the above-considered groups we have used the term 'real' principally as synonymous with 'existing', taken in the broad sense, i.e., that which is or exists in any way whatsoever. The extension of the term, then, is not limited to things having 'existence in themselves', but contains also the accidental, the properties, activities, and relations between real things.

One would be inclined to interpret the terms 'real' and 'reality', taken in this sense, so broadly that only the absolute nothing would be opposed to it. Usually, however, the interpretation is somewhat more restricted. 'Real' is considered synonymous with 'actually existing', in opposition to the possible, the merely imagined, and the ideal.[2] This last-named restriction will be especially important for us in Chapter VIII.

To arrive at a suitable description of the concept 'real' as opposed to that of 'ideal', especially in relation with the distinction between experiential and ideal sciences, the following formula is often used:

---

[2] Webster's Dictionary describes the philosophical meaning of real as: "actual existing; actual as distinguished from fictitious or imaginary, or the ideal". This description harmonizes with ours.

"Real is what exists independently of our perception or independently of our sensitive and intellectual knowledge". At first sight this description does not appear to be too bad. For, as was pointed out in the preceding explanation of 'experience in the objective sense', i.e., of the data of experience, this term applies only to things or entities, including properties, activities, etc., which are present independently of experience in the subjective sense, i.e., independently of our acts of perception and knowing, at least at the moment when their presence is observed. Perception presupposes the reality of the perceived at the moment of the perception.

Nevertheless, with respect to this description of the concept 'real', it is necessary to make a restriction or at least to offer an explanation regarding the words 'independently of our perception'. It may happen that a certain situation cannot be observed unless man interferes in a way which disturbs the actual situation, so that he does not perceive the objects as they were independently of his perception, but as they have become through his perception, or rather, through the interference required by his perception. If, for instance, one observes his own psychical processes, these processes will not remain unchanged, but undergo various modifications because of the observation. Something similar may happen in sense perception—namely, when the object can be perceived only through a preceding or accompanying preparation, e.g., through illumination or through the introduction of a measuring device.

Regarding this difficulty, we will limit ourselves here to pointing out that the restriction in question does not militate against the well-founded conviction that in experiential knowledge we are always dealing with a reality which exists independently of our knowledge, and that the content of the act of knowing or perceiving, is generally determined by the situation, as this situation is present to us at the moment of our cognitive act, i.e., whether it be modified or not by the act of cognition. In other words, the difficulty in question is not very important, it does not force us to modify the description of the term 'real'.

A more serious difficulty presents itself when we want to use the proposed description of the concept 'real' to distinguish it from that of 'ideal'. This difficulty will be considered in Chapter VIII when we will speak of the distinction of the real from the ideal. We may, therefore, limit ourselves here to a single remark: experiential sciences work with *real* concepts if this term is taken to mean concepts whose *contents* are a more or less abstract image of something which exists or can exist independently of man's cognitive activities, or outside the cognitive powers, as a subsistent being or as something which is in or pertains to a subsistent being. For more details, see Chapter VIII, Section I, pp. 210 ff.

3. *The Object of the Experiential Sciences*

Material and Formal Object. When we speak here of the object proper to the group of speculative sciences, called 'experiential sciences', we mean in the first place the so-called *material object* (Cf. Vol. I, Ch. V, pp. 43 ff.), i.e., the subject matter considered by these sciences, that to which these sciences pay attention. If, however, the subject matter considered in these sciences can be divided into rather heterogeneous groups, there will be a difference also in the aspects under which and the manner in which the subject matter must be viewed, i.e., in the *formal object.* The last-named difference is largely determined by the first. For this reason we may limit our attention to the material object insofar as the general division of the experiential sciences is concerned. In subsequent pages we will simply speak of the object without any further qualification.

Description of the Object of the Experiential Sciences. After the preceding explanations it should be clear without any further ado that natural *experience in the objective sense,* taken in its broadest meaning, must be considered to be the total object of the experiential sciences. By this expression we mean observed facts in the broadest sense, i.e., everything which in any way whatsoever is perceived by the external and internal senses or known in reality through intellectual intuition or reflection. Somewhat differently and more accurately formulated, the object of the experiential sciences is the totality of reality which exists independently of man's knowledge, insofar as it can be known by man's natural cognitive powers.

We speak here intentionally of 'natural' cognitive powers to exclude realities which are knowable only through a supernatural or divine revelation, because such realities are the object of the theological sciences mentioned in Chapter Five. Moreover, the words "which exists independently of man's knowledge" imply another restriction. They exclude, first of all, 'purely thought beings' or 'ideal beings', which are the object of the so-called 'ideal sciences' to be considered in Chapter VIII. Secondly, they point to a distinction from the natural operative sciences, for these sciences are not concerned with existing reality but investigate the possible realization of something which is not yet but can become real.

A further restriction has to be added to separate the experiential sciences from philosophy. For the philosophical sciences also are concerned with 'experience in the objective sense' and with "the totality of reality insofar as it can be known by man's cognitive powers". Philosophy, however, does not proceed in the same way as the experiential sciences. These sciences study reality in its specific and generic essence and sometimes also in its individuality and its individual and concrete properties, while the philosophical sciences consider reality under the aspect of being, i.e., as 'being' and further as 'human being', 'animal being', 'material being', etc.

If the above-mentioned restrictions are to be inserted in a description of the experiential sciences, it could be done in the following somewhat involved way: "experiential sciences are the speculative sciences which have as their object all real (i.e., independently of man's intellect existing) entities with respect to their specific and generic essence and even their individual and concrete essence, insofar as they can be known by man's natural cognitive powers". While it is true that even this description is not immune to all objections, it seems to me that it expresses the most important aspects of the experiential sciences, and especially those through which they distinguish themselves from the other groups of speculative sciences.

The Multiplicity of the Experiential Sciences. If we look at the natural speculative sciences which are based upon experience in the sense explained above in no. 1 (pp. 119 f.), we will find that they constitute a large collection of very heterogeneous sciences with manifold differences. The collection contains, for instance, physics, chemistry, geology, mineralogy, astronomy, paleontology, botany, and zoology, but also psychology, ethnology or cultural anthropology, and sociology, in addition to such sciences as history, archeology, literature, linguistics, economics, positive law, and many others. All these sciences are classified into different groups. In universities they pertain to separate faculties, schools, or departments. These divisions and departmentalizations point to a theoretical basis—namely, the awareness that, apart from their common features, these sciences have also important and profound differences, e.g., in their object, the foundation on which their knowledge is based, the character of their intelligibility, and their method.

The human mind always seeks order in multiplicity and therefore endeavors to classify or divide these sciences by means of a criterion. A good division leads to a measure of understanding but, reversely, a certain amount of insight into the matter to be divided is needed if we are to arrive at a suitable and justifiable division. For this reason it is necessary to reflect upon the proper nature of the various experiential sciences to discover whether there is a principle which can serve as the basis of a rational division.

Theoretically speaking, different divisions can be attempted based upon distinct criteria—as many as there are aspects in a science; for instance, according to object, method, procedure, degree of abstraction, and character of knowledge. As a matter of fact, various divisions have been proposed in the course of history. The choice of the dividing principle often depends, whether it is realized or not, to a large extent upon the view taken about the nature of the subject matter which is to be divided. Thus philosophical conceptions will make their influence felt in any division of the experiential sciences. Since the study of science is a typically human endeavor and man himself belongs to the objects of experience, a person's view of man may be particularly decisive in his effort to divide the experiential sciences. The subsequent pages will clearly illustrate this point.

Before proposing the division which for various reasons we consider most suitable, we want first to pay attention to a few divisions which were made toward the end of the nineteenth century and which still enjoy a considerable measure of favor in the philosophy of science. We mean the divisions proposed by Dilthey, Windelband, and Rickert. Guided by their philosophical views, these men proposed, each in his own way, a division of science, pointing out various aspects of the sciences. Although we are unable to accept their divisions unqualifiedly or even may have to reject some of their considerations entirely, certain aspects of the sciences to which they drew attention may be useful to us in working out the division which we consider most suitable.

II. Some Nineteenth Century Divisions of the Experiential Sciences

Reaction Against Previous Ideas. In the second half of the nineteenth century a few philosophical schools openly began to turn away from the conceptions which had largely dominated the philosophical life of the time. Opposition arose especially against the positivistic and Kantian trends of thought, and this opposition exercised influence also on the philosophy of science. New, or rather renewed, views began to make their appearance. In the following pages we will consider a few of these views, which are important for the division of the experiential sciences.

The opposition centered in part upon the hitherto predominant Kantian view of science. According to Kant, the criterion of science lies in apodictic certainty. This certainty can be found only in purely intellectual knowledge that is independent of experience, i.e., strictly speaking, only in mathematics. According to this view, only 'nature' can be considered the object of experience, and the considerations of 'nature' qualify as scientific only insofar as they have a mathematical character.

On the other hand, under the influence of positivism, there was also a tendency to treat all data of experience, even man himself and man's cultural expressions, in accordance with the methods of the physical sciences.

'Geisteswissenschaft'. Such one-sided conceptions of science, arising mainly from a physical orientation, led to opposition. Emphasis began to be placed on the proper character, distinct from that of the physical sciences, pertaining to certain experiential sciences and especially to history. The whole of the objects of experience was divided into two parts, indicated *inter alia* by the terms 'nature' and 'spirit' or 'mind'. (The last-named term indicated, but not of necessity, that a connection was sought with Hegel (1770-1831) or beyond Hegel with the ancient Greek philosophers.) This dichotomy of the total object of the experiential sciences was accompanied, of course, by a corresponding division of these sciences into two groups. The tendency to make such a division was not entirely new but could point to a number of precedents. As early as 1843, John Stuart Mill (1806-1873), in the first edition of his book, *A System of Logic,* had placed alongside the logic of 'natural sciences' that of the 'moral sciences', i.e., the sciences which study human activities and their motives. In translating this work into German, Schiel[3] used the term *'Geisteswissenschaften'* to render Mill's 'moral sciences'. In the singular the same term had already been used by Hegel's disciples. Because of the large circulation

---

[3]John Stuart Mill, *System der deduktiven und induktiven Logik,* übersetzt von Schiel, Braunschweig, 1877.

of Mill's book, even in its German translation, the term *'Geistes-wissenschaften'* became generally known, so that its common acceptance is due more to Mill than to the influence of Hegel.

Earlier Dichotomies. Even before Mill efforts were made to arrive at a similar division. Jeremy Bentham (1748-1832) opposed 'pneumatology' to 'somatology'. A similar dichotomy was suggested by the French philosopher-scientist André Ampère (1775-1836), who divided the sciences into 'cosmological' and 'noological' according as they studied either the cosmos or the mind. However, the influence of these two did not compare to that of Mill, whose ideas were widely divulgated in Germany, the country in which the new views of science were to originate.

It is rather surprising that such a dichotomy of the experiential sciences was not made at an earlier date. A few centuries before, René Descartes (1596-1650) had made a sharp—even too sharp—distinction between spiritual and material substances. However, his distinction did not immediately lead to a division of the sciences, because the time was not yet ripe for it. The sciences which could be called *'Geisteswissenschaften'* were not yet sufficiently developed to lay claim to a special status alongside the sciences of nature. More interest had first to be aroused in the typically human problems of a psychological, sociological, and historical nature. With the development of this interest and in interaction with it, there gradually arose a change in philosophical attitude which made man himself more the center of attraction. For our purpose there are three philosophers who deserve special attention in this respect—namely, Dilthey, Windelband, and Rickert.

1. *Dilthey's Division of the Experiential Sciences*

In his book, *Einleitung in die Geisteswissenschaften* (Leipzig, 1883) Wilhelm Dilthey (1833-1911) took over the term *Geistes-wissenschaften* as "the least unsuitable" (*die mindest Unangemessene*) of all available terms. By this term he meant "the whole of the sciences which have as their object historical-sociological reality" (p. 5). The central interest of these sciences was the analysis of the facts of consciousness given in internal experience. Dilthey was a forerunner of the anti-intellectualistic trends which later became embodied in philosophies of culture and of life. He attributed less value to the natural sciences than to the *Geisteswissenschaften,* because the former through their abstract concepts make us know merely a shadow of reality, while the latter grasp reality as it presents itself concretely.

For Dilthey, the distinction in question is not so much the opposition of material and spiritual things than that of the 'external world' (*Aussenwelt*), given to us in sensation, and the 'internal world' (*Innenwelt*) appearing to us in our reflection upon psychical events and activities.[4] In this way the *Geisteswissenschaften* acquire an independent place alongside the sciences of nature because they are given their own epistemological foundation.

Dilthey attributed the most fundamental place among these sciences to psychology—not to a psychology which proceeds in the same way as the natural sciences, but to what he calls a *"geisteswissenschaftliche Psychologie"*, i.e., a psychology which through emphatic sharing (*Nacherleben* and *Einfühlung*) in the concrete event attempts to arrive at an understanding of the meaning and value of the psychical structures. In Dilthey's view, the knowledge of individual and concrete reality which is acquired in this way is more important that that of the abstract uniformities attained by the natural sciences.

Within the *Geisteswissenschaften* Dilthey distinguished three classes of propositions. The first class refers to the facts given in sensation, i.e., to reality. This class, therefore, contains the historical part of our knowledge. The second group, which extends to the theoretical part of our knowledge, presents abstract formulations about uniform aspects occurring in parts of this reality. The third class contains value judgments and presents norms for man's actions. It constitutes the practical part of the *Geisteswissenschaften*.

By way of analogy with the structures studied in the *"geisteswissenschaftliche Psychologie"* Dilthey distinguished in history 'operative connections', (*Wirkungszusammenhänge*) which he called 'cultural systems' (*Kultursysteme*). As such he proposed political economy, law, science, art, and religion, each of which could be the object of a special science.

Dilthey's disciple Spranger elaborated and enlarged the ideas of his master and gave them a wider publicity. Spranger spoke of distinct "objective areas of culture", each of which could become a distinct object of scientific investigation. Moreover, he proposed certain modifications which made his views develop in the direction of a

---

[4]Dilthey used here the English terms 'sensation' and 'reflection', which he borrowed from Locke.

'philosophy of value'. For this reason his ideas are a transition to those of Windelband and Rickert, which we will now consider.

2. *Windelband's Division of the Experiential Sciences*

His Objection to the Opposition of 'Nature' and 'Mind'. Wilhelm Windelband (1848-1915) published his view about the division of the experiential sciences in 1894 in his rectorial address at the University of Strasbourg.[5] He looks with disfavor upon the opposition of 'nature' and 'mind', which was used in ancient and medieval times and which was maintained with great sharpness from the time of Descartes and Spinoza to that of Schelling and Hegel. First of all, he thinks, the opposition by object (*ein sachlicher Gegensatz*) is unsuitable as a foundation for the division of the sciences. Secondly, this distinction by object does not agree with the distinction in mode of knowing. Locke's distinction between 'sensation' and 'reflection' is, he thinks, unsatisfactory, for modern critique of knowledge does not justify the admission of 'internal perception' or 'reflection' as a special mode of knowledge. Finally, the division in question leaves no room for the important science of psychology. With respect to its object, psychology is a *Geisteswissenschaft* and may even be called in a sense the foundation of the other '*Geisteswissenschaften*', but with respect to its method it is a physical science (*Naturwissenschaft*)—namely, the "physical science of the internal sense" or "mental physical science" (*geistige naturwissenschaft*). Psychology is logically similar to physical science "with respect to the formal character of the purpose of its knowledge", for like physical science it seeks to establish laws.

The Proper Character of the Geisteswissenschaften. According to Windelband, the proper character of the experiential sciences known as *Geisteswissenschaften* lies in this that their aim is "to state fully and exhaustively a single, more or less extended event belonging to a temporally limited reality which is not repeated". Many things can be the objects of these sciences; for instance, a single occurrence or a whole series, the essence and life of a single man or of a whole people, the proper character of a language, a religion, a legal order, a product of literature, art, or science. Thus all historical sciences belong fully to the *Geisteswissenschaften*. For this reason Windelband sometimes speaks of "historical sciences" (*historische Disciplinen*) in

---

[5] Windelband, *Geschichte und Naturwissenschaft,* Strassburg, 1894, pp. 17-41. Two other addresses, delivered on the same occasion, were published in the same volume.

opposition to "physical sciences" (*naturwissenschaftliche Disciplinen*). In doing so, he classifies psychology among the physical sciences.

Nomothetic and Idiographic Sciences. In this way the formal character of the aim pursued by man's cognitive endeavors is seen as the criterion for the division of the sciences. Physical sciences seek general laws, while the other sciences devote their attention to particular historical facts. Using the language of formal logic, one may say that the first group of sciences aims at general apodictic statements, and the second at singluar and assertory statements. Or, to express it differently, the physical sciences seek "the form which always remains itself", "that which is always", while the other experiential sciences aim at "the unrepeated, determined content of a real event" (*den* einmaligen, *in sich bestimmten Inhalt des wirklichen geschehens*), at "that which was once". The former are "sciences of law" (*Gesetzwissenschaften*), the latter "sciences of events" (*Ereigniswissenschaften*): "the ones seek laws, and the others form (*Gestalten*)". Using newly coined terms, which subsequently were widely accepted, Windelband said that in the physical sciences our thinking is 'nomothetic', while in the other experiential sciences it is 'idiographic'.[6]

The Differences Between the Two Groups. According to Windelband, thought progresses in the physical sciences from the particular case to the establishment of general relationships, while in the other sciences it dwells "in the loving expression of the particular" (*bei der liebevollen Ausprägung des Besonderen*). So far as the physicist is concerned, the given particular object as such never has any scientific value, but serves only as a special case, an instance representing a species. The historian, on the other hand, endeavors to seize a picture of the past and to "relive it mentally in its entire individual expression". Accordingly, in the thinking of the physical sciences the tendency to abstraction predominates, while in historical thinking intuition (*Anschaulichkeit*) is prevalent.

The difference between the two groups of experiential sciences manifests itself, of course, also in their results. The physical sciences relinquish their intuitive starting-point and tend to the knowledge of law-like necessities which govern all events in timeless immutability. The aim of historical science, on the other hand, is always

---

[6]'Nomothetic' means 'establishing laws' (from the Greek *nomos,* law, and *tithenai,* to establish) ; 'idiographic' means 'describing what is proper or singular' (from the Greek *idios,* proper or singular, and *graphein,* to describe).

"to work over the mass of material until the true picture of the past arises in life-like clarity: what it produces is pictures of men and human life with the whole wealth of their own and proper forms, carefully preserved in their full and individual freshness".

Windelband realized that this methodic contrast classified only the procedure and not the content of man's acts of knowledge. Some objects can be investigated either nomothetically or idiographically. Language, for instance, is governed by laws in its special uses but, on the other hand, this particular language, taken as a whole with its special system of laws, is an unrepeated (*einmalig*) and passing phenomenon in the life of human language. The same applies to the physiology of the body, to geology, and in a sense even to astronomy; hence the historical principle can be applied also in the realm of the physical sciences. Thus, for instance, the science of organic nature, considered as the "doctrine of systems", possesses a nomothetic character, for in the course of thousands of years the same types and forms recur all the time, but as the "history of evolution" it is an idiographic and historical science.

Undoubtedly, many objections can be raised against Windelband's theory of the sciences. For instance, some sciences can hardly be placed in either of the two classes distinguished by him. Moreover, he did not pay sufficient attention to the difference in abstraction and universality in the various experiential sciences. The main objection, however, is, as will become clear later, against the very principle of his division. Nevertheless, Windelband's explanations contain so many valuable points that we do not regret the relatively large amount of space allotted to them. We even intend to revert to his views from time to time.

3. *Rickert's Division of the Experiential Sciences*

After Dilthey and Windelband attention must be paid to Heinrich Rickert (1863-1936). Like Windelband, he belonged to the School of Baden, which explains his strong inclination to 'philosophy of value'. In 1899 he published his book, *Kulturwissenschaft und Naturwissenschaft,* followed in 1902 by *Die Grenzen der naturwissenschaftlichen Begriffsbildung.*[7] Both works were reprinted several times and exercised great influence on the philosophy of science.

---

[7] I have made use of the sixth and seventh reprint of *Kulturwissenschaft und Naturwissenschaft,* Tübingen, 1926, and the second impression of *Die Grenzen der naturwissenschaftliche Begriffsbildung,* Tübingen, 1913.

Nature and Culture. Rickert was willing to accept the current terms 'nature' and 'mind' (*Natur* and *Geist*), provided a sharp distinction be made between 'mind' and 'soul' (*Geist* and *Seele*). 'Mind', he argued, is more closely related to what Hegel called 'objective mind' and means all that which cannot be grasped by external or internal perception but has 'meaning' and 'sense' (*Bedeutung* and *Sinn*) and can be 'understood' (*verstanden*) only independently of the senses, i.e., that which formerly was called 'intelligible' or 'noetic'. Thus the term 'nature' extends not only to the world of matter but also to "mere, still 'unspiritual' psychical life". The opposite of 'nature' is 'culture' (*Kultur*).

Any effort to determine the contents of the terms 'nature' and 'culture' more accurately encounters the difficulty that both terms have several meanings. Rickert himself formulated their opposition in two ways.

The first distinction is based on the original meaning of the terms. "A product of nature is what spontaneously grows up from the earth. A product of culture arises from the soil when man cultivates the land and sows". Accordingly, the term 'nature' extends to everything which arises or is born spontaneously, while 'culture' embraces whatever is purposively produced or taken care of by man because of the value it has. Products of nature may always be considered independently of their 'value' aspect, but products of culture always represent a 'value'. For this reason cultural products may be called 'goods'.

The second opposition formulated by Rickert has a more methodological nature. On the one hand, there are physical and psychical phenomena which are exclusively the object of perception but, on the other, there are objects which have a non-sensitive 'meaning' or 'sense' and can only be 'understood' immediately. The basis for the distinction, then, lies in the opposition between 'perceiving' and 'understanding' (*Wahrnehmen* and *Verstehen*). "Nature, then, would be being which is free of meaning, merely perceptible and not intelligible, while culture would be meaningful and intelligible being. And this is really the truth of the matter".

Both distinctions are, of course, closely connected. According to Rickert, the 'value' character must be assigned the first place, if only because 'meaning' and 'sense' have their foundation in 'value'. The opposite of 'value-free nature' *(Wertfreie Natur)* is 'value-bearing culture' *(Wertbehaftete Natur)*.

Natural and Cultural Sciences. In this way Rickert's view leads to two groups of sciences. On the one hand, there are the 'physical sciences' (*Naturwissenschaften*) which consider "value-free and mean-ing-free nature" and, on the other, the sciences whose object is "mean-ingful and value-related culture" and for which therefore the value problem is essential. To indicate the last-named group, Rickert gave preference to the term 'cultural sciences' (*Kulturwissenschaften*) over '*Geisteswissenschaften*', which because of its many meanings is misleading. The remainder of his book, *Kulturwissenschaft und Naturwissenschaft,* is dedicated to the investigation of the common elements of the cultural sciences.

Their Logical Difference. Apart from the above-mentioned dif-ferences, which refer more directly to the nature of the object, Rickert dwelled extensively on a difference which exists between the two groups of sciences from a logical viewpoint.

He characterized the logical feature of the method proper to the physical sciences by the term 'generalizing' *(generalisierend),* i.e., by means of abstraction these sciences endeavor to arrive at general concepts and propositions. These generalizing sciences have to be divided into two groups on the basis of a distinction in their object. One studies physical or corporeal realities, the other psychical or spiritual realities. According to Rickert, psychology belongs to the physical or generalizing sciences, no matter what objections be raised against this classification. For psychology endeavors to gather individual and particular psychical phenomena under general concepts and, whenever possible, to establish laws which from the logical point of view are 'laws of nature'. Therefore, he concluded, "it remains true that *every* reality, including psychical reality, in a generalizing way *can* be conceived as a nature and, consequently, it *must* also be conceived in the fashion proper to the physical sciences".

Accordingly, in Rickert's view, if there are any sciences distinct from the physical sciences, their existence cannot be justified by a difference in object but only by a difference from the logical view-point. But there are sciences which do not aim at the formation of general concepts and the formulation of universal laws—namely, the historical sciences, in the broadest sense of the term, which want to represent reality as it is in its concrete individuality. These sciences consider the same reality as the others, but under a different aspect. "Reality becomes nature when we consider it with respect to the general, but it becomes history when it is viewed with respect to the particular and the individual. For this reason I want to oppose the individualizing procedure of history to the generalizing procedure of natural science".

This distinction between generalizing and individualizing procedure was seen by Rickert as the formal principle dividing the experiential sciences. Moreover, he argued, in this way one arrives at the same division as by using the formal distinction between the methods of the physical sciences and history. He tried to show how the distinction corresponds to the more material division into 'value-free nature' and 'value-bearing nature'. The individualizing historical method is always guided by the aspect of value that is present in its object, while the generalizing method of the physical sciences precisely abstracts from all value relations. Because both the 'historical' and the 'cultural' features determine the proper character of the sciences in question, Rickert preferred to speak of 'historical sciences of culture'.

The Task of the Cultural Sciences. According to Rickert, the task of the cultural sciences is not to grasp the individual in its total reality—no science does or even can do this. These sciences consider the individual in a certain respect in the sense that, on the basis of a scientific *a priori*, they choose only those individual objects, and in these objects only those aspects which "really embody cultural values or are related to cultural values". In other words, we have to do here with an 'individualizing principle of selection'. The aim is not the individual reality itself but a certain view of this reality. According to Rickert, the historical-individualizing method is essentially a 'value-related procedure', although this does not at all mean that it has to lead to a value judgment, e.g., in an approving or disapproving sense. As for the objectivity of the historical sciences of culture, it is safeguarded by the fact that cultural values are de facto general or at least considered to be general for all members of a cultural society. Here also the requirement holds that, to be of scientific value, the particular must have a general meaning. "Like science of nature, history classifies the particular under a 'universal' ".

Rickert emphasized that he did not see the distinction between individualizing cultural sciences and generalizing sciences of nature as absolute but only as relative opposition. He considered them merely as two extremes of science. Nearly all scientific work, however, lies in between, and there are many intermediate forms of science. He thus differed from Windelband who admitted a far more acute opposition between the nomothetic and idiographic methods.

According to Rickert, "the two main tendencies of empirical scientific work both logically and with respect to content" are characterized much more profoundly and stringently by his proposed division than by the traditional division into sciences of nature and *Geisteswissenschaft*.

III. Division of the Experiential Sciences According to Their Object into Sciences of Man, of Nature, and of Culture

Introduction

The divisions considered in the preceding section made use of various criteria, such as the difference in mode of knowing (Dilthey), the difference in the formal character of the purpose aimed at by man's acts of knowledge (Windelband), and the difference from the logical viewpoint in the consideration of the same reality (Rickert). True, Rickert points also to a difference in object when he speaks of 'nature' and 'culture', but the emphasis is on the aspect of 'value' revealed by these objects as either 'value-free nature' or 'value-related culture'. All three of these philosophers reject a differentiation by object in the sense of an opposition between two or more clearly distinct groups of things, e.g., between material and spiritual things. Such a Cartesian distinction is more readily found in Bentham and Ampère.

The grounds upon which these philosophers reject distinction by object cannot be simply discarded as utterly unreasonable but deserve closer examination. On the other hand, each of the criteria which they themselves propose is open to so many objections that, in our view, none of them can be accepted without qualifications. The greatest difficulty appears to lie in the fact that these criteria do not allow a clear-cut distinction to be made in the experiental sciences, but merely allow us to distinguish different aspects in the object of one and the same science. A given science is nomothetic in one respect or part and idiographic in another (Windelband), it allows different modes of knowing (Dilthey), and it is sometimes generalizing and sometimes individualizing (Rickert).

Even for this reason alone it would seem better to attempt a division of the experiential sciences according to object. True, as we will see, such an attempt is not without difficulties, but nevertheless a distinction by object is more fundamental than any other division. Other aspects or qualities of a science, such as its method, mode of consideration, and the character of its scientific statements, are determined to a large extent by the nature of the object and the consequent relationship of this object to man's knowledge.

Accordingly, in this section we will investigate whether it is possible to make a rational division in the object of the experiential sciences. In the subsequent sections we will consider the differences in method and scientific character which are connected with the difference in object.

1. *Division of the Object of the Experiential Sciences*

As has been pointed out before, we may consider as the total object of the experiential sciences the totality of reality which exists independently of man's thinking, insofar as this reality is knowable by man's natural powers of cognition. To this, we must add a limitation in order to distinguish these sciences from philosophy— namely, that realities are investigated for their specific or generic essence and sometimes also for their individual and concrete essence.

The 'totality of reality', however, is an enormous complex of innumerable, varied and interconnected things which constantly influence one another and have manifold interrelationships. Hence at first sight it may seem extremely difficult to arrive at any useful dividing lines in this seeming chaos. Nevertheless, an attempt has to be made.

a. MAN AND NATURE

For those who, like the author, accept an essential difference between man and non-human beings, there is immediately a clear dividing line between two distinct groups of observable real beings. This line, then, could be the basis for a division of the experiential sciences into two groups: sciences of man and sciences of non-human beings. Upon closer inspection, however, there are a few difficulties which need to be considered first.

If the group of non-human things has to be indicated in a way that sounds positive rather than negative, it is customary to use the term 'nature'. We will follow this custom, although it offers some difficulties. First of all, this term has many meanings not only in every-day language but also in philosophical usage; secondly, and partly because of these many meanings, the opposition of 'man' and 'nature' can be interpreted in different ways. Let us consider both points.

The Different Meanings of the Term 'Nature'. Limiting ourselves to the meanings which are relevent to our problem, we may distinguish the following senses of the term.

1. In philosophical language 'nature' is often used to indicate the essence of a thing, especially insofar as this essence is the source of properties and activities. Thus we speak of the 'nature of things', the 'nature of man', etc. Occasionally the term is used in this sense in this book.

2. Chapter V showed us a theological usage of the terms 'nature' and 'natural' in opposition to 'supernature' and 'supernatural'. In this context both pairs of terms refer to the twofold relationship which a creature may have to God—namely, as a mere creature or as elevated to the status of a child of God. It goes without saying that in this chapter we are dealing only with what is the 'natural' order in theological parlance.

3. If abstraction is made of the above-mentioned philosophical and theological meanings, the term still retains several other senses both in every-day language and in the technical vocabulary of science and philosophy. Some of these are of importance for our purpose. Thus 'nature' may be used:

a. As equivalent to the terms 'universe' or 'world', as the sum total of all things and phenomena in space and time. In this sense man belongs to 'nature'.

b. As indicating the non-human things of this world, i.e., the non-living, plants, and animals.

c. As indicating the material part of the universe. In this sense it applies not only to non-human things ('nature' in the preceding sense) but also to what is material or somatic in man.

The last two meanings of 'nature' give rise to two different interpretations of the pair of opposites 'man' and 'nature'.

Different Meanings of the Opposites Man and Nature. 1. First of all, the totality of all things observable may be divided into two groups: human beings and non-human things. The last-named group contains the non-living, the kingdom of plants, and that of animals. Both groups are clearly distinct, while together they constitute the whole of the world of experience; hence the division in question is complete and adequate.

For anyone who shares the author's recognition of man's unique character this division is obvious. Through his spiritual principle or soul, which manifests itself in acts of understanding and free, purposive acts of will, man rises above non-human things and essentially transcends his surroundings and the world. Through his power of self-reflection man is conscious of his exceptional position in the world. He knows what he is and what he does. His intellectual power enables him to know his present situation in itself and from his past, at least in part, and thus to plan his future. This intellectual knowledge, which may grasp a limited good precisely insofar as it is limited, is by this very fact the basis and the condition of freedom for his intellectual appetitive activity, i.e., his freedom of will.

Man is not a pure spirit but a spirit-in-matter, an embodied spirit. Because of his embodiment, he is tied to his material surroundings in a spatio-temporal way. In this respect, therefore, he is related to and resembles purely material, non-human things, although matter in him is permeated by spirit. Contrary to what is held in the Cartesian view, the human body does not exist autonomously alongside the soul, but is a besouled body. Man is a spiritual-material being which is internally unified and identical with itself. All properties and activities of man possess this dual spiritual-material character. Not a single human activity, not even so-called body activities, are of a purely material nature. The material in man is raised by his spirit to a higher degree of being, so that man is indeed clearly distinct from non-human things, i.e., from animals, plants, and lifeless objects, which represent lower degrees of being.

Accordingly, the division of the experiential world into 'man' and 'nature', in the sense of 'human beings' and 'non-human beings', is obvious and well justified. It may be used, therefore, as we will see, for a division of the experiential sciences into sciences of man and sciences of nature. However, there is still another interpretation of the opposites 'man' and 'nature' which needs to be considered in this context.

2. The accepted use of language allows us to divide the world of experience into 'man' and 'nature' in a way which differs from the above-mentioned distinction. The term 'nature' may not be limited to non-human beings, but extended to include also what is corporeal in man. According to this view, man belongs with respect to his body, his material side, to 'nature', but transcends 'nature' with respect to his spirit. Thus the opposition between 'man' and 'nature' becomes

equivalent to that between 'typically human' or 'spiritual' and 'corporeal' or 'material'. For this reason the component parts of the world of experience are sometimes indicated by the terms 'nature' and 'spirit' (from the German *Natur* and *Geist,* as was explained in Section II). Thus man is at the same time 'nature' and 'spirit' or, in the words of a French philosopher, 'nature' and 'freedom' (*nature* and *liberté*).

This opposition of 'man' and 'nature' or of 'spirit' and 'nature' cannot be rejected as unreasonable. For, with respect to his bodily being, man is rooted in, and connected with non-human things in many ways; he is connected with 'nature', in the sense of the non-human, to such an extent that he could not be without it. Man, moreover, with respect to his body, is subjected to the same laws as material things; he manifests phenomena of life like those of plants and animals; he has sense knowledge and sense appetites similar to those of animals, etc. Despite his spiritual principle, by virtue of which he transcends matter, man has to accept everything by which he is material as 'given'. This relationship to the non-human is of inestimable value for the unfolding of his own human being but, on the other hand, it can also resist and hinder him in many ways in his efforts toward self-development. Although man is a principle of freedom by virtue of his spirit, he is at the same time determined with respect to his body. Obviously, this dual character of man will play an important role in all sciences which have man as the object of their investigation. We will have to point this out repeatedly in the following pages.

Comparison of the Two Views. The two interpretations given to the opposites 'man' and 'nature' may be schematized in the following way:

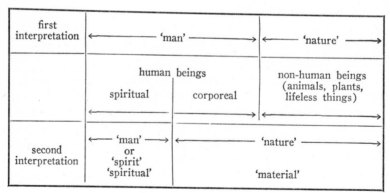

Both interpretations have their advantages and disadvantages. Personally we give preference to the first view, because in it the proper character of man and his spiritual-material unity are more clearly revealed. This point will become even clearer when we will consider the sciences of man (cf. pp. 150 ff.). Usually, therefore, we will refer to the opposites 'man' and 'nature' in the first sense. However, the second interpretation also has its usefulness and gives rise to a dichotomy of the experiential sciences into sciences of nature and human sciences (*Geisteswissenschaften*) which in some respects is not without advantages.

'Objective Spirit'. The proponents of the opposition of 'nature' to 'spirit' often do not limit the term 'spirit' or 'mind' to the spiritual in man (so-called 'subjective spirit', *subjektive Geist*), but extend it to everything which man's spirit produces in the non-human realm ('nature') and upon which he imprints a human character. In this sense the term 'objective spirit' (*objektive Geist*) or rather 'objectified spirit' is sometimes used. This expression is more or less equivalent to the concept 'culture', which we will consider now.

b. Man, Nature, and Culture

At first sight, the pair of opposites 'man' and 'nature', in the sense of the non-human, may seem to indicate the total object of the experiential sciences. Upon closer inspection, however, difficulties make themselves felt against this dichotomy. For the wealth of the world reached by 'experience' is not sufficiently expressed by these two terms. The following reflection should make this clear.

Man is not a self-centered and closed being which stands unmoved and inactive alongside non-human things. By virtue of his spiritual powers he is a free source of purposive activity, and through his bodily powers he is capable of acting in many ways upon non-human reality ('nature' or 'matter') and shaping it according to his ideas. By doing so, man imprints his own unmistakably human stamp upon the non-human world: he humanizes the matter and the surroundings in which he lives. New things are brought forth or 'nature' is given new aspects which it would not get without man's purposive interference or at least would not get in the same way. The modifications of 'nature' which arise in this way express man's typically human activity. 'Nature', at least that part of it which falls within man's reach is ennobled by the rational and purposive interference of man. (Sometimes, however, man's less well directed activity succeeds only in spoiling it.) 'Nature', insofar as it is thus ennobled or 'humanized', is often called 'culture'. It should be evident, therefore, that so-called 'culture' belongs to the objective data of experience.

Trichotomy of Experiential Data. These considerations should make it clear that the total object of the experiential sciences may be divided into three groups. We may describe them provisionally as follows:

1. 'Man', considered with respect to his whole essence, i.e., in both his spiritual and corporeal aspects.

2. 'Nature', as comprising all non-human beings, insofar as their proper character, i.e., their properties, activities, etc., is determined from within through their own specific or individual essence or independently of man's influence.

3. 'Culture', as 'ennobled nature' or as 'humanized nature', i.e., as 'nature' considered from the viewpoint of its being influenced by man's free and purposive activity. Provisionally we may be satisfied with this description. But, as we will see here below (under *c*), the term 'culture' should be understood in a broader sense.

A Few Additional Remarks. If preference is given to the view which extends the term 'nature' to the somatic aspect of man, the preceding considerations would have to be modified in the sense that the term 'man' would have to be limited to the typically human, i.e., to man in his spiritual character.

The groups 'man' and 'nature', taken according to the first interpretation, are 'materially' distinct, for they indicate separate groups of beings. On the other hand, there is only a 'formal' difference between 'culture' and that part of 'nature' with which culture coincides materially (Cf. Part. I, Ch. V, No. 1, pp. 43f.). We will revert to this point after enlarging the concept 'culture' in the following pages.

c. A CLOSER CONSIDERATION OF THE CONCEPT 'CULTURE'

Meanings of the Term 'Culture'. Hitherto we have considered 'culture' as 'ennobled nature', as 'humanized matter'. Although this idea is correct, it is too narrow. At any rate it is advisable to consider the meaning of the term 'culture' more fully. In doing so, however, we do not intend to offer an exhaustive study of the many meanings which this term has in ordinary language and in science.

1. According to its etymology (Latin *colere,* to care for, to till, to cultivate), the term 'culture' means first of all a human activity: care, tilling, cultivation.

2. In a more objective sense 'culture' means the result of such a human activity or 'culture' in the first sense: that which has been cared for, tilled, cultivated, etc.

In the subjective sense, therefore, 'culture' means the human activity which produces 'culture' in the objective sense; in other words, man's 'cultural' or 'culture-creating' activity. In the objective sense 'culture' means the result produced by such a culture-creating activity (culture in the subjective sense).

The term has its objective meaning especially when it is opposed to 'nature'. Unless indication is given to the contrary, it is in this objective sense that we will use the term here, enlarging it at the same time in the way which will be indicated presently.

The typically human 'cultural' or 'culture-creating' activity of man is of a very complex nature. Strictly speaking, it implies three kinds of activities.

1. An intellectual power that is capable of abstractly knowing the essences of the experiential objects, i.e., knowing their specific quiddities, and on the basis of this abstract knowledge is able to form an idea of something which does not yet exist and to recognize the possibility of realizing this non-existing thing. If the realizable object is seen as a good for man, because he sees in it an expression of ideal truth, goodness, and beauty, then the object will deserve to be tended-to and thus have the character of a 'purpose'.

2. An intellectual power of appetency—free will—which is capable of freely choosing such a good as a purpose to be realized and of selecting the means which the intellect considers necessary or useful for this purpose.

3. A transient body activity which the will sets into motion, insofar as the purpose and the means pertain to the realm of matter.

Summarized, man's activity that is creative of culture implies 1) intellect, 2) free will, and 3) transient body activities.

Broadening of the Concept 'Culture'. Thus the concept of culture always contains a typically human element, insofar as it expresses or realizes something which man has known and tended-to as true, good, or beautiful, and has given existence by means of his intellectual knowledge of purpose and means. Through this human influence the object has acquired a certain 'meaning' and 'sense'. There is, however, a possibility of differentiation and gradation in the way in which the human element is present. If we take this possibility into account, we arrive automatically at a broadening of our concept of culture.

1. Thus far in speaking about 'culture' we thought mainly about 'ennobled nature', i.e., material goods which man gave a certain shape or transformed in some way to make them suitable for a practical or artistic purpose. Examples are utensils, technical instruments, conveyances, horticulture, agriculture; also all kinds of material artistic products, such as statues, paintings, buildings, and parks. All these things may be indicated by the term 'material culture'.

2. 'Culture', however, should be conceived more broadly, so as to embrace also the whole of social and spiritual goods which are realized through man's purposive activity. Man, moreover, is capable of investigating the world around him without motives of self-interest, to apply himself to science, to the knowledge of God, and to religious activities.

In this broadened sense the term 'culture' applies also to all kinds of social and economic institutions, legal situations, customs, etc.; also to science, language, literature, music, religious institutions, education, etc. Taken in this sense, cultural activities have a more direct influence upon man himself either as an individual or as a member of a group. This type of culture is often indicated by the term 'civilization'. To distinguish it from the above-mentioned 'material culture', we could speak here of 'spiritual culture' or 'social culture'.

3. Finally, the term 'culture' may be given an even wider extension by being applied also to those human activities of which the acting person himself is the object. Such activities may be correctly called 'self-culture' or more generally 'culture of the mind'. By means of these activities man endeavors to realize the possibilities rooted in his own personality in the best possible way in order to become more 'human' and a better 'man'. Through his 'self-culture' or 'self-civilization' man raises, refines and ennobles the human 'nature'—the term is used here in a more philosophical sense—which is given to him in

his genetic disposition and developed through his surroundings and education (i.e., culture in the preceding sense). By means of this cultural labor man is oriented to his personal perfection and, consequently, to his final destiny, which he endeavors to approach more and more closely. This 'self-culture' is of a more immanent nature than culture in the preceding sense. 'Nature', as extending also to man, and 'culture', go hand in hand here in the individual human person: as 'nature', he offers possibilities of 'cultural' activities, and through this 'cultural' labor he perfects his own 'nature'. Thus man himself is at the same time both 'nature' and 'culture'.

In the following pages we will use the term 'culture' always in the broad sense, as applying to all three above-mentioned meanings. Thus 'culture' extends to 'material culture', 'social culture', and 'self-culture'.

In this broad sense the concept of culture refers to all objects and phenomena of experience insofar as their origin, content, or mode of being are due in one way or another to the 'human mind', i.e., to specifically human, intellectual, free, and purposive activity, and would not exist, or at least not exist in the same way, without this activity. It is this 'culture' in the broad sense which some philosophers indicate by the term 'objective spirit' or 'objectified spirit' (cf. p. 141).

Additional Remarks. As will become clear later, the study of culture in the second and above all in the third sense, is often inseparable from that of man himself, especially in ethnology or cultural anthropology.

In addition to the above-mentioned meanings, the term 'culture' is used also in various other senses. Although these senses generally are connected with one of the enumerated meanings, they usually restrict this meaning in some way, e.g., to the purely intellectual, moral, or artistic realms.

'Culture' is Formally Distinct from 'Man' and 'Nature'. These considerations show that 'culture', as object of the experiential sciences, does not indicate a new group of things outside the groups 'man' and 'nature'. In other words, we do not have to do here with a purely material distinction. It is true, of course, that there are things in the experiential world which pertain solely to 'nature'; for instance, the sun, planets, stars, and earth itself insofar as its external appearance has not been altered by man. On the other hand, there are no experiential objects which belong exclusively to 'culture'. What we have called 'culture' arises through the free and purposive activity

which man directs to himself, to the human society in which he lives, or to that part of nature which lies within his sphere of action. 'Culture', therefore, contains the groups 'man' and, in part, 'nature' insofar as these groups are modified by specifically human interference, i.e., from the viewpoint of their being influenced by man. Thus the group 'culture' arises alongside the groups 'man' and 'nature' by a distinction that is of a formal nature. The following diagram illustrates the point.

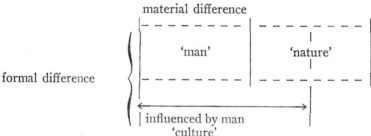

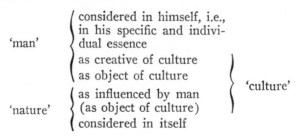

d. TRICHOTOMY OR DICHOTOMY?

Trichotomy. In the preceding pages we arrived for sufficiently good reasons at a division of the total object of the experiential sciences into three groups, indicated by the terms 'man', 'nature', and 'culture'. The objection against this trichotomy is that the three groups do not arise from the same criterion. 'Man' and 'nature' together constitute the entire world of experience, at least if these terms are taken in their first interpretation (cf. p. 140), i.e., as equivalent to the clearly distinct groups of human beings and non-human beings. 'Culture', however does not indicate a new group to be added to the realm of experiential objects, but considers the groups 'man' and 'nature' under a new aspect—namely, insofar as they are influenced and modified by man's free and purposive activity. Since 'nature' can become 'culture' only to the extent that it falls within the reach of man's activity, the resulting division may be schematically proposed as follows:

Despite the above-mentioned difficulty, the proposed trichotomy seems fully justified to me, because in this way man is assigned the place due to him with respect to both his own self and his achievements. Moreover, it seems impossible to divide such a complex whole as the world of experience adequately and completely by means of a single criterion.

It should be evident also that a division of the total object of the experiential sciences into 'nature' and 'culture' is very unsuitable. We cannot simply classify man under 'culture' and 'nature' in a broader sense, because by doing so the essential difference between man and non-human things is rendered obscure. The particular, wholly proper character of man is done justice only if man is assigned a place apart from non-human reality.

Dichotomy. Another division is arrived at when the 'human' aspect of 'culture' is emphasized. Culture owes its special character to the specifically human activities of thinking, purposive tending, and transient acting of man through his body. Without these activities the proper nature of culture cannot be understood. On the other hand, a better understanding of culture gives us a more profound insight into these activities and through them into man's essence itself. If, then, we want to study man, insofar as he can be known from experience, it will not be sufficient to consider him 'in himself', isolated, if this were possible, from non-human beings. Our considerations will have to include also the result of man's interference with non-human things, with fellow human beings and with himself. In other words, it will be necessary to study 'culture', in its broad sense, for it manifests clear traces of human activity and as such contains 'something human'.

Accordingly, the total object of the experiential sciences may also be divided into two parts: the human and the non-human. In this division the term 'human' must be understood in the broad sense as applying not only to man himself and especially the 'spiritual' element in man but also to the result of human activity. Putting the matter schematically, we get the following:

the 'human' $\begin{cases} \text{'man' (especially the human spirit)} \\ \text{'culture' (human influencing of man and nature)} \end{cases}$

the 'non-human' 'nature'

(considered in itself)

Here also the bipartite division is combined with a trichotomy, and here also the groups resulting from the division partially overlap materially, for 'culture' extends over both 'man' and 'nature'. The common parts of the groups are only formally distinct.

Usually the proponents of this division take the terms 'man' and 'nature' in the second interpretation (p. 140), i.e., 'man' is limited to the human spirit as the principles of man's being, and 'nature' is extended to include also the somatic element of man. In a terminology borrowed from Hegelian philosophy, the two main groups are then indicated by the terms 'spirit' and 'nature', the term 'spirit' being taken to mean not only man's mind ('subjective spirit') but also everything which in any way owes its existence or proper nature to man's mind ('objective spirit' or 'objectified spirit').

Recapitulation. By way of summary of the preceding and introduction to what follows, the following diagram may be proposed, in which is indicated the division of both the object of the experiential sciences and these sciences themselves according to the above-mentioned interpretations.

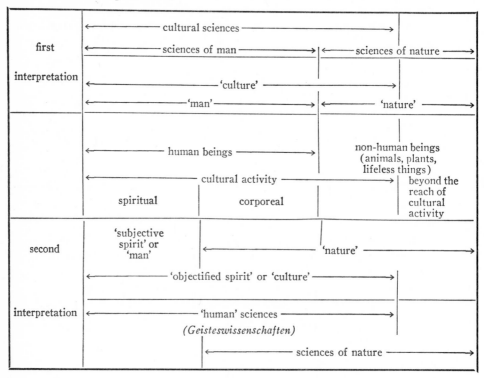

With respect to both the total object of the experiential sciences and these sciences themselves a trichotomy into 'man', 'nature', and 'culture' is preferable in some cases, while in others a dichotomy into 'human' and 'non-human' is more satisfactory. We will revert to this point in no. *d* of the next subdivision (pp. 157 ff.).

2. *Division of the Experiential Sciences*

As was already pointed out, every rational division of the total object of the experiential sciences gives rise to a division of these sciences themselves. Thus the trichotomy of the world of experience into 'man', 'nature', and 'culture' finds its counterpart in the division of the experiential sciences into sciences of man, sciences of nature or physical[8] sciences, and sciences of culture or cultural sciences.

In considering the object of the experiential sciences in the preceding pages, we noted that it is not possible to make a division by means of a single criterion into sharply distinct groups which contain a certain object exclusively and totally. One and the same object may belong, for instance, to both 'nature' and 'culture'. Although the division of the experiential sciences is not without certain difficulties, the situation does not present the same complexity. If the above-mentioned descriptions of 'nature' and 'culture' are kept in mind, generally speaking, there will be no reason to doubt whether a given science must be classified under physical sciences or cultural sciences. True, it may sometimes be a matter of taste whether a science will be considered to pertain to the sciences of man or to the cultural sciences. But no matter where the preference lies, the science in question belongs at any rate to the human sciences and not to the physical sciences. In this respect, therefore, there is no overlapping. For this reason the dichtomy into human sciences and physical sciences may be easier to handle than a trichotomy (cf. under *d*, p. 157).

The preceding pages have established in principle the division of the experiential sciences which we proposed to make on the basis of a distinction by object. We could, therefore, pass on at once to a consideration of the differences flowing from this fundamental distinction. Nevertheless, it seems advisable first to devote our attention

---

[8]From now on we will use 'physical' rather than 'natural', because the term 'natural sciences' was used in Chapter V to indicate the opposite of 'supernatural' or 'theological' sciences. However, we have no serious objections against the use of 'natural' in opposition to 'cultural'.

to the various distinct groups of experiential sciences. Because of the restricted scope and the purely introductory character of this book, we may limit ourselves to the few succinct considerations that are needed for a clear understanding of subsequent pages. It is not our intention, for instance, to present here a complete enumeration and description of the sciences pertaining to each of the various groups. It would not be possible anyhow. We will name only a few important sciences or systems of sciences which clearly represent the group in question. The three groups to be considered are the sciences of man, the sciences of nature, and the sciences of culture.

a. Experiential Sciences of Man or Anthropological Sciences

Their Object is the Whole Man. As was pointed out before, this group of sciences includes in the first place those experiential sciences which consider man in his typically human essence or in his spiritual aspect, as that by which man is distinct from non-human beings, insofar as experience can make this essence known to us. Man, however, is not a pure spirit but a 'spirit-in-matter', an 'embodied' or 'incarnated spirit'. If man is viewed from matter as a being which transcends matter, he may be said to be a 'besouled body' or 'besouled matter'. At any rate, he has to be considered as a spiritual-material being, in which the spiritual and the material are, despite their distinctness, united in inseparable unity, at least as long as man's earthly life lasts. The distinction, therefore, may never be made so radical that one falls into the Cartesian dualism of two separate substantial beings and principles of activity and consequently divides the sciences of man into sciences of the soul and sciences of the body. The whole man must always be the object of our consideration. Of course, this assertion should not be taken to mean that man cannot be considered in different respects.

Precisely because of man's essential unity and the consequent difficulties in making a sharp distinction between the spiritual and the material, the psychical and the somatic, in man, the sciences of man may not be limited to those which are especially concerned with man's spiritual aspect. While this aspect should evidently be assigned the first place, one may not leave out the sciences which consider man in his material or somatic aspect.

Sciences of Man's Spiritual Aspect. Among the sciences of man we must place first of all those sciences which study man in his typically human essence, insofar as this essence manifests itself to us in experience. Psychology and sociology certainly belong to this category. Cultural anthropology or ethnology could be added to them if so desired, although we would rather classify it under the cultural sciences (cf. below *b,* p. 154).

Psychology investigates how man presents himself empirically to us with respect to his sensitive and intellectual aspects, i.e., his external behavior and his conscious life. It studies these aspects in the various phases of his development from childhood through puberty to adulthood, in his relationship and dealings with others as a social being, and in many other situations. As a science, psychology tries to discover how the various forms of man's behavior and conscious life are conditioned or caused, how they become modified through internal or external influences, etc.

Sociology is the experiential science which studies the structures and functions of human groups and their phenomena both in themselves and in their mutual and perhaps variable interconnection. Because many cultural aspects enter into the formation and life of a group, it would be justifiable also to classify sociology, or at least certain social sciences, under the sciences of culture. If this point were to be the subject matter of a dispute, we would not like to take any irrevocable position but at most express a preference for considering sociology a science of man rather than a cultural science. However, the point is of little importance.

Sciences of Man's Somatic Aspect. Alongside these sciences which are more oriented to man's mind, there are others which are more closely allied to physical science. They study the external forms of man's body in the various parts of the world and in different races, often expressing their findings in measurements and numbers (physical anthropology), or study the development, structure, physiological functions, etc. of the human body (embryology, human anatomy and physiology). So far as their methods and character are concerned, these sciences are often not essentially different from their namesakes which consider the animal body. Nevertheless, even in a purely scientific study of the human body certain characteristics manifest themselves which are so strikingly different that for this reason alone it would not be unjustifiable to separate the sciences of man's somatic aspects from the physical sciences. Especially in physiology one may not discount the possibility that psychical factors will influence the vital functions of the body.

Man's Dignity and Scientific Investigation. Although these sciences do not essentially differ from the physical sciences in their method and character, there is a point in which an essential difference has to manifest itself—namely, the attitude of the researcher with respect to man as the object of his study. In his work on lifeless beings, plants, and even animals any interference is justified for reasons of scientific interest. But the person who studies living human beings will always have to maintain a definite restraint with respect to the object of his investigation. He will always have to keep in mind that he is dealing with a human being and that he cannot freely dispose of this being's life, its psychical and physical health, and its bodily integrity. This restraint will have to show itself especially when the question has to be answered whether or not certain experiments are ethically permissible. Scientific curiosity and even the otherwise so legitimate desire to advance medical knowledge for man's well-being may not be here the only motives of action. The investigation will always have to be guided by the pertinent ethical norms, which are based upon man's exceptional dignity. Thus, for instance, reasons of purely scientific interest can never justify the researcher in violating man's bodily integrity; he may never perform experiments which will seriously undermine man's psychical or physical health; he will have to abstain from actions which would jeopardize or destroy a man's fertility, from experiments with artificial donor insemination, from attempts to fertilize a human ovum in a test tube, etc.

What has been said here of living human beings applies also, but only in a greatly reduced way, to human corpses. A certain restraint and respect remains necessary, because the corpse once was the body of a human being.

The Human Character of the Somatic Sciences. These considerations show that, although the sciences in question appear at first to be of a physical nature, nevertheless they assume a special 'human' character because of their human object. For this reason it is rationally justified to classify them under the sciences of man or the anthropological sciences of experience.

The same conclusion is reached if we consider human pathology or the sciences which study man's illnesses. Human pathology could restrict itself to aspects which belong purely to physical science. It would, however, gravely fail in its duty if it did not pay attention to the more human or psychical aspects which reveal themselves in the origin, development, and cure of man's illnesses. Human pathology, therefore, has to be of a psychosomatic nature, i.e., it has to consider also the psychical or spiritual element of man. For this reason it is desirable to classify these sciences in the group of sciences of man.

Sciences of Man or Cultural Sciences? As was pointed out above, opinions may differ regarding the question whether a particular science must be classified under the sciences of man or under cultural sciences. Such a diversity of views is not unreasonable, because it is not always possible to draw a sharp dividing line through the subject matter in question. On the one hand, important aspects of man reveal themselves in the study of man's cultural activities but, on the other, man's mode of being is largely determined by the cultural character of the milieu in which he grows up, matures, and continues to dwell. For this reason, in general, the study of man will not be wholly separated from that of human culture, and vice versa. One and the same science, e.g., sociology or ethnology, will often have to extend its investigations to both man and his culture. According as either man himself or culture predominates in its research, the science in question will be classified either as a science of man or as a cultural science.

In the same way one could argue about the question whether the sciences of history must be considered as sciences of man or as sciences of culture. There is much to say in favor of the first view if attention is paid to the part of historical sciences which study historical man himself, i.e., peoples, groups of men, and individual persons. On the other hand, the second view can easily be defended, for the object of the historical sciences is very broad and extends also to manifestations of culture in the broadest sense. For this reason these sciences are usually, and in our view correctly, classified as cultural sciences. At any rate, they belong to the larger group of human sciences or *Geisteswissenschaften* if one prefers a dichotomy of the experiential sciences (see under *d,* p. 157).

Additional Remarks. In the preceding pages we have paid attention especially to the experiential sciences of man which are of a speculative nature and tend to knowledge for its own sake. Similar considerations, however, apply also to the operative sciences which aim at man's spiritual and corporeal well-being.

To prevent misunderstandings, it appears advisable to state again that not every science which has man as its object, not every 'anthropology', belongs to the above-mentioned group of experiential sciences. For instance, the philosophical study of man or 'philosophical anthropology' which is sometimes called 'philosophical psychology' or also 'rational psychology', belongs to the philosophical sciences. Theological anthropology pertains, of course, to the theological sciences spoken of in Chapter V. The same place may be assigned to the study of religion and religious phenomena (cf. Ch. V, Sect. IV, pp. 97 ff.). There is no need to mention here again the operative sciences referred to in the preceding paragraph.

b. Experiential Sciences of Culture or Cultural Sciences

According to what has been said about culture, this group contains all speculative sciences which have as their object culture in the broadest sense, i.e., all objects and phenomena of experience insofar as their origin, content, or mode of being is somehow due to the 'human mind', to man's intellectual, free, and purposive activity, in such a way that without man's influence they would not exist or at least not exist in the same way. 'Culture', as we have seen above (p. 143), may be conceived in a broader or more restricted sense. In this context, as the object of the cultural sciences, its scope has to be extended at least to the first two meanings of the term, to 'material' and 'social' culture. Frequently, however, 'self-culture' also will have to be considered, insofar as this kind of culture has aspects which can be experienced by other human beings.

Thus the group of cultural sciences contains the following:

1. The speculative sciences which study the 'ennobled nature' of material goods to which man has given a mode of being which they did not naturally have in order to make them useful for a practical or artistic purpose. As examples we may name archeology, history of arts, history of technology, agriculture, stock-breeding, etc.

2. The speculative sciences which devote their attention to all kinds of religious, social, and economic phenomena and institutions, to legal relationships, customs, language and literature, pedagogy and education, etc. Especially ethnology or cultural anthropology could be classified in this group. By cultural anthropology is meant the science which studies peoples, including primitive groups, to see how man exists in the spiritual, social, juridical, religious, moral, and economic realms, etc. Sometimes, however, the term 'cultural anthropology' is reserved for a more theoretical, general cultural science

which studies man as creative of culture, as well as culture itself in general, the comparison of different cultures, their mutual interaction, and the modifications of cultures.

In distinguishing these two groups of speculative sciences we merely intended to indicate in general the sciences which, according to the previously given division of cultural objects, must be considered to belong to the group of cultural sciences. The division does not mean that a particular cultural science has *per se* to belong to one of these two groups.

Moreover, as was already pointed out before (p. 153), it is sometimes merely a question of taste whether a particular science e.g., sociology, ethnology, or the history of a people, will be classified under the sciences of man or those of culture. The choice is not a matter of great importance. The main point is that one should not lose sight of the human aspect proper to both groups by virtue of the object considered, viz., either man himself or the result of typically human activity. This 'human' character of their object is what distinguishes both groups of sciences very clearly from the physical sciences.

c. EXPERIENTIAL SCIENCES OF NATURE OR PHYSICAL SCIENCES

In this group we may place all experiential sciences which have as their object 'nature' in the sense described above (pp. 138 ff.). According to the view which in our opinion deserves preference, 'nature' extends to all non-human things and phenomena, considered in their generic, specific, and even individual essence, properties and activities, including their origin, development, and passing away, insofar as they belong to the things independently of man's interference. (In the other view of 'nature', the term includes also the somatic aspect of man cf. p. 140.)

The Extent of 'Nature'. Taken in the first sense, 'nature' extends to all non-living, vegetative, and animal beings which man encounters in the realm of his experience and whose existence he merely has to accept as 'given'. A large part of this total object of the physical sciences is beyond the reach of man's interference; for instance, celestial bodies, the interior of the earth, and a substantial, albeit steadily shrinking, section of the earth's surface with its flora and fauna. This part is pure 'nature'. Another part of the earth, especially the area inhabited by man, undergoes in many ways the influence of a purposive human influence and thus acquires also 'cultural' aspects. In addition, the materials of the earth and the plants and animals living on it may acquire through man's influence a new mode of being, in the broadest sense of this term. Such objects are at the same time 'nature' and 'culture'. The physical sciences, however, study only the 'natural' substratum, the 'natural' being which lies beneath the new man-given forms.

Man and Nature. To disclose the secrets of 'nature', man often has to influence 'nature' in various ways. He has to 'question' it, i.e., force it through suitable experimental methods to 'reply' to a question which man raises about nature. For this reason it is sometimes said that the object of the physical sciences is not 'nature' without any qualification but 'nature as questioned by man'. However, as will appear from the following, the importance of this 'questioning' should not be exaggerated.

Man's influence on the object may assume a large diversity of forms. As we pointed out, in many cases a direct influence is not always possible; for instance, in the case of celestial bodies or the interior of the earth. Sometimes his influence is limited to modifying a thing's external form in such a way that it is more suitable for scientific examination; for example, in the case of magnetic needles. In other cases his influence consists in the actuation of potencies by exposing the object to external, usually artificial, forces in order to investigate its reactions and thus to learn about the potencies upon which these reactions are based.

The influence of the researcher may be much more profound. It may give rise to things and phenomena which would not occur without this human influence, at least not in the same way. We may think here of artificially produced chemical substances or physical states, e.g., extremely high or extremely low temperatures, or of the artificial modification of the genetic make-up of plants and animals in order to arrive at a better understanding of their development and heredity.

At first sight these types of purposive human activity may seem to fall under what we have previously called 'cultural activity', and their effects would seem to belong to 'culture' in the objective sense. Nevertheless, these terms are not used in this context, because these types of human influence are primarily directed to the investigation of 'nature', i.e., of the essence and properties which pertain to the material substratum independently of man's influence. It is only when they give rise to applications which in one way or another are valuable for man that we speak of 'culture'. It goes without saying, however, that man's research, the methods and instruments he devises for his investigation, and the results attained by it may always be considered as cultural achievements.

The Realm of the Physical Sciences. As was pointed out, the group of physical sciences contains all the sciences which study lifeless matter, plants, and animals; for instance, to name only a few, the astronomical, geological, physical, chemical and mineralogical sciences, paleontology, all botanical and zoological sciences, including the ethology and psychology of animals. Although animal psychology makes use of methods and—unfortunately—even terms borrowed from the psychology of man, and although one may find in animals phenomena which bear some resemblance to typically human phenomena, it appears to us that animal psychology must be kept distinct from human psychology. Each of the two must be classified in the group to which it belongs, as is required even by purely scientific interests. This separation, of course, does not prevent anyone from making use in one science of the results attained by the other, for any science is entitled to utilize the results of another.

From what has been said under *a* of this section (p. 150 ff.), it follows that in our view no sciences of man, not even those which study man's somatic aspects, should be classified under the physical sciences. This assertion holds true even if such sciences of man appear to be physical sciences with respect to their method and character. The unique, spiritual-material character of man co-determines what is material in him, imprints its stamp on it, and demands a special attitude of the researcher with respect to man as his object, even if he studies man's somatic aspects. It is this attitude which gives the science in question a value and dignity of its own.

d. Trichotomy or Dichotomy?

In speaking about the object of the experiential sciences we raised the question whether preference should be given to a dichotomy or a trichotomy (p. 146). As we suggested then and indicated in the diagram on p. 148, the same question may be raised with respect to the division of the experiential sciences themselves and receive a similar answer.

On the one hand, the experiential sciences may be divided into sciences of man, of nature, and of culture but, on the other, they may be divided into physical sciences and *Geisteswissenschaften*. The last-named group may be very suitably indicated by the term 'human sciences'. As such, it extends to the sciences whose object is man himself and especially the typically human, the spiritual, in man, to which must be added the sciences which investigate as their object the effects of human activity upon man himself and upon non-human things ('culture' in the broadest sense). Which division is to be preferred will often be a matter of taste and depend also on the immediate aim one has in mind. If, however, a bi-partite division is preferred, it will often become necessary later to distinguish the human sciences into sciences of man and sciences of culture. In other words, ultimately recourse is had to a trichotomy. For this reason we think that a tripartite division is preferable.

In the following two sections we will generally be able to have recourse only to the dichotomy into human sciences and physical sciences, because the differences which have to be considered are based precisely upon the presence or absence of the typically human aspects. In this respect the sciences of man and the cultural sciences have, of course, many common features; hence we may take these two groups together as 'human sciences' and oppose them to the physical sciences. This dichotomy, moreover, will simplify the consideration of the differences between the two groups.

A last remark. If the above-mentioned dichotomy is compared with the divisions of Dilthey, Windelband, and Rickert, it will become clear that it reveals a certain resemblance to each of these three without, however, coinciding fully with any of them. The reason for this difference lies in the fact that the criteria of division are not the same in any of these divisions. In the following pages we will have to refer constantly to the divisions of these German philosophers and compare them to our proposed classification.

IV. THE DIFFERENCES BETWEEN THE PHYSICAL SCIENCES AND THE HUMAN SCIENCES WITH RESPECT TO THEIR METHODS

Introduction

Object, Method, and Character of an Experiential Science. The fundamental difference in object of the experiential sciences gives rise to all kinds of differences in procedure and consideration, i.e., in method. Object and method, moreover, together determine the nature and structure of man's knowledge, the character of the sciences in question. For this reason it appears desirable to devote separate sections to the differences in method and in character of the two groups of experiential sciences. A consideration of method and character seems all the more necessary because most attempted divisions of these sciences are based on these differences. As has been pointed out in the introduction to the preceding section, such attempts are not justifiable, for the proper character of the object determines the method, and both object and method together determine the character of a science. Consequently, the division according to object must be granted priority.

Indefinite Boundaries. In this section we will show how the differences in method flow logically from the distinction according to object. At the same time, and this too is important, it will appear that the differences according to method cannot be defined as sharply as those according to the object. One could even offer plausible arguments showing that there are all kinds of transitions. Thus it should be clear that any proposed distinction according to method and mode of consideration can easily be attacked by showing that one or the other method or mode of consideration posited as characteristic of one group of sciences does occur also in the other group. However, the implied vagueness of boundaries which is often found to exist between the sciences does not, as we will see, militate against our proposed distinction of the sciences by their object. We may even say that *a priori* such vagueness was to be expected. Hence it does not invalidate what we have said in the preceding section.

Use of the Dichotomy. For the sake of convenience and brevity, we will follow here the dichotomy of the experiential sciences into physical and human sciences (cf. Sect. III, p. 147 and p. 158). The second group contains the sciences of man, especially those of his spiritual and psychical aspects, and the sciences of culture, while the first group considers non-human things but may, if necessary and with all due reserves, be extended to man's somatic aspects. The use of the dichotomy is justified in the present context by the fact that the differences in method arise precisely from the presence or absence of the typically human element, for this element is proper to man himself as well as to the human activities on which cultural achievements are based and even in a certain sense to the products of human culture.

In this connection it is important to pay due attention to a number of features which are fundamental with respect to the differences between the physical and the human sciences and at the same time explain why these differences are not always very clear. These features are the following.

a. *Method of the Sciences of Man and Man's Dual Nature.* As has been pointed out previously, man is a spiritual-material being, a besouled body or an embodied spirit. As far as his body is concerned, man is subject to the laws of nature, spatially and temporally limited and determined by his material surroundings. Through his spirit, however, man transcends matter, he is able to place himself 'at a distance' from his surroundings, and he enjoys a certain autonomy and freedom. But his freedom is not sheer arbitrariness: it is a motivated self-determination arising from man's present situation which is co-determined by his bodily character. Consequently, the act of will, as well as the transient and perceptible activities to which it may give rise, will be guided, on the one hand, by an intellectual deliberation about choice of purpose and means and by an insight into their value for mankind or for this particular man in this concrete situation. On the other hand, however, it can also be influenced, restrained, and more or less determined by the bodily element of man and especially by his sensitive knowledge and appetencies.

To summarize the point, as a spiritual-material being, man is at the same time and inseparably matter and spirit, nature and freedom, determined (with respect to his body) and non-determined (with respect to his spirit). This double character is always present, even in man's properties and activities, but not always in the same fashion. Sometimes the spiritual prevails, and sometimes the material. In the last-named case there will be more resemblance to the purely material, while in the first case the typically human element will manifest itself more clearly.

This complex dual structure will, of course, cause difficulties also in the experiential sciences which have as their object man himself and man's culture. It will influence the methods to be used and the general procedure to be followed. Especially the spiritual element in man's essence and activities will impose certain demands on the methods of research to be used in an effective scientific investigation. In this way it will determine the character of the science in question to a large extent. If scientific research aims more upon the material aspect of man, the methods used may be more like those of the physical sciences.

b. Method of the Cultural Sciences and Man's Special Character.
As we have seen in the preceding section (No. 1, pp. 141 ff.), by
virtue of his spiritual-material essence, man is capable not only of
self-knowledge and self-development but also of cultural activities.
These human activities give rise to effects which we have indicated
by the collective term 'culture'. As duly noted before, this term
extends to various kinds of culture: material, social, and even self-
culture, although the culture of the self may also be classified under
the sciences of man himself.

In cultural phenomena also, in the broadest sense of the term,
there will always be observable aspects which can be explained only
if they are viewed in relation to their human origin. We may name,
for instance, aspects of truth, goodness, beauty, relationships of end
and means, aspects which express freedom of choice and motivated
self-determination, and many others. It follows, therefore, that the
cultural sciences also will manifest a character of their own, insofar
as they consider the experienced objects from the viewpoint of the
influence man exercises on them. The methods of investigation will
have to be adapted, insofar as it is required, to the proper, 'human'
character of the object. In his scientific activity man will have to be
on the alert for the typically human element in the object. Of course,
all kinds of variations and gradations are possible with respect to the
presence of this typically human element.

c. A Fundamental Difficulty. Accordingly, the sciences of man
and those of culture, which we indicate together by the term *'Geisteswissenschaften'* or 'human sciences', possess certain common characteristics which generally are lacking in the physical sciences. In one
way or another these proper characteristics are connected with the
spiritual principle of man, which is the source of intellectual activities
of knowing and tending and the foundation of man's freedom and
autonomy. A special difficulty in the study of man and his culture
flows from the fact that every human being in his self-realization is a
unique phenomenon, and that it is impossible fully to understand the
inner spiritual life of the individual, because this life is only partially
accessible to the observer in perceptible phenomena and activities. As
we will see in the following sections, this difficulty entails certain
consequences for the proper character of the human sciences.

We must now consider a number of differences with respect to
method, but for brevity's sake we will limit ourselves to the main
points and a few illustrating examples.

1. *The Difference in the Method of Acquiring Knowledge*

Dilthey. According to Dilthey, the difference between the physical sciences and *Geisteswissenschaften* or human sciences lies in this that the former have as their object the external world known through sensation, and the latter the internal world revealed to us in reflection (cf. p. 128). In other words, he seeks the difference in the way in which knowledge is acquired, i.e., in an epistemological foundation. The special way of knowing shows itself most clearly, he thinks, in psychology, because the psychologist must try to arrive at an understanding of the concrete and individual structure of his human object by means of empathy ('*nacherleben*' and '*Einfühlung*'). The same difference is referred to by others, including Rickert, although in a somewhat modified way (cf. p. 133).

Physical Sciences. As should be abundantly clear from the preceding section, the human sciences must have a character which differs from that of the physical sciences, because the first group aims at knowledge of the human, and the second at that of the non-human. Obviously, a difference in the way of entering into contact with reality accompanies this difference in object.

In the physical sciences knowledge of nature is obtained through sense experience, not only in immediate perception but also in experimental research. Because of the material nature of the object, there is no need to emphasize this point.

Human Sciences. Sense experience is likewise indispensable for acquiring the first knowledge of the object in the human sciences. For instance, it is needed because we have to perceive human behavior or cultural achievements, such as manuscripts, books, inscriptions, lectures, tools, monuments, and artistic products. This experience, however, does not suffice as a starting point for adequate intellectual knowledge. What the human sciences aim at is to discover and understand the human element in the perceived phenomena, and this understanding will often be rendered easier by a confrontation with one's own human character known through internal experience, introspection, or self-reflection. This self-experience gives us knowledge of our own human mode of being, of knowing, striving, and operating. Because all fellow men agree with us in their specific essence, we may reasonably except that others will act more or less in the same way as we ourselves in similar situations. Thus, upon the basis of our own inner experience and self-knowledge, it will be possible to conclude to the presence of certain thoughts, feelings, motives, etc. in other human beings because of their perceived external behavior in a given situation. Of course, all kinds of deviations are possible here, because every human being has within himself a principle of freedom.

Accordingly, to seize the typically human element in the object of his study, the researcher who specializes in the human sciences will often have to endeavor to 'live', as it were, the situation which he investigates and to study his own sentiments and emotions, his own intellectual evaluation, etc., in order to arrive in this way at the most truthful interpretation of the behavior manifested by the individual persons or groups involved in the situation. This method of approaching the object will be required to a greater or lesser extent in all human sciences. Dilthey and his followers, therefore, are right when they stress this necessity. However, they become guilty of undue generalization when they claim that in the human sciences knowledge always refers to an internal world and is attained only by means of internal experience or introspection. If their position were true, the scientific value of these sciences would be exceedingly small.

From these considerations it seems to be sufficiently clear that the method of acquiring knowledge cannot offer a foundation for the fundamental distinction between the physical and the human sciences. The distinction in method, insofar as it exists, is one which flows logically from the difference in object.

2. *The Difference in the Purpose of Knowledge or in Scientific Attitude*

Dilthey, Rickert, and Windelband. Although the difference in question is intimately connected with the one considered in the preceding paragraphs, it contains enough proper aspects to justify a separate study (cf. Section II). Dilthey, as well as Rickert and Windelband, have pointed out certain aspects which we may use as the starting point of our consideration. Dilthey and Rickert drew attention to the fact that the specialist in the *Geisteswissenschaften* or *Kulturwissenschaften* attempts to arrive at an understanding of the 'sense' and 'meaning' or 'value' which the concrete and individual object has for man. In the physical sciences, on the other hand, we have to do with 'meaning-free and unintelligible being' (Rickert): there is no question of 'sense' or 'value', and abstraction is made of the individual and concrete to arrive at an abstract knowledge of

specific essences and properties. While the physical sciences operate
in a generalizing way, the cultural sciences individualize (Rickert).

This distinction is expressed in a similar way by Windelband
when he states that the physical sciences search in things for the
"form which always remains itself", for "that which is always" and
can be expressed in general laws, because these sciences are 'nomothetic' and 'sciences of law'. The other group of experiential sciences,
Windelband continues, devote their attention to the "singular, determined content of a real event", to particular historical facts, to "that
which was once", for they are 'idiographic' and 'sciences of events'.

Connected with these ideas is the view which bases the difference
between physical and human sciences on the distinction between 'explaining', the search for efficient causes and laws, and 'understanding',
the search for the meaning and finality of a thing, taking into consideration also its connection with the whole. In 'understanding' one
aims at knowledge of integral reality, of *Gestalte* (Windelband), of
the object in its totality insofar as it has 'value', 'sense', and 'meaning'
for man.

The views of these three German philosophers were widely accepted. Often the difference between the physical and human sciences
is presented in a way similar to their stand-point. It is easy to see
the reason why: the difference in object—the human versus the non-
human—will generally require a difference in the attitude of the man
of research. Undoubtedly, some characteristic features of this attitude
were laid bare by these philosophers. Nevertheless, here also it is
necessary to be critical and to be on guard against onesidedness with
respect to either one or the other of the experiential sciences. Let us
examine this point briefly.

Physical Sciences. It is true that in these sciences we usually
search for the specific elements of things, for universally applicable
rules and laws, for an explanation by means of efficient causes. However, it cannot be asserted that we always do so. In these sciences
also it is often the individual thing, that which is only once, which is
the object of research. We may think here, for instance, of the structure and evolution of the earth, of the sun, the moon, planets, and
other celestial bodies. Here also it will often be necessary to make
use of finalistic considerations and views of the totality, to proceed
according to the 'understanding' method. An example is biology, in
which the scientist deals with organized wholes, especially in animal
ethology and animal psychology.

Human Sciences. Insofar as the human sciences aim at the typically human element of the object, it is true that they often demand the attitude which the above-mentioned views describe so eloquently. In the historical sciences, for instance, which Windelband had especially in mind, the object is always something that is only once and, therefore, has to be studied in its individual concreteness. Through long and exacting studies, through 'reliving' and 'empathy' the historian has to become intimate with the historical periods and milieus, the persons and their world of thought, in order to be able to understand the actual course of events and the actions of its authors. With the appropriate changes, the same applies also to the literator, the exegete, the ethnologist, etc. Wherever a human person in his concrete and individual uniqueness forms part of the object of science, the researcher will meet difficulties which the physicist never has to face.

Nevertheless, this picture does not do full justice to the human sciences. It is too one-sided. What has been said here applies to a considerable extent to a few human sciences, e.g., the historical sciences, but it may not be unqualifiedly extended to all human sciences. These sciences rarely limit themselves to what is 'only once' as such, but wherever possible search for regularity and laws, so that the individual is considered also as representative of a species or of a group. It must be admitted, of course, that the laws in question are usually of a different nature from those which rule in the physical sciences (see Sect. V, No. 2, p. 175 ff.). Moreover, the human sciences attempt to explain what is 'only once' through 'general' efficient causes and by means of general principles, as is done by the physical sciences. Accordingly, the scientific attitude will more closely resemble that of the physical sciences in those parts of the human sciences which deal mainly with what is material, corporeal, and therefore determined.

Conclusion. Undoubtedly, there is a certain difference between the physical and the human sciences with respect to the purpose of their scientific activity or their scientific attitude. However, first of all, the situation is not such that one and the same scientific attitude occurs in all sciences of one group and not at all in any science of the other group. Secondly, as could be expected even *a priori,* whatever difference there is flows immediately from the difference in object. Consequently, the difference in method may not be considered as a criterion for the division of the experiential sciences but at most as a correlated and secondary difference.

3. *The Difference with Respect to the Use of Mathematical Means*

Another difference in method upon which sometimes a distinction between the two groups of experiential sciences is based is the difference in the use they make of mathematical means. According to proponents of this view, the physical sciences are the realm *par excellence* of mathematical treatment, while the human sciences offer no scope or very little scope for the use of a mathematical method. Of course, we readily acknowledge that in this respect there is a difference between the two sciences, but at the same time we must deny that this difference is suitable as a basis or criterion for the division of the experiential sciences. The difference in question again is merely secondary and logically connected with the difference in object of the sciences in question. The following considerations may clarify this point.

The Realm of Mathematical Method. In general, mathematical methods are applicable wherever we are dealing with quantities in the broad sense of the term. Quantity includes here discrete quantity or plurality, which is the basis of numerability, and continuous quantity, which is the basis of measurability.

There is question of discrete quantity or plurality wherever man deals with separate or clearly distinct things which can be numbered or counted by means of natural numbers. If the term 'plurality' is taken in a broad sense—so-called 'transcendental plurality'—it is applicable to every collection of arbitrarily chosen things, even if they belong to different species. In the strict sense, the term 'plurality' is limited to individuals of the same species and then it is called 'predicamental' or 'categorical plurality'.

The term 'continuous quantity' makes us think, first of all, of extension in the strict sense of the term which belongs *per se* and only to all material things and by virtue of which they have dimensions and shape. *Per accidens* or indirectly extension belongs also to the qualities and activities of material substances, because these qualities and activities are attached to the extension of these bodies. Moreover, an intensity can be attributed to these qualities and activities and this extension itself may also be considered as a continuous quantity (so-called 'intensive quantity').

With respect to continuous quantities which are homogeneous or considered to be homogeneous it will usually be possible to perform some kind of 'measurement'—namely, by comparing these quantities with a magnitude of the same kind that has been chosen as a standard. The result of such a comparison can be expressed by means of whole or fractional numbers. The same rule applies in general also to qualities and activities. In this case the comparison will succeed even better when it is possible to make a directly measurable representation of the activities by means of their action on a suitable medium. We may think here, for instance, of the measurements of temperatures or strength of currents by means of instruments on which a definite position or length can be read.

Physical Sciences and Mathematics. From these considerations it should be evident that the physical sciences by virtue of their object— matter—are eminently suitable for mathematical treatment, for their object is immediately affected by both types of quantity. The objects of 'nature' are, first of all, extended and therefore also measurable, because they are material. This character of extension is found also in the qualities and activities of material things. Secondly, these qualities and activities are also quantitative with respect to their intensity, so that, in principle at least there is always a possibility of measurement.

Moreover, in the physical sciences we are usually dealing with individuals which have a specific nature and whose plurality can be expressed in numbers; for instance, the number of atoms of the same element, that of the molecules of the same compound, and the number of electrons. Finally, the physical sciences study all kinds of interactions which can be described by means of mathematical relationships. This description can be exact, because it refers to determined material things whose properties and actions are always univocally determined.

Difficulties in the Use of Mathematics in the Physical Sciences. Accordingly, the physical sciences, because of the quantitative and determined nature of their object, offer almost unlimited possibilities for the application of mathematical means. On the other hand, mathematics cannot be applied to the same extent to all physical sciences or even to all parts of one and the same physical science. Without entering into many details, we may point out a number of difficulties which occur in various realms when mathematics is applied to them. They are chosen in a fairly arbitrary way.

First of all, we may mention the frequent necessity of having recourse to statistical methods. This necessity exists wherever one has to deal with an enormous number of similar things whose individual behavior, determined though it is, cannot be known exactly; for instance, in the kinetic theory of molecules, in the physics of neutrons and electrons, or in the physics of radiation. Very often, because the initial state is in principle unknowable, the subsequent course of events can be predicted only with a degree of probability. Moreover, physical science often also has to study pluralities of things which do not belong to the same species or at least are not wholly equal, although one considers or wants to consider them as pertaining to the same species. This happens, for instance, in astronomy and in the study of plants and animals. The result is that often one can work only by means of statistical methods.

In addition to the above-mentioned difficulties, there are others in the physical sciences of living bodies. They stem mostly from the enormous complexity of these objects. Although they are strictly determined, there is usually such a huge number of collaborating and mutually influencing factors that the ultimate visible result is not easily fathomed. It may even seem sometimes that there is a measure of freedom and spontaneity. This is especially the case with animals, whose concrete behavior is determined by sensations and instinctive reactions. In different individuals of the same species these sensations and reactions may differ and, moreover, in the same individual they are often dependent upon the animal's actual situation, which again can vary widely within broad limits. Because of all these factors, the results of experiments with living bodies, and especially with animals, are frequently difficult to reproduce repeatedly; hence here also we will often have to be satisfied with statistical descriptions or with rules that have merely a kind of probability. In several respects, e.g., individuality, spontaneity, knowledge, and appetency, animals foreshadow somewhat typically human properties. For this reason it is not surprising that in the zoological sciences one begins to encounter the difficulties which the human sciences find constantly in their path when they want to use mathematical methods.

Human Sciences and Mathematics. Reflection on the proper character of the object of the human sciences, on man and his culture, readily shows that this object is usually less suitable for the use of mathematical methods. Let us offer first a few examples illustrating the point insofar as man himself is concerned and then others taken from cultural sciences.

What is typically human in man, i.e., his 'spiritual' properties and activities, such as acts of intellectual knowledge and willing, as well as man's spirit or soul, as the source and origin of these qualities, are not extended. Consequently, they are not measurable either in themselves or in their intensity. The concept 'continuous quantity' cannot be directly applied to them. It is only insofar as the spiritual functions have a repercussion in the somatic and perceptible aspects of man that there can in a sense be question of 'quantity' and of mathematical treatment. Thus, for instance, a man's intelligence may be tested by proposing to him a number of problems which vary in difficulty, by counting the correct solutions, and comparing their number to a standardized average that has been obtained by analyzing a huge amount of research material. Although it is possible in this way to arrive at a kind of comparison and evaluation, it goes without saying that there can be question here of 'measurement' only in an analogous sense.

For a science which devotes its attention to groups of men the difficulty is that these human beings, despite the fact that they belong to the same species, are individually very different through differentiations resulting from ability, surroundings, education, selfculture, etc. In this realm it is hardly possible to arrive in a univocal way at divisions or classifications. Thus no one wants to claim that he is using univocal terms when he speaks of Americans, Greeks, or Romans, of Catholics, Protestants, or Jews, of intellectuals, middle class, laborers, or students, of boys, adults, or old men, etc. Insofar as individual persons are involved here, it is possible to count and to make use of mathematical methods, but the mathematical treatment and its results will have to be viewed with a certain amount of suspicion, because in general there exists no plurality of equal unities in this realm.

Cultural Sciences and Mathematics. If we look at the group of human sciences which are sciences of culture, we find that with the necessary modifications the same remarks apply to them as to the sciences of man, such as psychology and sociology, although often to a much lesser extent. It will be practically impossible to apply mathematical methods in those sciences of culture which deal with what is 'only once', with individual persons, or with particular groups of men. Such sciences are, for instance, archeology, historical sciences, ethnology, and the history of literature.

On the other hand, it will be easier to apply mathematical methods to parts of the cultural sciences which are concerned with a plurality of things that belong more or less to the same species or with similar tendencies in a plurality of persons. However, here also, because of the deviations from specific similarity, there will be great difficulties. We may think here, for example of the many variations covered by such terms as school, church, house, clothing, weapons and tools, marriage and family, war, revolt and revolution. Genuine univocity in the strict sense of the term exists only in uniformly manufactured industrial products.

In the cultural sciences the mathematical treatment will usually have to be limited to a statistical compilation of the data in numbers and graphs which facilitate a survey of the materials.

The cultural science which lends itself most easily to the application of mathematical methods is economics. Although the course of affairs in economics is determined by human beings, the human aspects which predominate here are egoism, the urge to acquire and retain money and material goods. The result is that in economic respects they behave more or less as determined things, which have only one mode of acting. The few exceptions which deviate from the general pattern of behavior have little or no influence because we are usually dealing with large numbers. Thus it will frequently be possible to predict how man will act in the realm of economics or how his way of acting will change under the influence of certain factors. There is in this area also a possibilty to formulate functional relationships, which may be called 'economic laws'. It is even possible sometimes to use in economics physical formulas if the physical symbols are given an economic content. The section of economic science in which the mathematical method is mainly used has acquired so much importance that it is indicated with a special name—'econometry'.

Conclusion. With respect to the use of mathematical means, there appears to be a general difference between the physical sciences and the human sciences. This difference, however, is not to be considered fundamental and cannot act as a suitable criterion for a good division of the experiential sciences. Insofar as there is any difference, it flows from the proper nature of the objects—nature, on the one hand,

and man and his culture, on the other. Likewise, the differences which exist in this respect within one and the same science can be reduced to differences in the quantitative character of the object. Thus it should be clear once more that a distinction of the groups of experiential sciences cannot be based on a difference in their method. On the contrary, as was *a priori* to be expected, it is again the object which determines the character of the method.

V. THE DIFFERENCE BETWEEN THE PHYSICAL SCIENCES AND THE HUMAN SCIENCES WITH RESPECT TO THE CHARACTER OF THEIR KNOWLEDGE

Introductory Remarks

The preceding section considered a few differences in method which exist in varying degrees between the physical and the human sciences. These differences in method, we said, cannot be held to be fundamental or to be criteria for dividing the experiential sciences into the two groups. To the extent that these differences exist, they can be explained by the differences in object.

Through the difference in object and the consequent difference in method the two groups, physical sciences and human sciences, acquire distinct characters which manifest themselves as differences in many respects. As we will see, these differences must be considered to be secondary, and the efforts to use them as a basis for the division of the sciences cannot be accepted. Although the differences in question may be very clear 'characteristics' in extreme cases, they allow too many intermediary forms to be suitable for a rational division of the sciences. Both these differences and the continuous intermediary forms which exist here and there can be rendered plausible by a consideration of the objects studied in both groups of sciences—viz., 'nature' or the non-human, on the one hand, and the 'human' with all the complications following from man's spiritual-material character, on the other. Thus it should not surprise anyone if we will have to appeal repeatedly to what has been mentioned several times already regarding man and his activity.

It is not our intention to offer here a complete enumeration of all differences. Completeness would not have been possible anyhow, for every aspect of science is likely to present some kind of difference. We have limited ourselves therefore to a few striking differences, presented in a very succinct way. The indications and examples will suffice, we hope, to initiate the reader to the question and stimulate him to further investigation. Any attempt to treat the subject matter more fully would make this chapter grow out of proportion to the remainder of the book.

1. *Difference in Abstraction and Universality*

The Physical Sciences. In general it is possible in the physical sciences to abstract from the individual and concrete and thus to arrive at univocal concepts of the specific essence or, through continued abstraction, of the generic essence. This so-called 'total abstraction' results in concepts which are universal from the logical viewpoint, i.e., they apply in a similar way to each of their inferiors. Examples are 'gold', 'atom of gold', 'atom' or 'molecule' in general, and 'energy' (the last three are examples of generic concepts).

The subject matter of the physical sciences is usually also suitable for 'formal abstraction'. In this abstraction an object of experience is considered with respect to one or the other constituent principle or an ontological mode of being, i.e., a 'formal aspect' or 'form' which in a particular respect determines what the object is. Such a form can play a role as a cognitive content and as the object of an investigation. Examples would be all kinds of essential forms as well as physical and chemical properties, such as elasticity, hardness, conductivity, color, valence; also quantitative aspects. Since here also abstraction is made from the concrete and individual, there is also total abstraction and universality.[9]

It will not always be possible in the physical sciences to arrive at abstract concepts in the above-mentioned sense or at universal statements in which such concepts function as subjects. For in the physical sciences also it happens frequently, as has been pointed out before, that the object studied is something individual considered in its concrete and individual mode of being. One has to think here only about such a science as geology. In speaking of such an object, however, we may use concepts which have been obtained through total or formal abstraction.

Moreover, it often happens in the physical sciences, especially in the initial stage of an investigation, that we cannot advance beyond so-called 'analytic abstraction', through which a totality or

---

[9]For a more detailed consideration of abstraction and universality, see **Part I, Ch. III.**

plurality of things is considered in separate, sense-perceptible aspects. This happens, for instance, in the study and the division of plants by the number of their stamina, the structure of their flowers, the shape and position of their leaves, in the study and comparison of animals according to their anatomic structure, in a provisional classification of stars according to color, strength of light, mass, etc. Complete induction and induction completed by analogy frequently are based upon such considerations.[10]

Analytic abstraction does not lead to abstractly general concepts but only to collectively general concepts, such as sea, island, river, glacial period, cloud, rainstorm, planet, star, constellation, etc. There can be no question of applying such concepts univocally to their 'inferiors'.

The Human Sciences. In general it will not be possible to arrive at strictly universal and univocal concepts in those human sciences which are concerned, not with man as such in his abstract essence, as is the case in philosophical anthropology, but with man in the concrete, either as an individual or as part of a group, or with real human culture in all the forms in which it appears. First of all, some sciences of man, e.g., psychology, and also some cultural sciences, e.g., history, aim precisely at man as he is and lives concretely in all his phenomenal variability, and study him in his concrete individuality. True, they use concepts which have been acquired by means of a kind of abstraction and therefore are in a sense universal. However, these concepts are significantly different from genuinely universal and univocal concepts. We may think here of ideas such as psyche, character, capacity, skill, intelligence, will power, of concepts indicating body characteristics, and of concepts such as child, adolescent, adult, man, and woman.

Secondly, the sociological and ethnological sciences which study man as a part of a group, peoples, and races, as well as several other cultural sciences suffer from the difficulty that they have to use ideas which cannot be sharply defined and consequently have a kind of vagueness resulting in a broad range of applicability. One has only to think here of the manifold meanings which within certain limits can be attributed to such terms as American, European, Dutchman, Greek or Roman, to laborer, farmer, intellectual, poet, professor, student, police officer, to democracy, liberalism, republic, kingship, peace war, revolu-

---

[10]Cf. Part I, Ch. VII, pp. 65-70.

tion, to marriage, family, household, to economic boom, devaluation, inflation, to sin, guilt, punishment, to literary 'categories', and to many other terms.

Moreover, in various cultural sciences man deals with events that happen 'only once' and with concrete not-repeatable situations which are indicated by singular terms and whose content often defies an exact description. To name a few examples, antiquity, the Middle Ages, Renaissance, gothic, baroque, romanticism, Marxism, the Greek character, the American War of Independence. Such concepts are not at all abstract in themselves, but in describing their contents we have to make use of concepts that are more or less abstract in the above-mentioned sense. Since these abstract concepts themselves are more or less vague, they can clarify only in a restricted way what they describe.

Even in the sciences which devote themselves to 'material culture' similar difficulties occur, although usually only to a lesser extent. Since man is capable of realizing a given idea in various ways in matter, a term and its corresponding concept may indicate a plurality of objects which can be widely different and sometimes may even be something that occurs 'only once'. The assertion may be illustrated by concepts expressing tools, such as knife, plow, spade, oven, axe; concepts of arms, such as bow, arrow, lance, rifle, gun; concepts expressing means of transportation, such as cart, wagon, motorcar, train, ship, aeroplane; concepts of dwellings or buildings, such as tent, house, church, school, factory. All these concepts have a certain content that can be more accurately described but, because of the many possible modes of realizing this content, there is always also a certain amount of vagueness. This vagueness affects even more generic terms, such as tool, weapon, means of transportation, room, etc.

Something analogous occurs even in a much stronger sense in original works of art. They have necessarily the character of something that is unique, so that it is only through analytic abstraction that one can arrive at terms and concepts applying to a plurality of them. Appropriate examples are poem, verse, essay, painting, woodcut, etching, statue and bust.

In the realm of material culture there is, strictly speaking, univocation only when there is question of the uniform reproduction of a given artistic object or of a technical concept; for instance, in the mechanical, uniform mass production of utensils or the mass reproduction of an artistic work.

Accordingly, in the human sciences it is only rarely that through total or formal abstraction an abstractly general or strictly universal and univocal concept will be reached. In general, one will have to be satisfied if through analytic abstraction one manages to arrive at collectively general concepts, such as those of the above-mentioned examples. Moreover, it happens very often and more frequently than in the physical sciences that one has to do with collectively singular concepts in which for a special reason a plurality of separate individual things or human beings are considered to be an accidental unit and indicated by a single name; for instance, the American people, the Democratic Party, the Faculty of Duquesne University, NATO, the capital or the wardrobe of Peter Johnson.

Analogy of Concepts. In the human sciences the fundamental concepts strongly reveal certain characteristics which makes us think of the analogy of philosophical concepts. Their content is to some extent vague, so that they can apply to a plurality of singular objects which are considered to have a similar essence; and they contain these objects not only insofar as their abstract essence is concerned but also in their individual concreteness, including the differences which distinguish one individual from another. The same thought content is realized all the time in a different way, and these different possibilities are included in the unity of the concept. This phenomenon occurs far less in the physical sciences, although even in them, as we have seen above, it is not entirely absent.

Conclusion. With respect to abstraction and universality, then, there clearly are differences between the physical and the human sciences, but these differences are not exclusively found in either group of sciences. Insofar as they are present, the differences in question can easily be explained through the proper character pertaining to the general object studied by the two groups of sciences. In the same way it is possible also to account for the similarity that is often found to exist between the two groups.

It is to be noted that the differences in abstraction and universality are connected with other differences, of which we will consider a few in the following pages.

2. *Difference in Character of Scientific Laws*

As we have seen in Section II, Windelband based the distinction between the two groups of experiential sciences upon the presence or absence of laws. He even named one group, that of the physical sciences, 'sciences of law' or 'nomothetic sciences', and used the terms 'sciences of events' or 'idiographic sciences' for the other group of experiential sciences, among which he paid special attention to the historical sciences.

Such a sharp distinction, however, with respect to the presence or absence of laws has to be rejected. Once more there is question not of a characteristic which would be wholly present in one group and wholly absent in the other, but only of its presence to a greater or to a lesser extent in both groups. Moreover, as we will see, the differences in value and scope of laws in the two groups flow again from the nature of their object.

Different Meanings of 'Law'. The term 'law' is an analogous concept, having different meanings which, in addition, allow all kinds of minor variations. We will abstract here from the meaning of 'law' as a norm of human activities, which is considered in the operative sciences and especially in those of law. At present we mean by 'law' any proposition which is 'generally valid'. The variable meaning which the expression 'generally valid' can have implies also differences in the concept 'law'. The nature of the validity in its turn is connected *inter alia* with the general character of the concept which functions as the subject of the proposition in question as well as with the type of necessity pertaining to the relationship between the subject and the predicate. A few words may be devoted here to both these aspects, which are partially interconnected.

With respect to *generality,* it makes a big difference whether the concept functioning as a subject is abstractly general or merely collectively general (cf. p. 172). In the first case we have to do with a proposition which is valid for the subject as such and, therefore, also for each of its inferiors. There is a relation of necessity. In the case of the collectively general subject-concept the proposition does not have a higher value than that of the sum total of the singular, usually empirical, propositions which it summarizes. If such a collectively general proposition is the result not of a complete induction, i.e., of induction through complete enumeration, but only of an incomplete induction that is completed by analogy, then its value will be even less, because of the possibility that there may be exceptions (cf. Part I, pp. 59 ff. and 66 ff.).

With respect to *necessity,* one has to pay attention, first of all, to the necessity and validity which a proposition may have in itself, according to the objective relationship between subject and predicate, as well as to the necessity attributed to it in our provisional and defective knowledge. It may happen, for instance, that a proposition which according to our knowledge may be considered only as being collectively general is in reality abstractly general or universal, so that it applies of necessity to all things pertaining to the extension of the subject-concept.

Secondly, a distinction has to be made between physical and moral necessity. If a *physical necessity,* which is an essential necessity in the physical order, belongs to the subject-predicate relationship, the proposition does not allow any exceptions. In the strict sense, such a necessity is present only if the subject is an abstractly general concept. If the necessity in question is a *moral necessity,* taken in the sense which we have attributed to this term and which, strictly speaking, is found only in propositions about human qualities and activities, then there will usually be a possibility of exceptions because of the complexity of man's nature and his freedom of will.[11] With respect to propositions which express merely a moral necessity or whose general validity for some reason or other is not fully waranted, many prefer to use the terms 'rule' or 'tendency' rather than 'law'.

This introductory consideration is sufficient to justify us in drawing certain conclusions regarding the differences which exist in these respects between the physical and the human sciences.

The Physical Sciences. In these sciences it is often possible by means of 'scientific induction' to arrive at an abstractly general proposition expressing a relationship of physical necessity. In such cases the term 'law' is often used or, if the propositions in question are very general, the term 'principle', as, for instance, in the principle of energy or of entropy.

We abstract here from the temporary character that such 'laws' sometimes have because defective knowledge makes us formulate them incompletely or incorrectly. If the laws correctly formulate the mutual relationship or the mode of operation proper to material objects, they are absolutely valid and universal, i.e., they apply to each and every object possessing the essence expressed by the subject-concept.

Such insights are more easily reached in the realm of inanimate nature than in that of living material beings. Living beings have an

---

[11]Cf. Part I, Ch. IV, pp. 37 ff. Because we are concerned here only with the experiential sciences, we may omit absolute or metaphysical necessity as well as mathematical necessity.

enormous inner complexity, they are extremely variable, and can be influenced in manifold ways by their surroundings, especially in the case of animals, whose sensitive life of knowing and tending is an additional source of complications. For these reasons living beings, although they are determined in themselves, will defy man's comprehensive grasp, so that it is extremely difficult to discover precise inter-relationships in the realm of the living. As a result, biological laws generally lack the character of precision which we are accustomed to in physics and chemistry. Biologists, therefore, often prefer to speak of 'rules' and 'tendencies' rather than 'laws'.

If in the physical sciences we have to deal with an object in its individuality and uniqueness, the result of the physical investigation can be expressed, of course, only in singular propositions, i.e., statements which apply to only one subject. In such a case there is evidently no question of 'laws' and 'universal validity'.

The Human Sciences. Man and his culture constitute the object of these sciences. Therefore, insofar as there can be question of generally valid laws in these sciences, their generality is of a much more complex nature. Moreover, because of the strictly individual character and the element of freedom that are present in every human activity, all kinds of deviations from a common 'rule' will occur. At most, there can be question of a 'moral necessity'. To avoid repetition, we will refer here to what has been said above in the first part of this section about abstraction and universality.

Only if there is a possibility of total or formal abstraction in the strict sense, leading to a univocal concept, can one arrive at genuine 'laws' possessing a universal validity. However, this possibility exists only rarely.

When through analytic abstraction collectively general concepts can be formed, the statements regarding these concepts will have the character of collectively general propositions. This happens very frequently. Products of material and spiritual culture, by virtue of certain similarities, may be put together under a single term and spoken about in a collectively general proposition; for instance propositions about houses or paintings. Likewise, human beings may be indicated by such a term because of certain common characteristics or identity of profession and referred to in collectively general judgments; for instance propositions about Americans, Negroes, Catholics, laborers, or professors. On the other hand, statements about a single person, a single event, or a single thing are logically speaking evidently singular judgments. Such statements are very frequent in the historical sciences. The same singular character belongs to a scientific statement whose subject is a collectively singular concept (cf. p. 175). In such a case there is, of course, no question of a universally valid law.

No human science is exclusively idiographic, in the sense that it leads only to singular statements because it is solely concerned with what is 'only once', with individual persons, things, or events (cf. Windelband's view on p. 131). Knowledge which aims only at the singular can hardly be honored with the term 'science'. True, investigation and knowledge of individual things are necessary, but a science will always try to explain the events or facts through general causes and to formulate 'rules' which apply to similar events. For example, there are rules governing the origin, course, and effect of revolution or war, rules about the vowel changes of a language, about the modifications of cultures, and many other phenomena. It may often happen that a large part of a science is of a descriptive character. Sometimes, if the part in question is important, it receives even a special name. For instance, a distinction is sometimes made between historiography and historical science, between sociography and sociology, ethnography and ethnology. The first of each of these pairs is idiographic, while the last of each is more nomothetic.

Contrary to what Rickert thought, the human sciences, therefore, also always reveal a tendency to 'generalize', to seek for 'tendencies', 'rules' or 'laws'. According to the character of the various human sciences, which is determined by their object, there will be a difference in the generality of its laws. This point should be clear from what has been said about it in the first part of this section.

Some Remarks About the Economic Sciences. There is one cultural science which many want to classify among the physical sciences precisely because of the character of its laws—namely, economics. A few remarks, therefore, must be made about this science in particular. In our view, such a classification must be absolutely rejected. For, according to its object, economics is a science of human activities in a particular realm, and its character is co-determined by this human aspect.

True, economic laws or rules resemble the laws of physical science, insofar as their universal character and necessity are concerned, much more than in the case of the laws formulated in other human sciences. It is even possible simply to transpose certain formulae from physics, e.g., thermodynamics, into econometry by giving the physical symbols an 'economic' content (cf. Sect. IV, p. 170). However, this 'physical' character of economics is easily explained if attention is paid to its object. As far as the economic realm is concerned, apart from a few exceptions which are without influence on the large numbers involved, human beings will always be guided by the tendency to acquire in a given situation as many goods or as much money as possible and to secure what they have acquired. Thus man acts here as if he were a determined being. As a result, it is often easy *a priori,* even without any experience, to formulate laws or rules which the economic behavior of a given group of men will follow in a given situation. However, this 'physical' character of economic laws should not be a reason to classify economics among the physical sciences.

Moreover, the similarity of economic and physical laws is not so great as it is often claimed to be. Experience shows that not only individuals but even large groups, precisely because of their freedom and motivated self-determination, frequently react quite differently from what was expected. Such reactions manifest the human character of economic activities and discomfit the assertions and forecasts of economic authorities.

Conclusion. As far as the validity of their laws is concerned, there is in general a clear distinction between the physical and the human sciences. This should not surprise us after what we have seen about abstraction and universality in the first part of this section. However, here also there is no exclusive distinction. Alongside clear differences, there are also all kinds of similarities. Both these differences and similarities appear as reasonable if attention is paid to the objects considered in the experiential sciences.

3. *Difference in Extension and Modality of Scientific Statements*

According to Windelband (Sect. II, p. 131), the physical sciences are characterized by judgments which are universal in extension and apodictic in their modality, while the results of the historical sciences are laid down in judgments which are singular and assertoric. This view is certainly too schematic. In its absoluteness it can only be rejected.

Insofar as in this respect there are differences between the physical and the human sciences, they flow from the differences in universality and in the character of laws which were spoken about in the preceding pages. Hence it will not be necessary to enter into too many details, but a brief explanation will suffice.

a. DIFFERENCE IN THE EXTENSION OF SCIENTIFIC STATEMENTS

With respect to extension, scientific statements are divided into abstractly general, collectively general, particular, and singular or individual statements according to the extension proper to their subject. As we have seen above (pp. 172 ff.), in neither of the two groups of sciences do one or more kinds of these statements occur to the exclusion of the other group. All four kinds are met in both groups, in one more and in the other less.

Abstractly general statements occur more frequently in the physical sciences, and especially those of inanimate matter, than in the human sciences. Collectively general assertions also occur in both groups, at least in the provisional stage of scientific investigation. In the human sciences they function more frequently in their final stage— namely, when it is not possible to make a transition to the abstractly general. However, this may happen also in the physical sciences, especially in biology. Particular statements, which apply to some individuals of a group but not to all, occur in both groups of the experiential sciences.

Singular assertions—among which we may include collectively singular statements, because they are logically equivalent to singular statements—result always when a single individual, or a plurality which is viewed as a unit, is the object of investigation. These singular statements do not exclusively belong to one group of the experiential sciences. However, they occur much more frequently in the human sciences, especially those of history. For further details we may refer to the examples and considerations of the first part of this section (pp. 172 f.). All that remains to be added is that the statements referring to concrete and individual things which are the starting point of every part of every experiential science have always a singular character (see also what follows here under *b*).

b. DIFFERENCE IN THE MODALITY OF SCIENTIFIC STATEMENTS

Types of Modality. A full consideration of the various modalities that may occur in speculative sciences would, strictly speaking, have to be presented before the differences in the modality of the two groups are treated. However, we will limit ourselves for brevity's sake to the ones that are most important for our purpose.

The first of these is the so-called *'alethic modality'* (from the Greek *alētheia,* truth), which qualifies the truth or falsity of a proposition. Four kinds are distinguished—namely, necessity (*S* is necessarily *P*), non-necessity or contingency (*S* is contingently *P* and can be also non-*P*), impossibility (*S* cannot be *P*), and possibility (*S* can be *P,* perhaps is *P*). With respect to the modality of necessity, further distinction has to be made between absolutely necessary and hypothetically necessary propositions, and the last-named group itself has to be further divided into physically necessary and morally necessary propositions (cf. Part I, Ch. IV).

Secondly, there can be a *quantifying modality.* It makes a distinction in the quantity or extension according to which a predicate is attributed to the subject. For instance, it is universally valid that *S* is *P;* it is not universally valid that *S* is *P;* there is at least one case in which *S* is *P;* or there is no case in which *S* is *P*.

There are several points in which these two modalities meet. For instance, a relation of S and P which is physically necessary is also universally valid; or if there is at least one case in which *S* is *P,* then it is certainly possible for *S* to be *P*. But the reverse is not always true. It may happen that a certain relation of *S* and *P* is *de facto* universally realized and, therefore, universally valid, without there being any necessity that it be so realized. However, the point is not very important for us here, so that there is no need to delve deeper into it.

Finally, we must mention so-called *'epistemological modalities'.* Scientific statements are expressions of the actual knowledge the man of research has about a given situation which is offered to the judgment of his intellect. The proper character which belongs objectively to a proposition in itself, e.g., its own modality of necessity, will usually not be clear at once to the man of research. Sometimes this modality will not even be known after a long and diligent inquiry.

As far as the objective relationships are concerned—and the experiential sciences are concerned precisely with these relationships—several epistemological modalities are possible. Sometimes it will be possible to prove that a proposed relationship is true or not true ('proved to be true' or 'proved not to be true'). Frequently, however, such a proof cannot be presented ('not proved to be true' or 'not proved to be untrue'). In such a case the question remains at least provisionally undecided. Accordingly, the way in which the intellect admits or rejects a proposed state of affairs is modally qualifiable according to the subjective state or degree of certainty which the knowing subject has of the situation. Thus we may distinguish here the modalities of certainty, probability, doubt, suspicion, etc.

All this goes to show that a consideration of the differences in modality existing between the statements of the experiential sciences would have to be very extensive if it is to lay claim to completeness. Evidently, we cannot go into such an extensive study. However, even without any further explanation, it should be clear that all the above-mentioned modalities are found in both the physical and the human sciences.

Assertoric, Apodictic, and Problematic Judgments. Sometimes the problem of these modalities is drastically—and not quite accurately—simplified by limiting it to three types of modal judgments, called **assertoric, apodictic, and problematic** judgments. In this case no explicit distinction is made between the character pertaining to a connection by virtue of its own nature and our knowledge of this connection. For brevity's sake we may follow here this trichotomy.

An *assertoric* judgment is an intellectual statement regarding a *de facto* connection ascertained through experience and accepted on the basis of this experience: *de facto S* is *P*. Such a judgment does not necessarily have to refer to a concrete and individual event. It may be the expression of empirical knowledge regarding a certain connection between phenomena which has been acquired through extensive and varied observations, without leading to an understanding of the connection. For instance, formerly the statement that there is a connection between sun spots and disturbances in the magnetic field of the earth was an assertoric judgment.

An *apodictic* judgment in the strict sense of the term is an intellectual statement in which the speaker, on the basis of an intellectual insight, fully assents to a proposed relationship or absolutely rejects it. Such a statement, therefore, presupposes that the speaker has knowledge of the essence of the subject and predicate in question and that he knows about the necessity or the impossibility of their being together: it is necessary that S be P, or it is impossible that S be P. Sometimes, however, the requirements imposed by the qualification 'apodictic' are not taken as strictly as has been explained here.

A *problematic* judgment is a statement which suffers from a defect of certainty. The intellect does not have a sufficient understanding of the situation to pronounce a definite, apodictic judgment. The investigator assents or rejects the proposed connection only partially or with certain qualifications. He colors his statements by such terms as perhaps, possibly, probably, etc. Statements resulting from complete induction or from induction that is analogously completed will usually have such a problematic character. Although one may be personally convinced that in such cases there is a necessary relation, one cannot express this conviction apodictically because insight into the essential connection is lacking. The same problematic character is found in statements regarding a relation which expresses merely a moral necessity, such as those that make assertions about the usual way in which human beings act.

Application to the Experiential Sciences. After this fairly long introduction, we may be brief, especially because we will consider only the last-named modalities and base ourselves on what has been said in the first two parts of this section. Evidently, in the experiential sciences there can be no question of a sharp distinction according to the modality of the judgments. In both groups all modalities can be found, especially assertoric, apodictic, and problematic modalities. We may limit ourselves therefore to the following remarks.

Because the experiential sciences have to derive their first data from the experience of the concrete and individual, man's first intellectual knowledge of the object will always be expressed in assertoric judgments containing statements about the perceived connections. This is true in both the physical and the human sciences. Moreover, in both groups assertoric statements will play a permanent role when the concrete and individual as such is the object investigated. Such an individual object is studied more frequently in certain human sciences, e.g., in the various historical sciences, than in the group of physical sciences. In the last-named group the individual as such is only incidentally the object of investigation. We may name geology and astronomy as examples of interest in the individual as such.

Wherever possible, both groups of experiential sciences endeavor to arrive at general statements regarding a certain connection between the subject and its qualities or between two phenomena in the broad sense of the term. The following rules apply to these statements.

If the statement in question is abstractly general, a genuine 'law', then it will have an apodictic character.

If the statement is merely collectively general or refers to human qualities and behavior, i.e., if it is a 'rule' or 'tendency' rather than a 'law' or concerned only with a 'moral' necessity, then the statement will have merely a problematic character.

From what has been said in the consideration of laws and rules in the preceding part of this section, it should be clear that proportionately there are more apodictic statements in the physical sciences and more problematic statements in the human sciences, although there can be no question of assigning either kind of statements exclusively to one of the two groups.

4. *Difference in the Use of 'Value' Judgments*

The aspect of value has been introduced into the philosophy of science especially by the School of Baden, represented by Windelband and Rickert. As we duly noted before (pp. 133 f. and pp. 163 f.), Rickert especially endeavored to make this aspect a criterion distinguishing the physical from the cultural sciences because it supposedly determined their method and character. According to Rickert, the physical sciences deal with 'meaning-free being', with 'value-free' and 'meaning-free nature'. The human sciences, on the other hand, aim at 'meaningful being', at 'value-bearing' and 'value-related' or 'meaningful culture'. Because Rickert's ideas were followed by many others who drew attention to the difference in 'value judgments' existing in the various experiential sciences, we will have to devote here some attention to this point. As we will see, there are clear differences between the physical and the human sciences in this respect, in the sense that genuine value judgments occur almost exclusively in the human sciences.

The Physical Sciences. In the study of the physical sciences man in general occupies an impartial position with respect to his object, whether it be inanimate, a plant, or an animal. Sense experience and the intellectual digestion of the empirical data lead to physical statements which, when they are duly verified, are accepted by everyone without any objection. There is nothing 'human' in the object, so that the man of research does not feel any special appeal to himself as a human being. His will and sentiments, in general, remain untouched. It is only rarely that the researcher will feel obliged to pronounce a value judgment.

And if any such judgment is made, the usual reason will be that the man of research, especially in physics and chemistry, has an inclination to operative science and with an eye upon practical possibilities qualifies something as suitable, useful, efficient, or as unsuitable, useless, ineffective, etc. However, when he makes such a judgment, he is, strictly speaking, no longer in the realm of the speculative sciences of nature. Sometimes also the man of research will qualify the object of his study as marvelous, mysterious, beautiful, etc. In doing so, he speaks not so much as a physical scientist but as a man with esthetic feelings, as a philosopher, as a believer, or in some other similar capacity.

The Human Sciences. When, on the other hand, man himself and human elements constitute the object of research, as is the case in the human sciences, the whole personality of the investigator plays a role in his scientific work. Not only his cognitive powers are engaged in it, but also his appetites or propensities, his evaluating or estimative power, his moods and sentiments. Often it is only through empathy (cf. Sect. IV, pp. 162 f.) that one will become acquainted with the personal attitude, the mentality, and motives of an individual human being, or with the meaning, importance, and value which a material thing has for man. This situation implies that the investigator faces the object of his study with his own sympathies and antipathies, his preference and disapproval, with a comparative evaluation. Thus he is spontaneously led to the making of value judgments. Obviously, this will happen especially in those sciences in which man and the typically human elements stand more in the center of interest; for instance, in history, in studies of art, literature, and culture, especially when they result in comparisons and critique. In other human sciences it happens much less or even not at all.

One's own philosophical, religious, esthetic and other views and, consequently, one's own evaluation of the object will manifest itself even in the organization, selection, and interpretation of the available material, in the choice of the methods to be followed, etc., at least when the subject matter allows any differentiation. In accord with the investigator's own world-view, certain qualities or aspects of the object may be neglected or strongly emphasized, evaluated very highly or dismissed as negligible.

De facto, therefore, the study of man and his culture is usually permeated with the personal philosophical attitude and world-view of the investigator. According to Rickert, knowledge here means an "interested recognition of values" *(stellungnehmendes Anerkennen von Werten),* so that the concept of truth becomes a concept of value. Although this view is not tenable in its generalizing extreme form, it contains nevertheless so much truth that proper attention has to be paid to it in studying the character of the human sciences. Evidently, there is great danger here of relativism and subjectivism, but the realization of this danger should induce the man of research to proceed in a critical attitude of mind and with all due caution (cf. below, No. 6, pp. 190 f.).

5. *Difference in the Relationship to the World-View of the Man of Science*

There is a striking difference between the physical and the human sciences with respect to their relationship to the world-view, in the broad sense, of the scientist. As far as the results of the physical sciences are concerned, the personal views of the researchers in philosophical, religious, ethical, and other similar matters have very little or no influence at all. In the human sciences, on the other hand, these views generally play an important role. This difference also, as will become clear from the following, flows logically from the difference in object.

The Physical Sciences. Non-human things or phenomena constitute the object of the physical sciences. This object is sense-perceptible and, in principle, is accessible to every observer in the same way. In the realm of the physical sciences one may justly demand that no statement can be accepted if, in principle, it cannot be verified by the methods proper to the physical sciences. This scientific attitude implies that philosophical views regarding matter or other world-views cannot influence the statements of the physical sciences. It does not matter whether the observer is a pagan, a Jew, a Protestant, or a Catholic, whether he is philosophically an idealist, a Thomist, a Kantian, a positivist, or an empiricist, so long as his statements remain limited to the realm of the physical sciences. In general, therefore, it is possible to arrive at perfect agreement, not only with respect to the actual verifiable phenomena, but also as regards their interpretation. Of course, there can be different interpretations if the phenomena in question are not sufficiently clear, if they cannot be reproduced or repeated. Such differences, however, are usually only of a provisional nature. The scientists always endeavor to devise experiments which can decide about the truth or falsity of competing theories and, as experience shows, if these efforts are continued long enough, they lead nearly always to success.

Opposing views which are difficult to reconcile occur practically only when the scientists leave the realm of the physical sciences and make statements referring to matter as matter or to the epistemological aspects of the physical sciences. These statements, however, are of a philosophical nature.

Philosophical and even religious influences will be felt most easily in those physical sciences which are concerned with plants and animal life, e.g., in considerations of evolution and animal psychical life. An interesting quotation taken from Bertrand Russell may serve to illustrate the last point:

"One may say broadly that all the animals that have been carefully observed have behaved so as to confirm the philosophy in which the observer believed before his observations began. Nay, more, they have all displayed the national characteristics of the observer. Animals studied by Americans rush about frantically, with an incredible display of hustle and pep, and at last achieve the desired result by chance. Animals observed by Germans sit still and think, and at last evolve the solution out of their inner consciousness".[12]

All this goes to show that many issues among the physical scientists are often a sign that the realm of pure physical science has been abandoned, whether consciously or unconsciously, and that the threshhold of philosophy or world-view has been passed. At times, they may be a sign that the object begins to show certain characteristics which reveal themselves fully only in the object of the human sciences. This is the case, for instance, in animal psychology.

The Human Sciences. Because of the special character proper to the object of these sciences, which is man and human elements, the situation is generally different here. As appears clearly from the preceding sections, the whole personality of the investigator enters into his work of research here. As this concrete and individual human being, with all that he is and has become through his own capacities, education, social and cultural status, he faces his fellow man, individually or in groups, as well as the products of typically human activities. As far as sense perception is concerned which everyone can equally have, the object of his investigation is accessible only in

---

[12]*An Outline of Philosophy,* London, Allen and Unwin, 1927, pp. 32-33.

one of its parts—namely, its material aspect, which in the human sciences is often the least important aspect of all. In its typically 'human' aspect the object is knowable only if it is approached and considered in a typically human way (cf. Sect. IV, No. 1, p. 162). The investigator must endeavor to enter empathically (*einfühlen*) into the personality and motivations of the other man, he must try to understand (*verstehen*) the meaning of the other's activity, he pronounces value judgments in accord with his own views (see above, p. 186), etc. All this implies that the personal world-view, in the broadest sense of the term, and even the very concrete personality of the scientist with all its aspects may play a role—we must even say, of necessity play a role—in the human sciences.

Although every science of man and his culture is exposed to the above-mentioned danger, there is a great difference in the degree to which the danger exists in various sciences. The danger will be greatest when concrete human situations or typically human activities have to be considered, as is the case in history. It becomes less according as the more material, sense-perceptible and sense-verifiable aspects are studied as, e.g., in the study of manuscripts, or according as human activities show a more determined character, as is the case in economics (cf. above, p. 179).

What could be expected even *a priori,* is confirmed by the facts. One has only to see how widely do the judgments and evaluation of a period of history differ according as it is treated by a believer or an unbelieving materialist, by a Catholic or a non-Catholic. It is not without reason that one may speak of a positivistic or of a Marxistic conception of history. Similar striking differences may be found in scientific treatises of a psychological, sociological, cultural, or philological nature and in many others. We may dispense here with examples and limit ourselves to pointing out in the following part of this section the differences in objectivity and subjectivity which flow from the above-mentioned diversity.

Additional Remarks Concerning Experiential Sciences and Philosophy. To prevent misunderstandings with respect to this diversity, it may not be amiss to add here a few remarks concerning the relationship of the experiential sciences with the philosophy or world-view of the scientist. Later, in Chapter IX, we will have an opportunity to revert somewhat more extensively to some of these points.

1. In former centuries, before the special sciences were autonomous, everything knowable was comprehended under 'philosophy'.

Thus philosophical views and 'scientific' data spontaneously inter-mingled.

2. The history of the development of the experiential sciences has shown that philosophical and even religious ideas can stimulate but also retard scientific investigations. Numerous examples could be adduced here to illustrate the point. The same statement is still true of our present time, although to a lesser extent.

3. The philosophical views of a scientist may determine his preference for one or the other of competing theories. Strictly speaking, this should happen only in a provisional stage of research when the data of experience are not yet sufficiently clear to determine the definite choice. In the final results and theories of the experiential sciences there should be no philosophical elements. However, as we have pointed out previously, in some sciences it is not always possible to avoid philosophical elements. Usually, the physical sciences are more readily purged of philosophical stains.

4. Because every man of science *de facto* always has a world-view as well as definite philosophical and religious conceptions, it may be difficult for him to see the boundaries separating his special science from philosophy. He projects his scientific data against the background of his world-view and thus is easily led to make statements which are mixed with philosophy or even purely philosophical. Such statements, consequently, are not fully, or even not at all, based upon the data of experiential science. This evil can be avoided only by reflecting upon the limits of the sciences.

5. It should be clear without any further explanation that philo-sophical world-views play a role in his speculations about man's mode of knowledge in any particular science. This fact does not cause any special problem for us, because such speculations evidently lie outside the realm of the special sciences and pertain to that of philosophy.

A more detailed consideration of these points would demand too much space. Hence we will limit ourselves to the preceding remarks and trust that, even without further explanation, they will be of some use to the interested reader.

6. *Difference in Objectivity*

In the question of objectivity one constantly meets the difficulty that the terms 'objectivity' and 'subjectivity' allow various interpretations. We must, therefore, determine more accurately what we mean here by these terms.

Meaning of 'Objectivity' and 'Subjectivity'. In epistemology 'subject' and 'object' are opposed to each other as 'he who knows' and 'that which is known'. In all created beings endowed with knowledge their knowing always implies a certain opposition or tension, even in the case of self-knowledge, and knowledge is arrived at by a kind of identification of the knower with the known. The object known is present to the knower in a sensitive or intellectual cognitive image. In his act of knowledge the knower is, in a sense, identical with the object known. The knowledge resulting from the cognitive act will always bear the marks of its twofold origin: it is ultimately determined by both the subject and the object.

Philosophers differ in their conceptions of the influence to be attributed to the subject and the object according to their general epistemological views. While idealistic epistemology attributes the lion's share to the subject, its realistic counterpart holds that the content of knowledge is determined mainly by the object. However, even in the realistic view, which we consider to be the only one that can be philosophically justified, the knowing subject always impresses its own character to a greater or lesser extent upon knowledge. For, as the classical saying expresses it, knowledge is always "according to the mode of the knower". Human knowledge is, first, permeated by the proper character of man's cognitive powers and, secondly, every new acquired item of knowledge is incorporated into the totality of previously present items of knowledge and insights, which influence the new knowledge.

Accordingly, perfect objectivity of human knowledge, in the sense that form and content of knowledge are determined solely by the object which exists independently of the knowing subject, is wholly unattainable. On the other hand, the realistic philosopher will always attribute so much objectivity to knowledge that its agreement with reality may be affirmed.

We will leave the general aspects of the subjectivity which is present in man's sensitive and intellectual knowledge to the consideration of ex professo studies of epistemology. The only aspects which interest us here are those which are important for the subject matter considered here. They are the differences in objectivity and subjectivity which characterize man's mode of knowing in the physical and the human sciences. Let us mention these very succinctly.

The Physical Sciences. In the sciences which are concerned with the study of the non-human or purely material, importance is, as a rule, to be attributed only to sense perception and to the abstractive digestion of the sense data by the intellect. This sensitive acquisition of experiential data is, in principle, possible in the same way for every observer, even at different times and places; hence there is a possibility of 'intersubjective' verification. Differences of opinion in this respect usually are not the result of a personal attitude but of insufficient or ambiguous data. In general there is always a possibility of new observations, because the physical sciences usually aim at generic or specific aspects which can be realized in many individuals. Moreover, it is often possible to reduce the share of the human observer to a minimum by carefully arranged experiments. In this way the chance of mistakes through subjective sensitive deviations or through differences in sensitivity, reaction time, and similar factors is rendered as small as possible.

If the investigations of the physical sciences were limited to the above-mentioned tasks, there would hardly be any difficulties insofar as objectivity is concerned. But the gathering, sifting and orderly arranging of sense data is only the first phase of physical research. What the man of research really wants is insight: he wants to 'explain' the observed properties and activities from the nature proper to things, or rather, he wants to deduce something about their nature from the perceived phenomena. This aim is usually implemented by means of a theory, which starts from a certain view or model and endeavors to deduce from it consequences that agree or disagree with old or new observations. Because this matter has been extensively considered in Vol. I, Ch. IX, Sect. II and IV, we may here limit ourselves to referring to these sections.

For the issue which interests us at present the important point is only that there is a possibility of subjective influences in the formulation of scientific theories or in the provisional choice between competing theories. As a rule, however, in one way or another an objective control will be possible and offer an unambiguous decision despite the influence of subjective factors. In general, the physical sciences do not suffer from the difficulties which, as we will see, the human sciences offer in this respect.

'Nature as Questioned by Man'. In Section I (pp. 123 f.), we pointed out a difficulty which presents itself in all experiential sciences —namely, that the object investigated is often not known as it is

independently of the observation but as it has become through the manipulation needed for its observation. Nowadays great emphasis is placed on this point in the physical sciences. Thus it is often said that the object of these sciences is not 'nature existing independently of man's knowledge', but 'nature as questioned by man'. An essential element of subjectivity is supposed to have entered into the knowledge provided by the physical sciences—namely, insofar as subjective factors will influence the questioning, and the 'answer' of nature will correspond to the 'question', making it one-sided and incomplete. Although we fully agree with this view, we find it necessary to make the following remarks.

1. As was pointed out in the preceding pages, the subject of knowledge will of necessity play a role in knowledge itself. This statement applies also to the way in which one tries to obtain knowledge, to the 'asking of questions', not only in the human sciences but also in the physical sciences.

2. The 'subjectivity' in question is not against the 'objectivity' of knowledge. The 'answer' of nature to the 'subjective question' makes us know something about nature as it is in reality, even independently of the question.

3. The interpretation of the 'question and answer game' is inter-subjectively controllable in the physical sciences. 'Objectivity', therefore, is present in them in the sense in which this term has been understood here. Thus the objection in question does not raise any new difficulty for us.

The Human Sciences. In these sciences it is always a question of a confrontation with man and human things. But the senses can make us know only material and corporeal aspects. The typically human element is discovered only through a 'human' contact with the data of the senses. This contact cannot be replaced by any registration apparatus. In this contact the scientific researcher will often be engaged with his entire personality, so that his origin, education, instruction, social status and a host of other factors of an emotional nature may play a role. Moreover, in the human sciences we have to do much more than in the physical sciences with something that is 'only once', something that is unique and cannot be reproduced, so that there is no possibility of control by means of new and different observations. All this makes an objective judgment difficult and contains great danger of mistaken interpretations.

Moreover, we may refer here also to what has been said in the two preceding sections about the use of value judgments and about the influence of the researcher's own world-view in the realm of the human sciences. Here also there are grounds that may cause subjectivity in the interpretation of the objective data. In modern philosophical trends there is even a tendency toward the individual and the subjective to the detriment of the universal and the objectively verifiable.

The danger of subjectivity will usually be greatest in the evaluation of human beings and their activities, e.g., in historical sciences and psychology; it will be smallest in the human sciences or their parts in which the typically human element stands less in the foreground, as happens, e.g., in economics, in the establishing of factual data, such as texts or portraits, in the dressing of chronological tables, etc.

The time which claimed that strictly objective knowledge of history is the ideal to be reached undoubtedly has passed. The most authoritative historians freely admit that it is impossible to escape from a certain amount of subjectivity in the interpretation and critique of historical data. Under the influence of his own world-view, in the broadest sense of the term, the historian will view the actual events from a special angle, he will select and consider the available data in a special way, he will place emphasis on some points and not on others, he will not evaluate persons and events in the same way as he would have done if his world-view had been different. The difficulty is especially great when it is a question of judging historical persons in their mental attitude, in the influences which they have undergone, in the motives of their deeds. It will hardly be necessary to give any examples here, for there is no one who seriously would question the presence of such subjective elements.

Similar difficulties are met in other human sciences, e.g., in literary critique, when persons are judged and texts interpreted. One may think here, for instance, of the widely different views about the persons and works of such people as Homer, Dante, Shakespeare, Pascal, and Dostoevski.

Nevertheless, even in the human sciences one must tend as much as possible to objectivity. A constantly critical attitude is needed. One will always have to ask oneself whether or not one's judgments are influenced by subjective factors of a philosophical, religious, or emotional nature. The researcher has to confront his own views with those of others and with the actual data; he has to investigate whether his views can stand critique; he must constantly return to the original sources and try to find new ones. He will have to be on guard against prejudices, aprioristic interpretations, unproved suppositions, emotional sympathies or antipathies, and other similar factors. Yet, despite all precautions and prudence, it will often not be easy strictly to verify a theory in broad areas of the human sciences. Thus it will often not be possible to reach here the objectivity which usually is attainable in the physical sciences.

It goes without saying that the subjective character proper to many statements of the human sciences is accompanied by a lack of unanimity among those who devote their time to such studies.

7. *Difference in Exactness and Communicability*

In conclusion we want to speak about one more difference between the physical and the human sciences, or rather about two joined differences—namely, those of exactness and communicability. They also are connected with one or more of the above-mentioned differences.

The Human Sciences. As we have seen in the first part of this section, the fundamental concepts of the human sciences often have a kind of 'analogous' character, which may be compared to the analogy of philosophical concepts. A consequent of this is that they lack in exactness. Such concepts are difficult to define and describe. They may even defy all description. Thus their content cannot be rigidly determined. Moreover, because of their intrinsic plurality of meanings, they do not always have the same meaning in the same author. In addition, it can easily happen that a reader or listener will give them another interpretation or association than the author or speaker intended. Thus the result is that communicability in the human sciences is more or less difficult to attain.

The Physical Sciences. In the physical sciences it is generally possible to stabilize the fundamental concepts in a univocal way through international agreements, as is illustrated by the concepts of meter, grammass, second, ampere, etc. Other concepts are connected with these fundamental ideas, e.g., through functional or quantitative relations in such a way that there is no possibility of misunderstanding for anyone. Moreover, the abstract concepts of things, substances, properties, and activities have a univocal character (cf. No. 1, p. 172). For these reasons the concepts of the physical sciences as well as these sciences themselves are endowed with a high degree of exactness and communicability.

The existence of this exactness is connected with the possibility of using mathematical methods and operations (cf. Sect. IV, No. 3, p. 167). These considerations should make it clear also why mathematics and the physical sciences are sometimes indicated by the term 'exact sciences'. We will revert to this point in an appendix to Chapter VIII.

Technical Language. The differences in exactness and communicability have consequences for the specialized language of the sciences. The physical sciences constitute the realm *par excellence* of standardized technical terms and symbols. The form and meaning of these terms or symbols are based on mutual, and often international, agreements, which make that they are easily understood by all. Almost every physical science has its own lists of clearly defined technical terms. Because of the far-reaching possibilities for using mathematical means and functional relationships (cf. Sect. IV, No. 3), physical treatises often exhibit a strongly mathematical character and are capable of expressing important results in a very succinct way, e.g., in a single formula.

The human sciences, on the other hand, have to rely mostly on ordinary language, which may or may not be supplemented by a few technical terms that are special to a particular science. With a multitude of terms that are often ambiguous or 'analogous' (cf. p. 175) the man of research has to try to clarify his views, while realizing that, no matter how careful and diligent he be, he will still easily be misunderstood. In recent times there have been repeated efforts to arrive also at a general standardized technical language in the human sciences. In our view, however, such efforts will never be fully satisfactory, because the very nature of the object studied in these sciences makes it generally impossible to attain the desired goal.

With respect to exactness and communicability also there are differences and grades in the various human sciences. Economics, as could be expected, approaches the physical sciences more closely.

CHAPTER SEVEN

SPECIAL OPERATIVE SCIENCES

INTRODUCTION

In the preceding chapter we spoke about the experiential sciences, i.e., the non-philosophical speculative sciences which have as their object reality as it is given in natural experience. Corresponding to this group of experiential sciences, there exists on the operative level a group of sciences which may be indicated by the term 'special operative sciences' or simply 'operative sciences'.[1] These sciences will be considered in the present chapter.

The aim of the special operative sciences is to formulate general norms for man's action with respect to himself and with respect to the things of man's world. Because this action itself and its results in one way or in another are subject to experience, there exists an evident correspondence between these operative sciences and the speculative sciences of experience. On the one hand, the data of the experiential sciences are needed to serve as the theoretical foundation of the operative sciences in question; on the other hand, the norms formulated by the operative sciences will lead to real results which in their turn may become the object of speculative investigation by experiential sciences, e.g., the cultural sciences.

The elaborate considerations of the preceding chapters permit us to be very brief here, for otherwise we would have to repeat too many things which have been treated previously in a more general fashion, especially in Chapter Four. However, to preserve the logical consistency of this chapter, we will succinctly summarize in Section One the principal points that are needed here for viewing the whole matter in its interconnection. In Section Two we will consider the division of the operative sciences in question, and in the last section we will add a few remarks about the relationship of these sciences to one another and to other groups of sciences.

---

[1] If the briefer term is used, it is taken in a narrow sense, for it excludes the operative sciences of theology and philosophy. Operative theology has been considered above, in Chapter V, Section III, and operative philosophy will be spoken of in Chapter IX, Section II.

197

I. The Proper Character of the Special Operative Sciences

The first section of Chapter Four indicated the difference between speculative or theoretical thinking and operative or practical thinking. The former has as its object a really existing being or an ideal being created by the mind and endeavors to investigate the essence and properties of such a being, while the latter aims at a being that has to be made real. In operative thinking, therefore, man's thought aims at investigating in what way a good which does not yet exist but is conceived as a purpose is capable of being realized through man's activity. The human activity in question may consist sometimes solely of rational acts of will or of deliberate bodily activities. In many cases the execution of the task can be accomplished only by bodily action upon matter, with or without the aid of material means (cf. Ch. IV, Sect. I., no. 1, pp. 45f). The fundamental difference between speculative and operative thinking entails other differences, such as those in orientation, truth character and necessity (cf. Ch. IV, Sect. I, no. 2, pp. 47 ff).

As has been explained in Chapter Four, Section Two, the distinction between speculative and operative thinking leads to the distinction between speculative or theoretical and operative or practical sciences. It has been convincingly shown there, we think, that there exists a fundamental difference between these two groups—namely, insofar as the sciences of the first group have as their object a being that is given, while those of the second group aim at a being that is still to be realized. This fundamental distinction is followed by other differences between the two groups with respect to the character of their truth and of their necessity, their objective tendency, foundation, general method, etc. (cf. Ch. IV, Sect. II, No. 2).

For a good understanding of the character proper to the operative sciences care must be taken not to lose sight of the interconnection of operative and speculative sciences and of the dependence of the former upon the latter. As we mentioned in Chapter Four (Sect. II, No. 3), any operative science needs a speculative foundation with respect to the area of human activity which it considers. In many cases this foundation may be readily borrowed from existing speculative sciences. In such a case there exists an immediate dependence upon the speculative science in question, as is exemplified by the technical sciences and their dependence upon physics, chemistry, mechanics, and mathematics.

When the necessary foundation is not readily available, the man who pursues the operative science will personally try to establish the required theoretical foundation. Thus, the resulting science will possess a speculative-practical character. However, these two aspects remain clearly distinguishable and will often be contrasted by the addition of the qualifiers 'theoretical' and 'practical'; for instance, we speak of theoretical and practical economics, pedagogy, and psychology.

The interrelationships of speculative and practical sciences, which have been briefly summarized here from their more extensive consideration in Chapter Four, flow spontaneously from the various spiritual powers of man. Apart from the power to think and investigate speculatively, man possesses also the capacity of devising ways and means which may lead to the realization of a purpose apprehended by reason. Although the two powers in question are distinct, they evidently are not to be separated. First of all, the knowledge acquired by speculative investigation will easily lead a man of a practical bent to search for possibilities in which this knowledge can be put to work, at least if he does not immediately see any such possibilities. As a natural consequence, a speculative science may sometimes acquire operative extensions which are not demanded by its own character and thus could be dropped without any loss as far as this science is concerned. Secondly, in his search for norms governing the realization of a particular purpose, man will make use of his power of speculative thinking in order to acquire the necessary knowledge of the purpose, methods and means. From this it follows that, as has been pointed out, an operative science demands a theoretical foundation, which may or may not be structurally incorporated into the science in question.

Finally, to avoid certain difficulties, one should keep in mind what has been said in Chapter Four (Sect. II, No. 4, pp. 65 ff.) about the notions 'theoretical' and 'practical', 'theory' and 'practice'. It would be advisable, moreover, to read again also the considerations of Section Three of the same chapter insofar as they refer to the operative sciences to be studied in this chapter.

II. DIVISION OF THE OPERATIVE SCIENCES

As was pointed out in Chapter Four (p. 60), in the operative sciences the purpose to be realized or the good to be attained is always the directing principle and consequently in a true sense is even the starting point of the scientific activity. The purpose to be realized through man's activity occupies the very center of scientific thinking, and it is in view of this purpose that man searches for the correct ways and means to attain the purpose. This operative way of thinking results in norms which have to be followed in a particular realm of human activities.

Accordingly, it should be evident that the content, character and scope of the purpose to be realized determine the nature of the operative science which takes this purpose as the object of its study. Because there is question here of sciences and not of man's concrete activity, the term 'purpose' does not indicate here a concrete individual goal but assumes a specific or even generic sense. Thus it follows that specifically or generically different purposes will give rise to specifically or generically distinct operative sciences. Accordingly, in our search for a suitable division of these sciences, we will have to pay attention to the diversity of man's powers as well as to the specifically or generally distinct purposes whose realization man wants to attain.

The fundamentally distinct activities of man are his immanent acts of thinking and willing and the transient activities by virtue of which man is able to utilize his bodily powers to interfere in his material surroundings. Of course, man's thinking and willing are present also in his conscious transient acts (cf. pp. 45 f.) but, nevertheless, the somatic and transient aspect of these acts endows them with a distinct character. The distinction in question flows from the very nature of man, so that its detailed study pertains to philosophy. Its operative aspects will be considered briefly in Chapter Nine, Section Two, where we will deal with operative philosophy. As we will see there, operative philosophy may be conveniently divided into three parts according as its object is the right order of thinking, of willing, or of man's transient activities.

As has been mentioned, we will limit ourselves here to the non-theological and non-philosophical operative sciences, which for the sake of brevity we will simply indicate without any further qualifier as 'operative sciences'. The activities which these sciences study contain, of course, the aspects of thinking and willing that exist in all human activity but, in addition, they will nearly always possess also a transient character, because the object of the sciences in question somehow has to be subject to the control of human experience. Accordingly, to arrive at a rational division of this group of sciences, we will have to pay attention to the specifically or generically distinct purposes which man wants or has to realize in this realm.

It remains true, of course, that all human activities in one way or another ultimately are ordered to man himself as their purpose, even when these activities are directed to material objects and find their experiential terminus in matter. For such material things are made the objects of human activity to render them more suitable for man's needs and desires. Nevertheless, it would be possible to make a dichotomy between human operations which directly aim at man himself and others that are primarily directed toward rendering material, non-human objects suitable for human purposes. In this way the operative sciences corresponding to the first genus of operations have the character of human sciences, and the operative sciences corresponding to the second genus of human activities are more like physical science.

This dichotomy, however, cannot be rigidly enforced because human activity has a complex psychosomatic character. Moreover, the division would have to be complemented by a more detailed subdivision. For this reason we will attempt here a different division which, although inspired by the above-mentioned dichotomy, is somewhat less rigid. The first three groups of this division refer more directly to man himself, group five aims more at material objects, and group four occupies an intermediary position. It goes without saying that we do not wish to propose this division as the only rational way or even as the best possible way of dividing the operative sciences.

For every group we will limit ourselves to a few examples. Evidently, it would be impossible to enumerate all the sciences that could be classified in a certain group. Moreover, such an enumeration would be superfluous for the scope of this work.

1. *Sciences Which Aim at the Education of Youth: Pedagogical Sciences*

Every human being is born as a little child who for many years will constantly need the spiritual and bodily care of his parents and of others if he is to grow up in a way worthy of man and capable of providing him with suitable opportunities for the realization of his innate potentialities. The combined activities of all those who guide the complex process of the development from infancy to maturity are grouped together under the term 'education'. According as education is concerned with different aspects of this process, it is known as physical, intellectual, moral, religious education, etc. Of course, as long as there is merely question of education with respect to concrete and individual cases, there is not yet any 'science'. There may be a kind of educational 'skill' that is either innate or acquired or even the mere concrete application of norms formulated by sciences which *ex professo* study the educational situation. It is these sciences which are known as 'pedagogical sciences'.

It is not our intention to investigate here the disputes that are concerned with the nature, scope and proper place of pedagogy as a science. Pedagogy, in its broadest sense, is still a young science and its status has not yet become definitely settled in all respects, so that there is ample opportunity to disagree about its proper character. · The point that interests us here is that undoubtedly pedagogy is a practical or operative science in the sense which we have given to this term. Like every other operative science, pedagogy has a speculative foundation. This foundation is usually, at least in part, developed within pedagogy itself (theoretical pedagogy), but it is partially also borrowed from other sciences, such as anthropology, psychology, and sociology. Moreover, sometimes elements of it are derived also from world-views and religion. In addition, the theoretical foundation will have to take into account man's historical experience with former methods of education. It has to be acquainted also with the actual needs of youth, for which sociological research may be able to supply important data. Finally, it may be desirable to engage in prudent experimentation with certain educational methods whose usefulness appears to be scientifically sufficiently acceptable.

2. *Sciences Which Aim at the Preservation or Recovery of Mental and Bodily Health*

Man has the obligation to maintain his mind and body in good condition and to preserve his bodily integrity by means of suitable nourishment, care, training, sufficient rest, etc. Even in the absence of scientific understanding, he will make use of certain means and methods to attain this goal, because experience has shown their usefulness to his ancestors and these have passed them on to their descendants, either explicitly by word of mouth and in writing, or at least through their actual application.

It should be evident, however, that the achievements of certain speculative sciences offer possibilities of arriving at the formulation of scientifically founded norms for the preservation or recovery of mental and bodily health. In this way there arises a group of special operative sciences, such as those of bodily and mental hygiene, of nutrition, of practical medicine, of athletics and sports, etc. In this group we must place also pharmacy insofar as this science aims at making medicine available for use in the most appropriate way and insofar as it endeavors to find easy and reliable ways to guarantee the identity, purity and grade of medicines.

3. *Sciences Which Aim at the Total or Partial Organization of Human Society*

Apart from the sciences aiming at the welfare and integral development of the individual human being, there are other operative sciences which devote their attention more especially to man as a social being. They endeavor to investigate scientifically in what way life in civil society can be rendered as suitable and as wholesome as possible for man. There are various ways in which these sciences can proceed and also various aspects that need to be considered.

Man's attention may be devoted, first of all, to the state as such and its structural organization. Thus, there arise operative sciences concerning the government of the state, administrative law, political science, etc. A well-organized society demands, moreover, a complex system of positive laws or norms governing the relationship between authority and subordinates or between different subordinates. This situation leads to a whole of practical or operative legal sciences concerning civil rights and legal procedures, trade laws, criminal laws, law suits, and many others.

A more immediate purpose which man has to attain in society is the best possible care for the material welfare of the citizens. There are many operative sciences which are concerned with this purpose. We may name, for example, practical economics, government management, economic policy, company management, sciences of money and banking, accounting, and taxes.

The aims to be realized may be conceived even more broadly than the confines of a single political society or state and extended to international problems. In this way there arise operative sciences which devote themselves to international law, the *ius gentium*, international private rights, the rights and laws governing conflicts, aerial rights, etc. In the realm of economics there are, likewise, international interests to be attained. The norms governing these interests are formulated by the sciences which devote themselves to international economic politics.

Many of the above-mentioned sciences have a speculative-operative character, and others borrow their theoretical foundation from various special theoretical sciences, such as theoretical political science, theory of law, and theoretical economics.

4. *Sciences Which Aim at the Ordering of Artistic Activities*

Man is capable of knowing and desiring beauty, as well as embodying ideas of beauty in material things through the transient activities of his body. It is possible to make such activities the object of a scientific study and thus to formulate norms for the correct and rational use of these activities. In this way there arises a group of operative sciences aiming at the creation of beauty.

This group contains the sciences which aim at the formulation of norms governing the creation and pursuit of art in general as well as its specialized forms, such as poetry, painting, architecture, music. To these we may add also logopedics, the science of style and mastery of language, and others.

The sciences in question may be able to borrow their theoretical foundation at least in part from speculative sciences, such as the history of art and music, literature, etc. Frequently, however, they have to build their own foundation, so that they assume a speculative-operative character.

5. *Sciences Which Aim at the Transformation of Material Things*

It is characteristic of man to make material objects subservient to himself in all kinds of ways. Relying upon understanding acquired in the speculative sciences of nature, man is able to visualize a material object which may possibly be produced or rendered useful to his purposes. In such a case he may attempt to deduce scientifically the norms which should govern the human activities that tend to produce such an object. Thus, there arise special operative sciences for each of the realms in which man's various transient activities seek their development. Examples of these sciences are the technical sciences of technical mechanics, mechanical and chemical technology, the science of raw materials, electrotechnics, road and canal engineering, practical architecture, the sciences concerned with mining and oil production, ship and plane construction; also the sciences of agriculture, truck farming, cattle breeding, dairy technology, forestry, etc. There can be no question, of course, of listing all the pertinent sciences here. Moreover, many of those named could be subdivided into various subordinate branches.

III. RELATIONSHIP OF THE SPECIAL OPERATIVE SCIENCES TO ONE ANOTHER AND TO OTHER GROUPS OF SCIENCES

In this section we will briefly consider the operative sciences in order to clarify their interconnection and their relationship to other groups of sciences.

1. *The Hierarchy of the Operative Sciences*

With respect to the operative sciences, the aim to be achieved in a given realm of human activities is the determining factor. Accordingly, there can be question of a hierarchy of the special operative sciences only insofar as there exists a hierarchy of aims or purposes. The character of the purpose, however, depends upon the 'value' which a particular good possesses for man; consequently, the hierarchy to be proposed for the operative sciences will be based upon the view one has regarding the hierarchy of 'values' i.e., it will be based upon philosophical considerations.

As we pointed out in the preceding section, the special operative sciences could be divided into two genera: one which aims directly at man himself, and one which aims more immediately at making material things subservient to man. Undoubtedly, everyone will attach a higher value to the first genus than to the second. Moreover, sciences which aim at what is typically human in man, i.e., at man's spiritual aspect, will be valued higher than those which aim more immediately at man's bodily well-being. For this reason an internal hierarchy could be formulated in each of the first three groups. Many undoubtedly also would attach a higher value to the group that aims at the creation of beauty than at the group which is guided by utilitarian considerations. This question is rendered even more complex because there are innumerable interdependencies between the various groups. However, we do not think that the matter is important enough to delve deeper into the problem.

2. *Relationship to Other Groups of Sciences*

Relation to the Experiential Sciences. As we have pointed out in a general fashion in Chapter Four and in particular for the special operative sciences of nature in Section One of this chapter, the operative sciences depend on a scientific investigation of a speculative character for their required theoretical foundation. Usually this speculative knowledge will be borrowed from the speculative sciences which investigate the realm in question. On the other hand, it may happen also that the need to provide the operative sciences with a theoretical foundation will stimulate a greater development of an existing speculative science or lead to the creation of a new theoretical science. In this way there arise all kinds of interconnections between the operative sciences considered here and the group of experiential sciences.

Some operative sciences—those which are concerned especially with the welfare of man himself—are more dependent upon the group of cultural or human sciences, while others depend more upon the physical sciences. For this reason it would be possible to divide the special operative sciences into groups of cultural and physical sciences. As a matter of fact, authors who do not attach any relevance to the distinction between speculative and operative sciences classify the special operative sciences among the cultural or the physical sciences, as required by their particular character. Nevertheless, it seems to us more preferable to retain the existing use of language and to reserve these two terms for corresponding groups of experiential sciences.

Relationship to Philosophy. The special operative sciences have a relationship also to operative philosophy. Each of these sciences in its own realm attempts to formulate norms of human activity in connection with a definite and limited purpose to be attained or realized by man. In one way or another this purpose ultimately refers to the well-being and perfection of man. Human beings, however, are limited in their understanding, and the purpose they pursue may be co-determined by all kinds of less worthy or short-sighted motives. Hence it may very easily happen that man is misguided in formulating the norms governing a special realm of activity. Experience shows that such misconceptions occur all too frequently.

A few examples may serve to illustrate the point. The operative sciences of fine arts frequently pay not enough attention to ethical values. In the realm of economics the norms are often too much determined by the interests of certain groups or, on a wider level, by the interest of a single nation. In the problem of overpopulation quite a few people attempt to reduce the population by artificially diminishing human fertility or through recourse to abortion.

Accordingly, it should be evident that the special operative sciences should be guided by higher norms of goodness and beauty, deduced from a knowledge of man as an individual and as a social being which is not onesided but takes all of man's aspects into consideration. For a believer there are, moreover, fundamental norms contained in divine revelation. Operative philosophy, in addition, has the task of formulating rationally the general norms which man must follow to reach his ultimate destiny. This point will be considered more in detail in Section Two of Chapter Nine.

Operative and Applied Sciences. Frequently the term 'applied sciences' is used instead of operative sciences. As we have indicated in Section Two of Chapter Four (pp. 68 ff.), the use of this term can easily give rise to misunderstanding. What was said there with respect to the operative sciences in general—including theological and philosophical operative sciences—applies also to the special operative sciences considered in this chapter. Chapter Four, moreover, made mention of several points, illustrated by examples, that apply in particular to the special operative sciences. We may, therefore, refer the reader to the remarks made in that chapter.

Nevertheless, we want to remind him particularly of the meaning of 'applied science' indicated there (p. 70) as referring to a scientific system which is a particularization and concrete expression of an operative science. In this sense it is likely to be true that every operative science has an extension which is an 'applied science', i.e., an extension in which the more abstract data of the operative science are rendered suitable for practical use and in which by means of sample problems a student can acquire the necessary skill and inventiveness to discover the correct solution in the usual situations facing him in daily life. Such training is very important, for instance, for future lawyers and engineers.

When the term 'applied science' is understood in this sense, there will often be no clear difference between this science and the corresponding operative science. An added reason for this lack of distinction is also that the various parts of an operative science readily lend themselves to a consideration of their possible 'applications'. Thus, it is not surprising that a science with such a mixed character is often called an 'applied science'.

Finally, we may remind the reader of what has been said in Chapter Four (p. 71) about certain kinds of 'applied science', such as criminalistics, the 'sciences' of advertising and of preserving museum objects. The science of jurisprudence may be added to this group, at least if it is understood as the critical study of actual law suits and their verdicts as examples that are useful for future similar cases.

CHAPTER EIGHT
IDEAL OR FORMAL SCIENCES

INTRODUCTION

In a passing way this book has mentioned several times a group of sciences called 'ideal' or 'formal' sciences. These sciences lie within the reach of man's unaided natural reason, i.e., they are non-theological, 'natural' or secular sciences. They are, moreover, theoretical or speculative, for they aim to study the essence and properties of one or the other being proposed by the human intellect. In a previous chapter we have divided the 'natural' speculative sciences into experiential, ideal, and philosophical sciences, and we have also indicated the proper character of the ideal sciences and their difference from the other two groups.[1]

In the present chapter we will examine the group of ideal or formal sciences in a more extensive fashion. We will attempt to determine their proper character by means of a consideration of their object and the characteristics connected with this object, such as method, structure, and character of knowledge. This consideration will oblige us to make various comparisons between the ideal sciences and the experiential sciences, and especially between the ideal sciences known as the 'mathematical sciences' and the group of experiential sciences called the 'physical sciences'. The reason lies in the great danger that these two groups will be confused. In ordinary speech and even in learned terminology mathematics and physical science are usually indicated by the single term 'exact sciences' or simply 'sciences'. The Anglo-American College of Science, for instance, as well as the French 'faculté des sciences', comprehend both mathematics and physical science. Thus, the impression is easily created that the difference between the two groups of sciences is minor and not essential. To counteract this false impression we will carefully indicate the differences between the two groups in each of the aspects that will be considered here.

For obvious reasons we will again have to limit ourselves to the main issues. Specialists may be disappointed, because they may find

---

[1] Cf. Chapter III, Sect. III, pp. 40 ff.; the schematic division on p. 42; the Introduction of Chapter Six, p. 117. See also Part One, Ch. III, Sect. IV, No. 4, pp. 29 f.

our considerations too brief or even too superficial. However, we see no way in which this risk can be avoided without having this chapter develop beyond all proportions into a philosophy of the ideal sciences or at least a philosophy of mathematics. All we can do is remind the reader that this book intends merely to be an introduction to a philosophy of science and to stimulate him to further study.

Division of this Chapter. The first section will consider the distinction between the 'ideal' or 'formal' and the 'real'. The second will devote its attention to the 'ideal' insofar as it is the object of the ideal sciences. In Section Three we intend to investigate the proper character of the ideal sciences and the various differences between the ideal sciences and the experiential sciences, especially the physical sciences. Finally, in an appendix we will dedicate some pages to exact sciences, positive sciences and operative ideal sciences.

I. The Meaning of 'Ideal' or 'Formal'

1. *The Opposition Between 'Ideal' and 'Real'*

Both in ordinary language and in scientific usage the term 'ideal' has many meanings. Most of these, however, are irrelevant to our question. Of those which Webster enumerates in his dictionary the following come closest to what concerns us in this chapter: "existing as a mere mental image"; "existing in fancy or imagination only"; "pertaining to, or of the nature of, mental images; conceptual". Nevertheless, even these descriptions do not exactly indicate what 'ideal' means as the object of a group of sciences which differ from the sciences of the 'real' or experiential sciences. For the sciences of the 'real', precisely as sciences, as products of man's intellectual activity, also are concerned with concepts and images. Without further explanations and qualifications the above-mentioned descriptions certainly would not suffice accurately to determine the object of the ideal sciences and to distinguish it from the experiential sciences. For this reason it is necessary to contrast the concept 'ideal' with that of 'real' and to indicate the boundaries between these two concepts.

Above, in Chapter Six, Section One, we spoke of 'real' and 'ideal' and indicated that "real is that which exists independently of our perception or independently of our sensitive and intellectual knowledge" (p. 123). This description revealed itself suitable at the time, and we were able to reply at once to an objection raised against it.

Another difficulty, however, merely received mention there and a promise of being considered in the present chapter. It was concerned with the problem of finding descriptions of the concepts 'real' and 'ideal' which could serve to distinguish the two groups of sciences that are concerned respectively with the 'real' and the 'ideal'. We must now try to solve this problem.

Provisional Description of the Concept 'Ideal'. The above-mentioned description of 'real' is sometimes supplemented with the following description of 'ideal': "ideal is that which comes into existence through intellectual activity and can exist only in thought". Although at first this description may seem to be suitable, it gives rise to the difficulty that in this way all concepts (and even all phantasms if we slightly reword the description) would be 'ideal' in this sense. Hence the concepts of all sciences, even those of the experiential sciences, would be 'ideal', for every concept arises through intellectual activity and can exist only in the intellect. Phantasms, likewise, exist only in and through our cognitive powers. Thus, it should be clear that the description in question cannot be considered satisfactory without further qualifications.

To escape this difficulty, it appears necessary to make a distinction between concepts considered in themselves and in their contents. Only with respect to content the opposition of 'real' and 'ideal' reveals itself meaningful and capable of acting as a foundation for the distinction between 'real' and 'ideal' sciences.

It is not subject to doubt that our intellectual concepts come into existence through our intellectual activity, through knowing and thinking. They are produced by the knowing and thinking intellect. Because the activity of the intellect is strictly immanent, these concepts cannot exist outside the intellect. Their origin and continued existence is fully dependent upon the activity of the intellect. If, then, we compare concepts with the above-mentioned provisional description of the 'ideal' as "that which comes into existence through thinking and can exist only in thought", we would have to conclude that the description applies pre-eminently to our concepts.

Adapted to the imagination, the same conclusion applies also to the sense phantasms. They originate through the imagination and can continue to exist only by virtue of the imagination's activity. Freely formed phantasms, moreover, depend also on the intellectual powers of understanding and willing.

A further consideration, however, shows that concepts and phantasms, taken in themselves, have to be conceived as something 'real'. For they are the results of a real activity either of the intellect or of the imagination,[2] and therefore they themselves are real, at least as long as the producing activity in question continues to exist. They are not less real than the light of an electric bulb or of a magnetic field which arises from current flowing through a solenoid and depends for its existence and strength entirely upon the existence and intensity of the current. Accordingly, 'thought-being' and 'imagined-being' are 'real-being'—although of a special kind—and as such they pertain to the object considered in a realistic ontology.

Thus, we see that the above-mentioned provisional descriptions of 'real' and 'ideal' give rise to difficulties. We must, therefore, continue to investigate this matter critically and endeavor to arrive at a distinction which clarifies the issue.

Moreover, the remark must be made that, if concepts and phantasms are unqualifiedly considered to have an 'ideal' mode of being, it becomes difficult to see how one could escape from a kind of idealism in the sense of Kant or Hegel.

2. 'Real' and 'Ideal' Concepts

Concepts Considered with Respect to Their Content. Before we can present a modified and more suitable description of the terms 'real' and 'ideal', it will be necessary first again to devote our attention to concepts and phantasms in general. Apart from being considered in themselves, i.e., in their own mode of being, concepts may be viewed also with respect to their content, their intentional meaning or their expressive power. This consideration will have to be somewhat more extensive, because the matter itself is less simple than appears at first sight.

In the above-mentioned sense all concepts must be said to be 'real', but with respect to their content they may be divided into two groups, which for good reasons may be indicated by the terms 'real' and 'ideal'. Of course, the term 'real' here no longer retains the same meaning as it had above. The division in question may be made in this fashion:

------

[2]The reality of the imagination and of the intellect is an undeniable fact of experience. Cf. Ch. VI, Sect. I, No. 2, p. 120.

a. A concept is 'real' with respect to its content if this content is in a more or less abstract way a representation of something which exists or can exist independently of cognitive activity, outside the cognitive power, in a concrete and individual fashion, i.e., either as a subsistent thing or as pertaining to a subsistent thing.

b. A concept is called 'ideal' with respect to its content if to this content there does not and cannot correspond adequately any individual and concrete extramental reality. Or perhaps more clearly expressed, 'ideal' is what can exist only as the content of thought, as 'being-thought'.

Regarding phantasms we may remark that, strictly speaking, they are always real in the sense now given to this term. For a phantasm is always built from elements borrowed from former sense experiences; consequently, it is, at least in its constituent parts, always a representation of something that exists or can exist in reality. For this reason phantasms must be considered to be always 'real' even with respect to their content. We may therefore limit our attention here to concepts and investigate which concepts are 'real' or 'ideal' with respect to their content.

a. 'REAL' CONCEPTS

In accord with the description of 'real', we must call real, first of all, the intellectual representations of individually existing entities. Likewise, all specific or generic contents of concepts derived through abstraction from the immediate data of internal or external sense experience. For these specific or generic contents are intellectual representations of really existing things in their specific or generic essence or at least of properties, activities, relations, etc. of really existing things. Examples of such concepts are man, dog, house, water, red, warm, hard; animal, color, object, energy. Such concepts are called 'experiential' or 'intuitive' concepts. Each of them is an intellectual grasp of a material reality which exists independently of man's thinking and, consequently, is an expression of this reality in a spiritual or intellectual way, i.e., in accord with the proper nature of the spiritual intellect.

It is to be noted that the abstraction which by way of sense experience leads to the origin of the concepts in question is, on the one hand, so-called 'total abstraction'—it leaves behind the concrete and individual—and, on the other, 'formal abstraction' on the physical level or 'physical abstraction'—it intellectually seizes the 'form', i.e., that which determines the mode of being of a real thing. For a more detailed explanation we must refer the reader to Volume I, Chapter III, Sections III and IV.

In the second place, 'real' also are so-called 'negative-positive' concepts. These concepts express in their contents existing entities but do so in a negative-positive fashion: positively, insofar as the thought content contains elements which through abstraction have been derived from experiential data, negatively, insofar as certain elements ('imperfections') contained in the data have to be thought away in order to express the proper perfection of these entities. An example to the point is the concept 'spirit' conceived as an intellectual subsistent being which is not-material and not-extended. As a rule, it is easier for us to say what such a being is not than to express what its positive ontological perfection is.

Insofar as the content of the two groups of 'real' concepts described here is in any way subject to 'natural experience', they constitute principally the subject matter of experiential sciences.

Thirdly, we must consider as 'real' concepts also so-called 'philosophical' concepts, such as being, substance, cause, quantity, quality, material being, living being, etc. Such concepts are analogous and include, at least confusedly, all their realizations in their comprehension and extension. Concepts of this type are fundamental in the philosophical sciences.

Fourthly, 'real' are so-called 'theological concepts,' i.e., the concepts containing divine revelation or concepts formed to explicitate the data of revelation, such as the concepts of God, Creator, Redeemer, Providence, prayer, grace, sin, eternal happiness, heaven, hell, purgatory, faith, hope, and charity understood in the theological sense. Such concepts are essential to the theological sciences.

Fifthly, the term 'real' may be applied to a group of contents of concepts which have not been derived through direct abstraction from sense data, but which the intellect, aided by the imagination, forms by modifying and combining directly abstracted concepts in such a way that the resulting combination could correspond to reality. This group contains the concepts or ideas which guide man in the operative sciences. They are intellectual representations of something which must or can be made real, e.g., the concept of a new kind of machine or aeroplane. The group contains also the ideas which guide the production of certain artistic works and, in general, the ideas of a good that has to be attained, that is a 'value' for man and thus can have the character of a purpose.

Sixthly, the group of 'real' concepts contains also concepts whose contents represent 'possibles', i.e., entities which do not exist and which will perhaps never be realized—for instance, because there exists no cause capable of producing them or no suitable matter— but which nevertheless do not imply an intrinsic impossibility or contradiction. Examples of such concepts are a mountain of gold or an airplane flying with the velocity of light. These concepts are, of course, without any importance for science, but they may play a role in science fiction.

Seventhly, the group of 'real' concepts may be said to include the conceptual contents of individual persons, things and events created or expressed by art; for instance, in literature or paintings. With some hesitation, we would like to include also the concepts of mythical or legendary beings, fairies, etc. True, the contents of such concepts may not always be capable of real existence because they contain internally contradictory properties: for instance, a centaur conceived as a being which is at the same time man and horse, or animals which think and speak. However, generally it is possible to conceive these contents in such a way that the contradictory elements disappear: for instance, if a centaur is conceived as a rational being having the external form of a horse. In this way it becomes possible to pronounce meaningful judgments about such beings. Of course, they do not belong to the philosophy of science, although they may be discussed in the philosophy of art.

Summary. 'Real' concepts are all concepts whose contents concretely or abstractly present intellectual representations of something that exists extramentally or at least can be thought to exist in such a way because it is without any internal contradiction.

From the viewpoint of the philosophy of science, the first two groups named above are important for the speculative sciences, whether theological or non-theological, and in part also for philosophical sciences; the third group is important for the philosophical sciences, and the fourth is essential for the theological sciences, and the fifth group is fundamental in the operative sciences.

b. 'IDEAL' CONCEPTS

As has been mentioned above, with respect to its content a concept may be called 'ideal' if this content, considered in its expressive function, can exist only as a product of the intellect, as 'being thought'. Hence no extramental reality adequately corresponds or even is able to correspond to this content. In other words, 'ideal' is that which can exist only as the content of thinking, as a thought concept. It is something which in its pure essence and properties, possessed in thought, does not exist in reality and cannot be made real.

In this chapter we will frequently have to speak about such 'ideal' concepts. Provisionally we may illustrate the kind of ideas mentioned here with such fundamental mathematical concepts as number, mathematical body, plane, line, and point.

Insofar as the entities expressed by these 'ideal' concepts exist, they are constructs or creations of thought. They exist solely in and through and in utter dependence on an act of thinking. For this reason they are often also referred to as 'thought beings' (*entia rationis*). The being of such entities is a 'being-thought', an 'ideal being'. The function of the intellect here is purely active, without any passivity, safe insofar as there is a general dependence upon accompanying phantasms which are memories of past sense data.

Dependence upon Experience. A general epistemological principle states that nothing is or can be present in the intellect which was not first in one way or another grasped by sense experience. In accord with this principle, we must admit that ideal concepts are not only always accompanied by, and based upon sense phantasms, but in their first origin and at least in their elements are also always connected with the sense perception of an extramental reality, no matter how remote this connection may be.

As a matter of fact, the most fundamental ideas of any existing system of ideal concepts are always derived from experience. This derivation takes place by means of a special kind of 'formal abstraction', i.e., a certain 'form' or constituent principle which determines a real being to a certain mode of being is abstracted from a material datum of experience in such a way that every material realization of this form is left behind. Hence the form itself, idealized and schematized as it is, can now exist only as the content of thinking.

Because it is especially so-called 'mathematical concepts' which arise in this fashion, the abstraction in question is often spoken of as 'mathematical abstraction'. This term distinguishes this abstraction, on the one hand, from 'physical abstraction', through which a specific or generic form is abstracted from the complex datum of experience in such a way that the material nature of the whole is retained. Examples of such physical abstraction are coloring, liquidity, hardness, elasticity, as well as the forms through which a particular being is, e.g., a dog, a cat, or a man. Such forms cannot be thought of without matter.

On the other hand, mathematical abstraction is distinct from the so-called 'philosophical abstraction', i.e., the abstraction which makes it possible to consider anything that is, under the 'aspect of being', as being in general (metaphysics), as material being (philosophy of nature), as living being (philosophy of life), or as human being (philosophical anthropology).

Because 'ideal concepts' especially have the character of forms, pure forms without implying matter, they are sometimes called 'formal concepts'. For the same reason 'ideal beings' are known also as 'formal beings'. However, the term 'formal' could refer to many other entities than the formal concepts in question, and for this reason we prefer to use the term 'ideal'.

The reason why such 'ideal' thought contents cannot represent any extramental reality lies in this that the way of conceiving them gives them a mode of being which is such that they cannot adequately be realized in matter and, on the other hand, they do not represent purely immaterial or spiritual beings. The expressed 'forms' are pure products of thought, results of the way in which the intellect idealizes or schematizes data of experience to such an extent that the resulting thought contents can exist only as 'thought beings'.

Kinds of 'Ideal Thought Contents'. Mainly two groups of 'ideal thought contents' or 'beings of thought' may be distinguished. The first of these pertains to the domain of logic, and the second to that of the 'ideal' sciences.

To the domain of logic belong, for instance, the concepts of genera and species and all kinds of logical relationships, i.e., relations between ideas or judgments, such as identity and opposition. These categories of 'beings of thought' supply the material with which the 'theoretical' part of formal logic is concerned. We will not consider them here, but will refer to them in Chapter Nine, Section II, No. 1.

The second group of 'ideal' concepts constitutes the object of the 'ideal' or 'formal' sciences. It contains, for example, the concepts which are the fundamental building blocks of mathematical sciences and also of other sciences, such as theoretical mechanics.

This group, moreover, contains in general also all entities which can be arbitrarily conceived and endowed with properties by simply postulating or defining them by means of more or less freely conceived relationships. Such entities function in all kinds of sciences that are 'formal' or 'ideal', e.g., in logistics.

In the following section we will speak more extensively about the second group of 'ideal' concepts, limiting ourselves nevertheless to the most important aspects of the mathematical sciences in their most simple form.

II. The Proper Object of the Ideal Sciences

In this section we will first explain what must be considered to pertain to the object of the ideal sciences. We intend to do so mainly by enumerating a few groups of 'ideal' concepts' which may function as the fundamental building blocks of such sciences. Next we will make a comparison between the ideal sciences and the experiential sciences in reference to their object.

1. *The 'Ideal' as the Object of the Ideal Sciences*

Among the 'ideal' conceptual contents which may function as objects of the ideal sciences the following groups should be enumerated:

a. Fundamental mathematical concepts or objects. Although these concepts are formed by the intellect on the occasion of a sense datum by means of 'mathematical abstraction' or through a special schematizing or idealizing process, their proper essence cannot exist in reality. For instance, the concepts of number, mathematical body, surface or line, as well as particular numbers and particular mathematical bodies, surfaces and lines, such as sphere, prism, circle, ellipse, and parallelogram. The concept 'number', for example, undoubtedly has been derived through abstraction from the sense experience which makes us perceive a plurality of things: two, three, four . . . things. By disregarding everything material in the perceived things, we obtain positively a concept of 'plurality', and this plurality may then be more closely characterized by a 'number'. The number as such, however, say, two or three, cannot exist in reality, but exists only in the intellect when and as long as it is thought of.

The same applies to the fundamental concepts of geometry. If in perceiving real bodies, we abstract from everything material, except extension, we arrive at a concept of a 'geometric solid' as a closed tri-dimensional area. Such a metric body without any material content and material properties, of course, cannot really exist. A division in thought of such a solid or its boundary supplies us with the concept of a mathematical surface as a two-dimensional extension; the division in thought of a mathematical surface or the boundary of one part of such a surface gives us the concept of a mathematical line as a one-dimensional extension; the division in thought of such a line or the boundaries of a line supply us with the concept of a point. It may be subject to dispute whether or not such a geometric surface exists in real physical bodies as a 'boundary surface' and a geometric line exists as a one-dimensional 'boundary' of such a 'boundary surface'. Nevertheless, as such, as geometric surface and line, they cannot exist in reality. These geometric concepts, as such, i.e., with respect to their mathematical essense, are products of the intellect. Even if it were true that in one way or another they would exist in reality as, say, a 'boundary surface', it is still possible to abstract completely from such an existence. As mathematical entities, the content of these concepts exists only in and through thought.

b. What has been said above about natural numbers, applies likewise to combinations of numbers in arithmetic and to number systems, whose properties are determined by more or less arbitrary rules. The same must be said *a fortiori* about 'numbers' or 'number structures' which arise by virtue of a thought operation and to which no real model can even show any resemblance. An example to the point are so-called 'imaginary numbers'. The intellect itself here simply creates new 'ideal' objects.

c. What has been asserted regarding the fundamental geometric concepts in reference to geometric solids, surface, and lines of arbitrary form applies also *a fortiori* to bodies of a particular shape, such as cubes, spheres, and cylinders; to particular surfaces, such as flat surface, revolution surface, saddle surface, and well-defined parts of such surfaces; to particular lines, such as straight line, circle, ellipse, parabola, and hyperbola. The intellect, moreover, discovers in the tri-dimensional space that is present through our imagination the possibility of letting geometric objects move and consequently create new figures and new geometric objects by way of constructions.

d. The 'ideal' character which reveals itself in elementary mathematics, such as Euclidean geometry, ordinary arithmetic and algebra, becomes even more pronounced when we progress beyond elementary mathematics. For then we turn away from the mathematical forms and properties which everyday sense experience suggests and from the number manipulations which this experience teaches, to devote ourselves to, e.g., the construction of a non-Euclidean geometry or a more abstract kind of algebra.

e. The above-mentioned 'ideal' or 'formal' character is not limited to the mathematical sciences but may occur also in others, for instance, in theoretical mechanics. This science also manipulates objects and units which as such do not exist and cannot exist in material reality, although here also the fundamental concepts have been derived from the data of experience. By means of a thought schematization or idealization these concepts have been given their own 'ideal' character. For example, a 'material point' having mass but no dimensions is a product of thought. Nothing equivalent corresponds to it in reality. An ideal uniform or uniformly changing motion along a mathematically defined orbit, considered by theoretical mechanics, cannot exist in reality, but is a thought idealization or simplification of a real situation. Reality, likewise, does not know any fully elastic collision or a frictionless motion. The principles upon which mechanics is based, such as the principle of inertia and the laws of conservation of energy or of momentum are not formulae expressing *a priori* insights, but are idealizations of the rules according to which the phenomena of the really existing world take place. (Parenthetically speaking, everything points to the correctness of these laws, and nothing militates against them; hence the scientist is justified in postulating their 'truth'.) In this way man thinks or creates idealized, not really existing objects, properties, situations, etc.

It is true, of course, that mechanics endeavors to maintain the closest contact with experience. The reason is that the results of the theoretical considerations are wanted for the sake of practical applications. However, in principle there would be no objection against a different kind of mechanics, based upon other, more or less arbitrarily chosen principles. In such a mechanics, like in many parts of mathematics, there would be an element of playing a game. For instance, one could construct a mechanics in which motion would follow different laws and in which mutual attraction would obey another formula than that of Newton. All such mechanics would be fully equal as ideal sciences, but it would not be probable that the results of such sciences would prove themselves valuable for the solution of practical problems.

f. As a last example of 'ideal' concepts we would like to refer to the contents of concepts which constitute the structural elements of the 'logistic' sciences. Here also man creates 'ideal' objects— namely, concepts whose nature is exactly determined in an axiomatic way by means of definitions, and here also 'rules of deduction' pre- scribe how the symbols may be used. In a 'real axiomatic deduction' one attributes a 'meaning' to the definitions and axioms and assumes that this 'meaning' is related to reality, but in 'formalized deduction' the logician abstains from assigning any meaning to the symbols used. Such a logistic calculus or logistics becomes a game, albeit a game which is rigorously determined by self-chosen rules. These rules do not claim to be any true statements about meaningful things, but are nothing but accepted rules and agreements.

In the following pages we will not devote our attention to mechanics and logistics but will limit ourselves to the more elementary mathematical sciences. However, the essence of what we will say will be valid for the ideal sciences in general.

2. *The Difference Between Ideal Sciences and Experiential Sciences With Respect to the Object*

From the preceding considerations it should be evident that there is a profound and essential difference in object between the ideal sciences and the experiential sciences and especially between mathematics and the physical sciences. Nevertheless there is real danger that the way in which these groups of sciences differ from one another will not be clearly perceived.

Experiential Sciences. The object of these sciences is human and non-human things which exist independently of man's acts of knowing and can be experienced by his cognitive powers. We acquire our first knowledge by means of the external and internal senses through which we become acquainted with things in their concrete and indi- vidual existence, i.e., as individual things having a concrete shape in concrete conditions, at a certain time and in a certain place. Through abstraction from the individual and concrete the objects of experience become suitable material for intellectual acts of knowl- edge. Through physical abstraction we are capable of taking as objects of our acts of knowing certain formal modes of being or forms which constitute a thing in a special way. The proper object, then, of the experiential sciences is, in general, the 'specific' aspect of the essence, properties and activities of the things of experience, but sometimes—more so in the human sciences than in the physical sciences[3]—also the individual and concrete.

The man of research is tied down to existing reality. It is here that he finds the starting point of his scientific endeavors and it is here also that he must return to control the progress of his work. His imagination may aid him in devising models and analogies to explain what is given in reality, but it may not proceed beyond the boundaries set by reality. It is meaningless, for example, for the scientist to imagine another world containing different objects, governed by different laws. Such intellectual games may provide him with some personal satisfaction or supply him with material for a science fiction story, but so far as the experiential sciences are concerned, they are devoid of value. Only reality which can be experienced is the object and norm of the experiential sciences, and any intellectual activity which neglects or disregards this principle is foreign to these sciences. For creative imagination and the element of play there is, generally speaking, no room in the sciences of experience.

The Ideal Sciences. As we have noted above, the proper object of these sciences is a product of human thought. In its proper essence this object can exist only in and through man's thinking. The 'being' of an 'ideal' entity is a 'thought being'. Once thought, however, they may be considered as a 'given being' whose essence and properties can now be more closely investigated. In this investigation and in his pertinent scientific activity the man of research is restricted, of course, in his liberty, because he has to respect the essence of the thing as it has been thought. For instance, a quadrilateral formed by four straight lines which are two pairs of parallel lines—a parallelogram—has of necessity the property that opposite angles are equal or that the diagonals bisect each other.

Species-Individual Relation. There is also an essential difference with respect to the relationship of the individual to the specific perfection. Like all fundamental concepts, 'species' and 'individual' have arisen from reflection upon the data of the world of experience. A philosophical consideration of the character possessed by material things shows that they have a species-individual structure, i.e., that every individual is at the same time a representative of a species. Or

[3]Cf. Chapter VI, Sect. V, Nos. 1-3, pp. 104 ff.

to say it differently, a particular individual is merely one of the possible realizations which the specific perfection may have, and by virtue of this particular realization the specific perfection is limited in space and time. Even if an object occurs *de facto* only once, e.g., the earth, we realize that in principle there could be other objects which in all details agree with the thing in question. This species-individual structure presupposes that material things are composed in their essence of prime matter and essential form, that they have a so-called 'hylomorphic' structure. One and the same specific perfection, communicated through the essential form, may express itself in a multitude of individuals, because the essential form is individuated through the prime matter with which it enters into an internal union. The same conclusion would be reached if we considered the essential change to which material things are by their very nature subject.[4]

With respect to mathematical objects there is, of course, no question of a hylomorphic structure. If one insists that the same terminology still be used, he would have to say that the objects of mathematics are 'pure forms', forms not connected with any 'matter'. A particular specific perfection or specific 'form', e.g., that of a circle with a radius of two inches or that of the number of 'two' itself, is fully expressed by an act of thought in a single individual; hence this individual represents the whole species. A multiplication of the same species in many individuals is possible only through new acts of thought of the same or of different persons. It is only by means of analogy that one may speak here of multiplication of the specific perfection through union with 'matter': for instance, when several circles of the same radius are drawn on different parts of a black board. Moreover, it should be kept in mind that the drawn circles are not genuine mathematical circles.

The remark may perhaps be added that not all possible circles constitute together a species 'circle', but every circle of a particular radius, e.g., two inches, represents a whole species. The possible circles of all conceivable radii constitute a genus.

With appropriate changes the foregoing remarks apply to all ideal sciences, at least if their objects are to be considered pure 'forms'. If, however, there is question of 'thought *material* objects', then, philosophically speaking, the matter that is included in the thought has to be conceived as hylomorphically composed and pos-

---

[4]Cf. Andrew G. van Melsen, *The Philosophy of Nature,* Pittsburgh, 1961, Ch. IV, Sect. 4.

sessing a species-individual structure, in the same way as is the case with real material things. This situation may arise, for instance, in an 'ideal' mechanics.

III. THE MODE OF KNOWING IN THE IDEAL SCIENCES. ITS DIFFERENCE FROM THE EXPERIENTIAL SCIENCES.

It goes without saying that, precisely because of the peculiar character of the object, the way in which man knows in the ideal sciences possesses a special nature and is fundamentally different from the way in which knowledge is had in the experiential sciences.

A multitude of problems are concealed behind the expressions 'mode of knowing' or 'the way in which man knows'. To do full justice to all their implications would require a long treatise in which the entire scientific activity of man in the ideal sciences would have to be examined. Within the limited scope of this book, however, we will have to limit ourselves to a few of the most important problems.

We will begin by examining the foundations of the ideal sciences and then proceed to consider the character of scientific activity proper to these sciences and their structure. These parts will be followed by a discussion of the type of truth possessed by the ideal sciences as well as a consideration of the methods used in them. Finally, we will draw attention to two important characteristics of the ideal sciences, viz., the type of necessity and of exactness which pertains to these sciences. Throughout these discussions and considerations we will often make comparisons with the experiential sciences and in particular with the physical sciences, in order to show more clearly the special character of the ideal sciences.

1. *The Foundation of the Ideal Sciences*

As was indicated in Chapter Six of Volume One, by 'foundation' of a science we mean here both its 'starting point' and 'presuppositions'. In both respects the ideal sciences differ considerably from the experiential sciences.

a. THE STARTING POINT

The Experiential Sciences. In these sciences the starting point lies in the experience of the real world, for it is this world which man attempts to know through these sciences; consequently, he remains dependent upon this world in acquiring the necessary initial knowledge. This knowledge is obtained by means of the external senses and, especially in the case of the human sciences, also through the inner senses, through introspection and self-reflection. To the extent that this knowledge is obtained through the senses, it refers immediately only to concrete things in their qualities and activities, i.e., to the 'external side' of these things. Even in self-reflection man knows immediately only himself in his activities. However, in this case there is also an intellectual knowledge of an immediately present datum, so that it is easier here to find access to the concrete essence.

The concepts which are used by the experiential sciences are obtained through total and formal abstraction—the kind which is called 'abstraction of the first degree' or 'physical abstraction'.[5] This is a kind of intellectual activity which, on the one hand, negatively removes the concrete and individual from the experiential datum and, on the other, positively attempts to seize the specific element of things, e.g., gold, helium, horse, rose. Generally speaking, the concepts obtained through ordinary, non-scientific experience will be rather vague and barely say anything explicit about the essence of things. A better knowledge of the essence will be acquired only by means of an intellectual analysis and examination of the data by means of the principle of sufficient reason. Research is needed to discover the reason for the observed qualities and activities. Only in this way is it possible to arrive at some insight into the essence of the object considered. As a rule, moreover, it will be necessary to conduct a very careful scientific investigation and to treat the data according to the method of scientific induction.

The results of sense experience are expressed in empirical or assertoric statements. While the scientific investigation continues, there is constantly need of further sense experience to obtain more accurate knowledge, or at least to check hypotheses or theories, based upon the available material, against new data.

The Ideal Sciences. Undoubtedly, even in the ideal sciences the primordial beginning likewise lies in experience. Here also applies the ancient saying that there is nothing in the intellect which was not first in the senses. Nevertheless, the contribution of experience differs here considerably from that made in the experiential sciences. In the ideal sciences experience merely supplies the raw material from

---

[5]Cf. Part One, Ch. III, Sect. II-IV.

which the intellect through a special kind of formal abstraction forms the elementary concepts that are fundamental in these sciences.

The formal abstraction in question is the so-called 'mathematical abstraction' or 'abstraction of the second degree'.[6] This abstraction negatively leaves behind everything sensitive in the sense perception, except quantity. Positively it seizes quantity in its double meaning of discrete quantity or plurality and continuous quantity or extension in various dimensions, as well as certain fundamental properties which pertain to these quantities, such as numerability, divisibility, and form. The contents of the concepts acquired in this fashion retain quantity but nothing else of whatever sensible qualities belong to the objects experienced, such as their heat, cold, hardness, elasticity, and color, nor the specific essence of the matter from which the concepts have been abstracted. As examples we may name the concepts of natural numbers; of surface, line, etc., which have arisen through idealization of experiential data, but in their mathematical essence are not at all data of experience. Once acquired, such elementary concepts are known in themselves, i.e., 'in their essence', by the intellect. By means of further intellectual idealizations, man then proceeds to more complex concepts, such as flat plane, straight line, parallel lines, and circle, and these concepts also are known 'in their essence'.

It is possible also to make fundamental 'ideal' entities arise by formulating a number of relationships (axioms or postulates) which the entities to be defined have to satisfy. However, to do this meaningfully, it will be necessary to possess at least some idea of these entities before formulating the relationships in question.[7] A certain degree of arbitrariness may preside over the formulation of these relationships, as long as care is taken that none of the proposed relations goes counter to the proper nature of the ideal objects and that the whole system remains free from internal contradiction. For instance, by substituting another postulate for the fundamental postulate of parallels proper to Euclidean geometry it became possible to create a non-Euclidean geometry.

In addition to the fundamental concepts, the ideal sciences determine also the operations indicating in what way these concepts should be used. This determination may at first take place in close connection

---

[6]Cf. Part I, Ch. III, Sect. IV.

[7]This point is often overlooked by proponents of 'formalization'. A further discussion of it would lead us beyond the scope of this book.

with the operations performed with the things of experience; for instance, the elementary operations of adding, subtracting, multiplying, and dividing. From these operations other operations may be deduced; for instance, involution or raising to a power as the multiplication of equal factors, the operation of finding the root as the reverse of raising to a power. Such operations are defined as much as possible independently of experience and they are, moreover, posited as universally valid. This universal validity often leads to an extension of the realm of numbers. Sense experience teaches us only about so-called 'natural' numbers (one, two, three, etc.), with respect to which the operations in question are possible only in certain cases or on a limited scale. The generalization, however, of the operations occasions the acceptance of new species of numbers. For instance, 'negative' numbers arise by permitting subtraction when the number to be subtracted is greater than the number from which the subtraction is made; the generalization of division gives rise to 'broken numbers' or 'fractions'; by permitting to draw the root of negative numbers, we obtain the group of 'imaginary numbers'.

Geometry proceeds in an analogous fashion. For instance, one accepts a few fundamental operations, usually called 'fundamental constructions', and by means of these then proceeds to build ever more complex geometric figures or bodies. In Euclidean geometry, for example, the following fundamental constructions are accepted: through two given points it is possible to draw a straight line (by means of an 'imaginary' rule); with a given point as center and a given line as radius it is possible to describe a circle (by means of an 'imaginary' compass). Solid geometry also has its own fundamental constructions, such as that a plan is fixed if it passes through three points not collinear or through two intersecting straight lines, and that a sphere can be constructed when the center and the radius are given.

'Experience' Always Remains Necessary. In the preceding pages the term 'starting point' has been taken in the sense of the 'point of departure' or 'the beginning' of a science from which we must proceed when we begin to build the science in question. However, the term could be conceived more broadly and extended to include that which in every phase of scientific activity in an ideal science must be considered to be the starting point. In this broader sense of the term we must admit that in the ideal sciences scientific activity is always accompanied by, and essentially based upon 'experience', but 'experi-

ence' of a very special kind. The 'experience' in question is offered mainly by the imagination, aided by visible models, drawings, or formulae when the number or complexity of the data is such that the imagination alone is unable to cope with them. As we have pointed out in Part One,[8] the imagination plays a special and indispensable role in mathematics and in the ideal sciences in general. Only exceptionally it may happen that a phantasm or even an experiment is capable of supplying us with an insight that is immediately useful for the ideal sciences. For instance, when it is a question of determining what actually does result in cases where intuitive insight makes clear to us that a certain univocal result must follow. To speak more concretely, the result of an addition, multiplication, or other arithmetical operation can be obtained by experimenting with real objects or by means of a machine; the possible divisions of a Moebian strip may be found through an experiment in which a real strip having a similar shape is appropriately cut.

In general, however, the phantasm or the experiment, taken by themselves, will not be able to motivate the consent of the intellect and will be insufficient to allow exact statements, because phantasms simply lack the necessary exactness. An intellectual assimilation and idealization of the phantasmal data always remains indispensable. More will be said about this point in Section III, no. 5, b (pp. 243 ff.). Meanwhile it should be clear that in the ideal sciences the two cognitive powers which play essential roles are the intellect and the imagination. The external senses, on the other hand, merely exercise an auxiliary function, insofar as they aid the imagination by means of observable data of experience.

b. The Presuppositions

Among the foundations of a science there are always also numerous insights which, as a rule, are not explicitly formulated but are merely implicitly present in the intellectual elaboration of the subject matter. These insights may be called 'presuppositions'. It is the task of philosophy to render them explicit. With respect to the group of sciences considered here, this explicitation could be performed in a philosophy of the ideal sciences or, on a more limited scale, in a philosophy of mathematics. We will have to limit ourselves here to a few presuppositions which we consider extremely important and

---

[8]Ch. III, Sect. IV, pp. 30. ff.

with respect to which there is a clear difference between the experiential sciences and the ideal sciences.

General Presuppositions. There are presuppositions that are common to all scientific activity and even to all intellectual knowledge. Such are, first of all, metaphysical principles, insofar as they express something which belongs to every being as being; for example, the principles of identity, of contradiction, of sufficient reason, and of intelligibility. Secondly, there are epistemological presuppositions, which refer to man's cognitive power; for instance, the openness of the intellect to all that is and the trustworthiness of the intellect. With respect to these general presuppositions, there is little difference between the various groups of sciences.

Special Presuppositions. Apart from the general presuppositions, there are others that are less general but still common to entire groups of sciences, such as to all theological sciences, all experiential sciences, or all ideal sciences. We will limit ourselves here to those of the ideal sciences, but compare them to those of the experiential sciences.

In the *experiential sciences,* precisely because they devote themselves to the observable world, there is no escape from accepting the trustworthiness of the senses. These sciences, moreover, have to compare and combine present data with past observations. This necessity implies the presupposition that memory and the images which the imagination reproduces from the past are trustworthy.

Next, since the experiential sciences want to explain the phenomena of observation, the conviction is important to them that the principle of causality possesses universal validity. This point may be emphasized here especially with respect to the physical sciences, because it is sometimes incorrectly said that in certain areas of physics it has become meaningless to speak of a true causal connection.[9] The principle of causality says nothing about the nature of the required causes. These causes may be either non-necessary (free) or necessary in their working. If they are necessary, then their operation is determined in all its details. It is an implicit presupposition of physical science that material nature is determined. The human

---

[9]Cf. P. Henry van Laer, *Philosophico-Scientific Problems,* Pittsburgh, 1953, Ch. V; Andrew G. van Melsen, *The Philosophy of Nature,* Pittsburgh, 1961, Ch. VIII, pp. 229 ff.

sciences, on the other hand, at least if they do not want to lose their proper character, must presuppose that in man's spiritual part there is an element of freedom.

Finally, we must mention that the experiential sciences, in the quantitative elaboration of their results, presuppose also the trustworthiness of the theorems and operations of mathematics.

The *ideal sciences* with respect to presuppositions differ in an important point from the experiential sciences and especially from the physical sciences. It may be true that the ideal sciences assume, for example, the trustworthiness of the senses and of memory, but they do not do so in the same way as the experiential sciences. For in the ideal sciences it is at any moment possible—of course, with the aid of the imagination—to reconstruct the necessary objects and to deduce again from them their essential properties. The presuppositions of the species-individual structure and of the determinacy or indeterminacy of the object are irrelevant to them. Likewise, there is in general no question of causality, in the ordinary sense of efficient causality, for the objects do not have any activity (unless one creates an ideal mechanics or another ideal science which supplies its objects with activities). If one wants to speak of causality in the ideal sciences in general and in mathematics in particular, there can be, as a rule, question only of so-called 'formal' causality. The objects of mathematics, as 'forms', as thought entities and structures which do not include matter, 'produce' their own essential properties as long as these objects are thought by the mathematician.

The presuppositions of the ideal sciences have to refer, of course, to the proper character of the object and to the characteristic method of these sciences. For this reason the presuppositions of mathematics, insofar as mathematics is concerned with quantity, refer also to quantity. As examples of these presuppositions we may name: the whole is greater than the part; and quantities of the same kind may be added and their sum is another quantity of the same kind. Geometric sciences assume also implicitly that the extended is divisible; that a mathematical object can be placed differently in 'geometric space'; that Euclidean 'space' is homogenous and isotropic, so that a geometric figure moving in it does not change its form and properties. These examples may suffice to illustrate the presuppositions of this type of sciences.

2. *Purpose of the Scientific Activity Exercised in the Ideal Sciences. The Structure of the Ideal Sciences*

In the experiential sciences the purpose of research activity is to arrive at an understanding of the component parts as well as the whole of the real world. For this reason research endeavors to obtain a certain knowledge of the essence proper to reality by studying observed phenomena and properties. In the ideal sciences, however, the aim is quite different. True, subjectively many of those who study, e.g., mathematics may be able to make the knowledge they acquire useful for a correct description of the real world in its quantitative aspects. This situation, however, does not change anything at all in the proper objective purpose and structure assigned to the ideal sciences by their disinterested creators and students.[10]

The purpose pursued by the creators of the ideal sciences is, by starting from a rather arbitrarily chosen point (cf. no. 1, p. 225 ff.) and by following operative principles which have to satisfy only the demand of not going counter to the proper nature of the object, to construct new entities and to deduce from them as many consequences as possible in order to build up a logically coherent system. As we pointed out in Part One,[11] an ideal science, such as a particular mathematical science, as a whole has the character of a theory which —abstracting from its presuppositions—is based upon a set of fundamental concepts and postulates and in which a consistent whole of theses is deductively arrived at; hence these theses are interconnected and in this particular system are valid of necessity. As to the role which deduction plays in the ideal sciences and the character of necessity proper to these sciences, later we will have an opportunity to speak more in detail about them.

3. *Truth and Verification in the Ideal Sciences*

A question which arises in connection with these considerations is to what extent the statements of the ideal sciences are true and capable of being verified.

Truth of the Ideal Sciences. More than one meaning could be assigned to the term 'truth', but in this context it may be described in the traditional fashion as an "agreement between intellect and the thing known". An intellectual statement, S is P or S is not P, is true

---

[10]Cf. Ch. IV, Sect. I, No. 3, pp. 52 ff.
[11]Ch. IX, Sect. I.

if the relation between subject and predicate is actually as it has been conceived by the intellect. In connection with this definition one generally thinks here first of all about the cognitive relationships of the intellect to the real world which are expressed in the experiential sciences or in everyday language. However, the definition, properly modified, applies to all speculative sciences[12] and therefore also to the ideal sciences, provided that the term 'thing known' be understood correctly, i.e., in accord with the character proper to the object in the ideal sciences. The object in question contains entities which are either immediately or by means of a series of logical deductions produced by thought. Thus, we have always to deal here with things that may be considered as 'given beings', capable of functioning as subjects of judgments and to which through predicates we may ascribe all kinds of properties and relationships. If, then, the predicate does pertain to the subject in the system in question, we must say that the statement in the system is 'true', i.e., that in this statement there is an "agreement of the intellect with the thing known".

It is to be noted that we have added here the limiting qualifier 'in the system'. This limitation should not be taken to mean that one and the same objective relation could be true in one ideal system and not true in another ideal system. It is possible, however, that identical terms may have different meanings in distinct ideal systems. Let us illustrate this possibility by means of a few examples.

For natural numbers the following relationship is valid: $5 + 3 = 8$. But, if the numbers 5 and 3 represent the lengths of two vectors, then their sum total will be eight only if the two vectors have the same direction. If their directions are opposed, then their sum total will be equal to two, and in all other cases their total is a real number whose value lies between two and eight.

Another example may be taken from geometry. The sum of the angles of a triangle, formed by three 'straight lines', is equal to two right angles in Euclidean geometry, greater than two right angles in the elliptical non-Euclidean geometry of Riemann, and smaller than two right angles in the hyperbolic non-Euclidean geometry of Lobatschewsky. All three of these statements are equally 'true', but each of them in the system to which it belongs. There is no question of contradiction, because the entities in question are not the same. The concept 'straight line', for example, has each time a different content, because in each of the three geometries

---

[12]Cf. Ch. IV, Sect. I, No. 2, p. 47.

it is determined by means of a distinct set of postulates. The 'straight line', for example, of Riemann's geometry may be considered to be analogous with a large circle on a spherical surface in Euclidean geometry.

Verification in the Ideal Sciences. This point has been mentioned in Part One, Chapter Nine. We must now consider it somewhat more extensively here.

First of all, in general there can be no question of exact verification by means of experience. For the objects of the ideal sciences are not experiential data and therefore cannot be sensitively observed.

Secondly, the only strict kind of verification possible in the ideal sciences is to control whether or not all successive steps from the starting point to the statement to be verified have been taken in a logically correct fashion. If the reply is in the affirmative, then this control has verified that the statement in question is really 'true' in the system in which it occurs.

Thirdly, *per accidens* it may be possible for a result obtained by an ideal science to be verified by means of perceptible data; for instance, if there is question of the correctness of a number calculation. The result of an addition, a multiplication, or a division can be controlled by means of a mechanical calculator. Such a verification, however, does not greatly interest the pure mathematician, for he is concerned only with the correctness of his mathematical statements and not with their possible applications.

Fourthly, sometimes experience may indicate that a particular thesis, the truth of which has not yet been proved but is merely surmised, is certainly not true or at least not true in its universal form. This happens when the application of the thesis to reality does not produce the result that could be expected upon the basis of the thesis, or when it is found that the thesis in question certainly does not apply to this or that particular case. A very carefully drawn figure, for example, may show that a given statement, say, that a number of points, obtained in a particular fashion, lie in a straight line, is certainly not true. In this way it could be evident that somewhere in the deduction of this statement a mistake was made.

Fifthly, from the fact that a particular statement of an ideal science has never been found to be false by whatever real application and control it permits, we may not yet conclude that this statement is 'true' according to what an ideal science demands for verification.

Of course, it may happen that in this way the statement in question is suspected of being 'true' and that this suspicion stimulates the ideal scientist to attempt the deduction of the statement by means of the methods that are at his disposal. For instance, there are several statements about prime numbers which probably are true because experience has never found any exception to them. Nevertheless, the mathematician will accept such statements as 'true' only when they have been correctly deduced in the theory of numbers.

4. *Methods in the Ideal Sciences*

In the first volume (Ch. VII) we have spoken about scientific methods in general as well as in particular about the deductive, inductive, analytic, and synthetic methods. We pointed out there that no science is exclusively deductive or inductive, analytic or synthetic. This assertion applies also to the ideal sciences. If, as far as methods are concerned, there is a difference between the ideal sciences and other groups of sciences and especially the experiential sciences of nature, it will be a question of greater or lesser use of either methods, of a clear shift toward one of the two opposite methods, but not a question of exclusively using only one method.

Whatever differences there are will have to arise from the proper nature of the objects studied in these sciences and from the method that is required by the knowledge of these objects. In the following pages we will first speak about deduction and induction and then about analysis and synthesis, indicating, where necessary, the differences from the experiential sciences and especially from the sciences of nature. However, we will not repeat here the general considerations presented in Chapter Seven of Part One. Finally, we will add a few general remarks about special mathematical methods.

a. Deduction and Induction

The use of the deductive or inductive method is to a large extent determined by the nature of the starting point and the purpose of the scientific activity. Thus, our considerations here are necessarily connected with the preceding remarks about these points. In the experiential sciences thought proceeds at first from the particular, the concrete and individual, to the general and therefore uses primarily the inductive method. Next, if there is question of applying an established general law or rule to a particular case, or if a particular consequence has to be derived from a general truth, thought proceeds deductively. In other words, the experiential sciences use the inductive method mainly to arrive at general insights and proceed deductively in their more theoretical parts. These deductions are more readily possible in the physical sciences than in the human sciences. In the last-named group there is a great danger of pseudo-deduction, because their statements are rather frequently not abstractly general but merely collectively general.[13]

In the ideal sciences the situation of scientific activity is generally quite different. Building upon foundations that have been obtained through schematization or idealization of experiential data or that have been chosen in a fairly arbitrary way, the ideal scientist, as we have seen, endeavors to deduce new propositions and in this fashion to construct a logically coherent system. Moreover, whatever the reason why he is convinced that a proposition is valid, he will not recognize this proposition as on a par with the other propositions of his science until it becomes possible to deduce it from the foundations of this science. Thus, there is every reason to say that the ideal sciences, and especially mathematics, are deductive sciences. It is hardly necessary to insist upon this point, for scarcely anyone would attempt to deny it. The danger exists even that the deductive character will be exaggerated to such an extent that there hardly remains any room for inductive elements. For this reason it appears desirable here to draw attention also to these inductive aspects. In order not to prolong the discussion unduly, we will limit ourselves to mathematics, but, with due changes, our remarks apply also to the other ideal sciences.

Inductive Aspects of the Mathematical Sciences. If the term 'induction' is taken in a broad sense to include also the formation of concepts upon the basis of experience, induction occurs also in the ideal sciences. For here also, as we have seen above (pp. 225 ff.), experience, albeit in a different sense, is the starting point of the first concepts. Moreover, under the guise of phantasms, experience is an indispensable aid in the use of these concepts and in the formation of new concepts and propositions.

Secondly, if the term 'induction' is supposed to indicate any kind of knowledge arising from experience, the ideal sciences offer a broad

---

[13]Cf. Ch. VI, Sect. V, Nos. 1 and 2, pp. 172 ff. and Part I, Ch. VII, Sect. I, No. 1, pp. 57 ff.

area in which induction is used. We may refer here to p. 227, where the question has been considered.

Thirdly, as the progress of thought from the particular to the general judgment, induction plays an important role in mathematics with respect to the search for new propositions and problems, and especially in the exploration of virgin mathematical realms. In such a search one has to use his imagination, to try this or that, to experiment with the known, e.g., with numbers, figures, and symbols. By chance or through a kind of intuition the man of research discovers something special in a particular experiment; he then investigates whether the same happens in other similar cases and thus begins to suspect that this or that proposition is probably universally valid. In this method an indispensable role is played by visualization or experience, i.e., an intellectual viewing of a datum supplied by the imagination (a phantasm) or sometimes by an external sense perception, e.g., looking at drawn figures or at models, and occasionally even an experiment, e.g., the division of a complex body, say a Moebian strip.

In passing we may note here that an actually observed connection is expressed in an assertoric judgment; a thesis which is probably true but not yet proved, in a problematic judgment; and a proved thesis, in an apodictic judgment.

Induction Followed by Deduction. The inductive labor of finding new problems is indispensable in an ideal science—just as indispensable or perhaps even more than the work of deduction, for the latter type of work is stimulated by the former. The 'result' that is intuitively or inductively discovered has still to be proved universally valid by means of logical deduction. Through the analysis of the *a posteriori* discovery the way has to be sought to the foundations, to the set of axioms, from which the discovery has to be proved *a priori* and deductively. The ideal scientist will not be satisfied until his efforts meet with success and the result can be stated apodictically. It is through the search for the proofs of a problematic proposition that ancient realms of mathematics sometimes acquire an unexpected growth or that new realms are discovered and developed. It may even happen that the search will lead to a revision of the set of axioms serving as the foundation or to the creation of an entirely new foundation.

Success does not always attend the efforts to prove the universality of inductively discovered propositions, even when one is convinced of their validity. A well-known example is Fermat's proposition that it is impossible to find natural numbers a, b, c and n which can satisfy the equation $a^n + b^n = c^n$ if n is greater than 2. The proposition has been proved for certain series of values of n, but hitherto no general proof has yet been found which would apply to every natural number n. As long, therefore, as such a proof is not given, the proposition will retain its problematic character. Meanwhile the efforts spent in searching for such a proof have been very fruitful for the evolution of mathematics, for they have initiated the development of entirely new realms of mathematics, such as the theory of ideal numbers and modern algebra.

In conclusion we may draw attention to a method used in mathematics which is called 'complete induction', 'mathematical induction' or 'successive induction'. This method is based upon the following principle: "If a proposition is valid for a natural number a, and it can be shown that the same proposition is valid for $n + 1$ if it is valid for the natural number n, then this proposition is valid for every natural number that is greater than a." The use of the term 'complete induction' for this process is misguiding, for the procedure is entirely different from what is usually understood by 'complete induction'.[14] In reality, we have to do here with a genuine deduction, in which the above-mentioned principle functions as a major, and the minor expresses that the condition is actually fulfilled for proposition P. The conclusion then indicates that this proposition is generally valid for every natural number greater than a.

b. ANALYSIS AND SYNTHESIS

Because analysis and synthesis have been considered in general in the first volume of this work (Ch. VII, Sect. II), we may restrict ourselves here to a few aspects which are important for the ideal sciences.

From the fact that the ideal sciences are mainly deductive it follows that they proceed intensively according to the synthetic method. For every deduction is a synthesis, because the conclusion arises from the combination of the two premises. The truth of the assertion becomes apparent also if one takes into consideration that the term 'synthesis' indicates a progressive or *a priori* process of thought, i.e., the passage from the general to the particular, from genus to species,

---

[14]Cf. Part I, Ch. VII, Sect. I, Nos. 4 and 5, pp. 65 ff.

from law to application, from essence to properties. Especially the last point may be emphasized because it manifests again a clear-cut difference between the ideal sciences and the experiential sciences. In the sciences of experience the objects can be approached only from their sense-perceptible 'outer side', so that one has to reason from the perceived properties and activities to their ground, the essence of things. In other words, one proceeds *a posteriori*, regressively or analytically. The procedure of the ideal sciences, however, is usually just the opposite. In these sciences man himself creates the essence of the objects through his intellectual operations and it is from the essence of these objects thus known by him that he deduces *a priori* their essential properties. In this respect, therefore, the procedures used by these two groups of sciences are clearly opposite.

The ideal sciences are synthetic also insofar as constructive thought builds simple structures from the fundamental elements and uses the simple structures to raise ever more complex structures. As an example we may refer here to the way in which ordinary Euclidean geometry operates.

Alongside the synthetic method there is ample room in the ideal sciences for the use of the analytic method. This point should be evident from the preceding considerations about deduction and induction if one keeps in mind that induction plays an important role also in the ideal sciences and that every process of induction makes use of an analytic, regressive or *a posteriori* method. The results discovered by observation or 'experience' have to be logically analyzed to reduce the complex to the simple, to elements and principles, in order to make it intelligible. When problems are to be solved or mathematical constructions to be made, one begins regressively by analyzing them in order to find the way to a progressive and synthetic solution and construction.

Many problems deal with entities, such as figures and formulae, which in certain respects are variable. In such cases one may arrive at particular instances by investigating the various implied possibilities. In so-called 'analytic geometry', for example, we may start from a general equation of the first or of the second degree. By making one or more of the coefficients in the equation zero or by making them satisfy certain conditions, one can investigate which particular cases are implied in the general formula.

Accordingly, we see that in the mathematical sciences analysis and synthesis work closely together. Usually, the initial phase will be more analytic, and the final phase more synthetic. No branch of mathematics is exclusively either analytic or synthetic, although one or the other may be prevalent.

c. SPECIAL MATHEMATICAL METHODS

The methods described above are used in the ideal sciences, but they have a general character and in one way or another serve all sciences. In addition to these general methods, every group of sciences and even every particular science has its own special methods. While the scope of this work does not permit us to speak extensively of them here, nevertheless it may not be amiss to draw attention to a special point which is characteristic of the special nature proper to the ideal sciences—namely, the element of freedom which prevails in the choice of methods and rules to be followed in these sciences. 'Freedom' here does not mean absolute arbitrariness, for here, too, man is limited by the laws of logic and by the fundamental demands made by the proper nature of the object studied by these sciences. Nevertheless, there is in the ideal sciences a certain latitude, there is room for an element of play. This latitude may be restricted by freely chosen additional rules of play, inspired by aesthetic or methodic motives, such as the desire to keep a theory free from foreign elements, by a quest of adventure to see how far one can go in this way, or by philosophical insights. A few examples may suffice to illustrate the point.

In ordinary Euclidean plane and solid geometry mathematicians allow only constructions which can be executed by means of a compass and a ruler. The result is that the construction possibilities are limited. For instance, it is impossible to divide any given angle into three equal parts. The same limitation makes it impossible to solve a number of other mathematical problems, such as the doubling of a cube (the Delian problem), the rectification and the quadrature of a given circle. If construction methods of a different kind were permitted, such problems could be solved.

In the number theory it is often demanded that a proposition about real numbers must be proved also without making use of non-real functions. In the 'intuitionistic mathematics' of Professor Brouwer no use is made of the principle of excluded middle, in part for philosophical reasons, because he claims that this principle is not reliable at least with respect to infinite systems. According to Dr. Brouwer, something is 'mathematically existent' only if it can be shown that the construction of the entity in question can be performed in a finite number of steps. Because of this restriction on demonstration, large and important parts of classical mathematics have to be rejected as invalid. These consequences are the reason why most mathematicians refuse to accept the intuitionistic limitation of method.

Many other examples could be adduced to illustrate the point we want to make. However, these few should suffice to show that ideal scientists enjoy freedom in the choice of their methods and that this freedom is something characteristic of the ideal sciences.

5. *Some Important Characteristics of the Ideal Sciences*

Because of the proper nature of their object and of their structure, the ideal sciences have also certain features which set the mode of knowing proper to these sciences apart from those of other groups and especially from that pertaining to the experiential sciences. Here again it is very instructive to compare mathematics, as representing the ideal sciences, with physical science, as representing the experiential sciences, because mathematics and physical science are frequently considered together and thus their essential differences may be lost sight of. We will consider here only the characteristics of necessity and exactness, limiting ourselves to a few pertinent remarks.[15]

a. THE CHARACTER OF NECESSITY

A general consideration of the necessity characterizing a science has been proposed in Volume One, Chapter Four, where attention was drawn also to the difference between the physical and the mathematical type of necessity. It may be useful to develop a few points here somewhat more extensively, because they are likely to provide us with a more profound understanding of the character proper to the ideal sciences.

When there is question here of the character of necessity, this expression should be taken to refer to a property pertaining to the connection between subject and predicate in judgments expressing

---

[15]For a more extensive treatment we must refer to *ex professo* works on the philosophy of mathematics. We may mention by name a few publications of Dr. Peter Hoenen, whose considerations we have found to be very fruitful: "De problemate necessitatis geometricae", *Gregorianum,* vol. 20 (1939), pp. 19-54; "De problemate exactitudinis geometricae", *ibid.,* vol. 20 (1939), pp. 321-350 and vol. 24 (1943), pp. 171-234. These articles were published also in book form under the title *De noetica geometriae origine theoriae cognitionis,* Rome, 1954.

assertions of the ideal sciences. Moreover, a distinction should be made here between necessity as it is present objectively, independently of our knowledge, when the connection is demanded by the essence of the subject and the predicate, and necessity insofar as it is known to us. For it is possible that there exists objectively a necessary connection which is not known to us. The ideal, of course, is that the objective necessity be known to us, for then the statement expressing the connection between S and P is not only apodictic in itself but also with respect to our knowledge.

It should be evident that the ideal in question, generally speaking, can be reached in the ideal sciences, at least in their deductive parts. For these sciences start from evident truths about a subject matter that is open to intellectual understanding or they take as their starting point a set of axioms or postulates that are posited as valid. Whatever statements are deduced from such starting points with rigorously accurate logic evidently share in the evident and apodictic character of these starting points. In certain parts of mathematics, e.g., in the theory of numbers, one could even speak of a known absolute necessity, because the foundations here are chosen in such a way that they agree with the really existing and known relationships between the real pluralities symbolized by the natural numbers.

In other cases it is better to speak of a hypothetical necessity, because in them the known necessary connection between S and P of a judgment is present only within the system in which these judgments have been deduced. For example, it is only in Euclidean geometry that the sum of the angles of a triangle is equal to two right angles (cf. p. 232). In all cases, however, it is true that in a given system the predicate is demanded or 'produced' through formal causality by the subject and that we understand this necessity because we ourselves through our thinking have created the essence of the ideal entities and therefore are capable of deducing from the known essence the essential properties which pertain to it of necessity.

To the extent that ideal sciences are still in the inductive stage (see p. 235), the inductively acquired general statements provisionally have, as a rule, only a problematic character. There may be objectively a necessary connection and there may also be a subjective conviction about the validity of the statement in question, such as that of Fermat, but in this stage the formal insight into the nature of the connection is still lacking. This insight is not present before man succeeds in deducing the statement from the foundations of the ideal system.

As a further clarification we may remark that the object of the ideal sciences is always something 'necessary'. There is no room in them for contingency in the ordinary sense of the term. There is 'contingency' only in the sense that within a given genus, e.g., that of triangle, an infinite variation is possible, but insofar as this genus ('triangle') is concerned, there are necessary generic relationships, and with respect to any species within this genus, e.g., an equilateral triangle with a base of five inches and an angle of 30° at its apex, there are necessary specific relationships. [16]Insofar as in the ideal sciences intellectual insight is derived from experience, from the phantasm or the sensed object, the consequent contingent qualities do not prevent intellectual understanding. For by means of a particular kind of formal abstraction the intellect manages to separate the relevant from the irrelevant. If, for instance, one tries to find the result of a mathematical operation, such as an addition, or a division of a Moebian strip, by experimenting with real things, one knows *a priori* that a certain result is necessary and also that this result depends only on the quantities in question or the essential structure of the object and not on the material from which the things are made, from their color, hardness or temperature, or from the time and place of the experiment. For abstraction is made of all these material and sensible aspects. Thus, a single experiment suffices to arrive at a conclusion whose necessary character is readily recognizable.

Difference from the Physical Sciences. The *sui generis* character of necessity proper to the ideal sciences manifests itself even more clearly when it is compared with that proper to statements pertaining to the experiential sciences, and especially to physical science, which at first seem to resemble those of the ideal sciences most closely. In the experiential sciences the starting point lies in empirical and assertoric judgments about an actually observed connection. In general, it is not immediately evident which aspects of experience are relevant and which ones irrelevant. As a rule, a very careful investigation is necessary to reach here the required level of 'physical abstraction' by way of scientific induction and to arrive at statements expressing a necessary connection. Frequently the most that can be obtained is knowledge that a particular relationship discovered by induction

---

[16]Cf. what has been said above in Sect. II, No. 2, p. 222, about the species-individual structure of ideal objects.

de facto has the character of necessity, without there being any way of understanding the how and why of this necessity.

Moreover, the scientist must always keep the possibility in mind that the discovered 'laws of nature' are valid only within the limits of the investigated area and of the conditions under which this area was searched. Outside this area more accurate observation may oblige him to revise or supplement the laws in question. Even the most solidly founded statements of physical science, therefore, only rarely if ever attain a strictly apodictic character at least with respect to our knowledge. In the human sciences, as we have seen before,[17] it is usually possible only to arrive at a so-called 'moral necessity', which permits exceptions. Thus, these sciences are even farther removed from the necessity proper to the ideal sciences.

b. THE CHARACTER OF EXACTNESS

We do not intend to examine here the meaning which could justifiedly be attributed to the term 'exact' in the much-used expression 'the exact sciences'. Instead we will restrict ourselves to a brief consideration of a kind of exactness that is very clear and with respect to which there is a clear-cut difference between the ideal sciences and the experiential sciences, and especially again between mathematics and physical science. In an appendix to this chapter we will devote a few words to the expression 'the exact sciences'.

By exactness we mean a property which belongs to mathematics because of the precise character of its object and consequently also because of the absolute precision with which a given relationship can be fixed in scientific statements. Regarding this exactness the following brief remarks may suffice.

Insofar as the object of the mathematical sciences is derived from sense experience or phantasms, it is through 'mathematical abstraction' (cf. p. 226) freed from sensible matter and from all the inaccuracies inherent to this matter. In the process from an observed discrete plurality to the mathematical natural number there is exactness even in the sensible starting point, because such a real plurality consists of clearly distinct things, at least if suitable objects are chosen.

Insofar as mathematical entities arise through an intellectual process, e.g., by means of the idealization or schematization of experiential data or through an intellectual definition or construction, it should

---

[17]Ch. VI, Sect. V, Nos. 2 and 3, pp. 175 ff.

be evident that such entities cannot be subject to inexactness.[18] For instance, a mathematical line does not have a very small thickness that can be neglected, but has no thickness at all. Defined lines, such as a straight line, a circle, and an ellipse, are in all respects exact by virtue of their definition. The same applies to other entities which through more or less complex operations are constructed from elementary concepts.

The mathematical sciences are not merely exact in the essence of their objects but also in the knowledge of these objects because mathematical objects originate in the intellect. This 'knowledge of the essence' makes it possible to have knowledge of the essential properties, and this knowledge also is exact. It is on this exactness that is based the exactness pertaining to the statements of the mathematical sciences. No one will be able to doubt the exactness with which, for example, are determined the results of an arithmetical operation or the absolute exactness proper to a geometric proposition regarding the collinearity of points or the concurrence of lines.

It may be useful to add that the impossibility of expressing certain magnitudes in whole numbers or in ordinary and decimal fractions does not at all make those magnitudes themselves less exact. For instance, the relation of the circumference of a circle to its diameter is a determined and wholly exact real number (π), although this number cannot be exactly expressed by means of ordinary or decimal fractions, or even by means of a geometric method exactly fixed on the line of real numbers.

Difference from the Physical Sciences. The great difference in exactness between mathematics and physical science should be obvious from the preceding considerations. True, in physical science we are dealing with determined matter, which is at every moment determined in itself and does not allow any moment of freedom in its activity. However, our knowledge of this matter is deficient in many respects, so that the ideal of absolute precision or exactness is not attainable. First of all, the contact of our intellect with the object has to take place through the senses, so that our knowledge is subject to the same inaccuracy which affects our sense perception. This assertion applies also to quantitative measurements. Although the unities of such measurements may be theoretically defined in a fully exact way, the

---

[18]We abstract here from the various theories with which the philosophy of mathematics endeavors to give a foundation to this exactness.

actual determination of the number of units in a particular magnitude can be indicated only by approximation.

There are special difficulties in microphysical research, which deals with the smallest particles, such as molecules, atoms, protons, and electrons. First of all, observation requires here certain operations which disturb the situation in a way that cannot be fully grasped by our intellect. Secondly, we suffer from the difficulty that our imagination is unable to make a suitable model of these elementary particles. The result is that even questions about fundamental points, such as the size of these particles cannot receive an unequivocal reply, for the outcome of the research depends upon the type of measurements.

Inductively obtained statements, even the best known and most generally valid 'laws', do not enjoy absolute exactness (cf. p. 242). The highest that can be attained here is the conviction that all observations point to the absolute and exact validity of such laws within the investigated realm and that there is nothing which goes positively counter to it. However, it remains always advisable to take into account the possibility that new and more accurate research will be able to show deviations from a 'law' established by physical science.

These remarks suffice, we think, to illustrate the difference between ideal and physical sciences with respect to exactness and thus to throw some light upon the exclusive character of the exactness proper to the ideal sciences.

APPENDIX

I. Exact Sciences

Mathematics and physical science together are often referred to as 'the exact sciences'. We must confess that we do not know who first made use of this term and what qualities he wanted to indicate by means of it. At any rate, it is certain that at present there is no agreement about the meaning of the term and that one could discuss at length which meaning would be most appropriate. According to Webster's dictionary, 'exact' means "capable of great nicety or precision". Vague as the description is, it expresses an acceptable meaning and indicates what most people mean by it in the present context. Thus, the ideal of precision would be present in mathematics. The physical sciences would share in this character insofar as they resemble mathematics or offer a possibility of using mathematical methods. The difficulty, however, of this view is that these mathematical aspects are not present in the same way in all sections of physical science. Moreover, they are not wholly absent from the human sciences,[19] so that these sciences too would be in part exact.

There are also other views about the reason why physical science should be called exact. Some claim that this reason may be found in the experimental character of this science, while others seek it in the fact that in this science it is possible to appeal to sense perceptions which can be interpreted only in one way, and others again refer to the presence of arguments that are unanimously accepted by all experts in the field. However, none of these reasons is such that it justifies a sharp distinction of physical science from the human sciences.

In our view only the following two reasons offer a kind of justification for the use of the term 'exact' with respect to physical science and mathematics: first, the fact that in both groups of sciences one has to deal with univocal concepts and is able to use 'exact' definitions; second, the fact that in both groups the object is absolutely determined. Let us add a few words about both points.

With respect to the exactness of the definitions and relationships in mathematics we may refer to what has been stated above on pp. 243 ff. The ideal of exactness is truthfully within reach here.

---

[19]Cf. Ch. VI, Sect. IV, No. 3, pp. 166 ff.

Although the physical sciences certainly cannot match this exactness of mathematics, it is often possible to approximate it somewhat. In general, and especially in the physical sciences of non-living matter, such as physics and chemistry, it is not difficult to fix the fundamental concepts univocally in definitions in such a way that even internationally there is no danger of misunderstanding. We may refer, for example, to the definitions of meter, second, calory, and ampere. Other concepts allow themselves to be connected with these fundamental ideas in a univocal way, such as by means of functional relationships. Moreover, the abstract specific concepts of substances, properties and activities, used by physics and chemistry, are of a univocal character.[20]

Regarding the determinism of the object, mathematical sciences have a deterministic character in a *sui generis* fashion: they are logically coherent creations of the human mind, which has seen to it that the concepts and axioms used as a starting point have a well-defined meaning that remains invariable in a given system. The human mind, moreover, takes care that the deduced propositions are univocally and in a precisely known way connected with the starting point.

Physical sciences, on the other hand, have as their object material things, in which, apart from possible human interference, only causes operating by physical necessity determine the course of events. These causes, then, are without any element of freedom. The whole course of events, therefore, takes place in a deterministic way, i.e., it happens precisely, 'exactly', in accord with the inherent properties and activities of the material objects. Thus, an investigation of the phenomena occurring in non-living matter is an inquiry into a problem which in itself is fully determined and univocal. The same could be said of living matter, with the execption of man, although in this category the situation is not so clear as in that of non-living matter. Thus, on the basis of the analogy that is present here to the mathematical sciences it would be possible to speak of 'exact' problems.

The two above-mentioned aspects are the only ones which in our view can serve as a basis for the similarity of mathematics and physical science with respect to exactness. The other aspects of 'exactness' named at the beginning of this appendix, insofar as they exist in physical science, may be based upon these two fundamental reasons

---

[20]Cf. Ch. VI, Sect. V, No. 7, p. 195 ff.

for exactness. This assertion applies especially to the 'similarity' of physical science with mathematics which reveals itself in the use of mathematical means in physical sciences. For the possibility of treating a problem mathematically finds its main basis, on the one hand, in the exactness and univocity of the concepts used and, on the other, in the deterministic character of the object studied by the physical sciences. We may refer here again to the considerations about this subject matter presented in Chapter Six, Section Four (pp. 166 ff.).

One point raised in that chapter may be brought up here again. We mentioned there that quantitative aspects are present also, although to a lesser extent, in some of the human sciences. A strong case in point is economics. Nevertheless, this presence does not appear to us to be a sufficient reason to enumerate economics among the exact sciences. If anyone insists that the use of mathematical means and methods must be considered the criterion of exactness, he would have to be consistent and apply the term 'exact science' not only to mathematics and physical science but also to a number of other human sciences. Hardly anyone, however, appears willing to do so.

From all these considerations it should be evident that the term 'exact sciences' can be applied in the full sense only to mathematics and other ideal sciences. Any broader usage of the term, without a precise indication of what is meant, can easily lead to misunderstanding and therefore should be avoided.

II. Positive Sciences

The term 'positive sciences' is frequently used both in ordinary language and in philosophical studies. It is meant to indicate a group of sciences which distinguish themselves from others by their 'positive' character. In the preceding chapters we have not applied this term to any group of sciences—though in passing we spoke in Chapter Five of 'positive' theology—and in the subsequent pages likewise we will not make any use of it. Others use the term in various ways but always to indicate sciences which either in whole or in part pertain to the groups considered in the preceding chapters. We may therefore devote a few lines to the term here.

The term 'positive' became popular in philosophical studies around the years 1820-1830 in the school of Saint-Simon and Auguste

Comte. In his *Discours sur l'esprit positif* Comte analyzed the various meanings of the term. Since we have mentioned Comte's conception of science in Chapter Two (Sect. IV, pp. 24 ff.), we may refer the reader to this place for further details on Comte's view.

Under the influence of the positivistic school the term 'positive' received various meanings, such as, that which is posited or given, that which can be perceived and verified by the senses, that which through logical deduction can be derived from accepted premises. In the positivistic view, the term definitely does not apply to the thinking of traditional philosophy, to that which cannot be univocally determined or verified. Thus, 'positive' came to mean 'non-philosophical', 'free from philosophical content', and sometimes even 'anti-philosophical'. Anything theological is, of course, even more excluded.

In this way the term 'positive sciences' mean 'non-philosophical sciences'. This meaning, however, allows still a certain latitude, so that the following scale of views about the extension of the concept 'positive science' may be drawn up:

1. All non-philosophical and non-theological sciences, whether they be speculative or operative.

2. All non-philosophical and non-theological speculative sciences, i.e., the experiential sciences and the ideal sciences, especially mathematics.

3. The experiential sciences, whether they be human sciences or sciences of nature.

4. Only the sciences of nature, and not the human sciences, for these are tainted by philosophy.

5. The sciences of nature and of mathematics.

We do not consider it necessary to add much to these brief remarks, for what has been said above about the experiential sciences, special operative sciences, and ideal sciences applies in part also to the 'positive sciences'. The various meanings, however, listed above, show that the term is not at all used in a univocal way. Thus, to prevent misunderstanding, it would be necessary to indicate each time the sense in which it is used. The best procedure would be to abstain from it entirely.

III. Operative Ideal Sciences

When in the preceding pages we considered the various groups of sciences we constantly saw each group of speculative sciences accompanied by a corresponding group of operative sciences. For instance, alongside speculative or dogmatic theology there is operative or moral theology (Ch. V), and alongside the speculative sciences of experience there are the special operative sciences (Chs. VI and VII). As we will see in the following chapter, the speculative philosophical sciences likewise find their counterpart in operative philosophical sciences. Thus, it becomes obvious that we must ask whether or not, alongside the speculative ideal sciences, considered in this chapter, there exist also operative ideal sciences. In our view this question must be answered in the negative.

As we indicated in Chapter Four (Sect. II, p. 54), the term 'operative sciences' indicates those sciences whose aim is to derive norms to guide man's activity in the various realms of his life, so that he will be able to attain or realize certain purposes that are valuable to him. Ideal sciences, however, by definition are concerned with 'ideal' objects, i.e., objects which arise and exist solely in and through man's thought. Therefore, 'real' aims cannot be directly attained through such 'ideal' thinking. It is true, of course, that in the ideal sciences there are all kinds of more or less arbitrary rules according to which thought must construct its ideal objects. Nevertheless, this 'operative' method pertains essentially to these speculative sciences. Thus, there is no reason for making a distinction between speculative and operative ideal sciences.

An entirely different point is that the results of the ideal sciences can be made scientifically suitable for application to real problems occurring either in daily life or in the special operative sciences. It would be better, however, to speak in this connection of 'applied science' or 'applied mathematics' than of 'operative ideal science' or 'operative mathematics'. We may refer here again to the considerations presented in Chapter Four, Section Two (pp. 68 ff.).

CHAPTER NINE

PHILOSOPHICAL SCIENCES

INTRODUCTION

The completeness of this book and the interconnection of philosophy with other branches of knowledge require that in the present chapter we devote our attention to the philosophical sciences. A special difficulty, which did not occur in the other groups of sciences, presents itself here. We mean the fact that for many people it is even doubtful that philosophy has any right to existence or at least to be called a science. This tendency manifests itself more strongly in our time than it used to do in past centuries.

Is Philosophy Possible? Many (usually, they are adherents of some kind of positivism) haughtily reject everything that has been traditionally presented as philosophy or metaphysics with the disparaging remark that all this is nothing else than the valueless and useless mental gymnastics of degenerated and erring minds. If they do not have recourse to such crass language, they will at most consider so-called philosophy as something possessing only a passing value, as the first hesitant step toward genuine science, as "incipient science". In their view, the progressive evolution of science steadily leads more and more parts of philosophy to secede and to develop as autonomous sciences. Thus, the area in which philosophy labors constantly shrinks, and ultimately the time will come when it will no longer have any right to exist.

Even for those who do not wish to let themselves go to such far-reaching assertions the existence of a philosophical science alongside the many special sciences will often present a problem. Is it not true that the entire potential realm of human knowledge is covered by the various groups of special speculative and operative sciences considered in the preceding chapters? These people may be willing even to make room, alongside the many 'natural' sciences, for 'supernatural' or theological sciences, whose object transcends the 'natural' sciences. But, they ask, what could possibly remain to become the object of another science or group of sciences that is clearly distinct from the above-enumerated sciences?

Against such views and in reply to such questions it will be necessary to defend the existence of a subject matter which cannot be

251

studied by the special sciences or, at least, the existence of an intellectual approach and method of explanation of the same subject matter as is studied by the special sciences, which differs very clearly from the approach and method of these sciences. Such a distinct approach and method could then suitably be indicated by the traditional term 'philosophy'. In Sections One and Two of this chapter we will endeavor to proceed in this fashion with respect to various groups of the special sciences, so that the right-to-exist of speculative and operative philosophy should become clear. We will do so more by means of examples than by a systematic and exhaustive presentation of philosophy, for the scope of this book would not allow us to present an exhaustive study of philosophy, even if such a presentation were possible.

Is Philosophy a Science? Even if the discussion of the approach and explanatory method of philosophy should lead to the conviction that the existence of something like philosophy is possible, the question may still be raised whether or not this intellectual activity or the results it attains deserve to bear the honorable title of 'science'. As a matter of fact, there are many who refuse to recognize so-called philosophy as a science or who make a distinction between 'scientific' philosophy and other types, such as philosophy based upon a world view, which do not merit to be called 'science'. Thus, it will not be superfluous to devote some attention to this point. We will do it in Section Three of this chapter.

It may be useful to add here that in our view also not everything presented as philosophy may appropriate the title 'science', just as, strictly speaking, it should not assume the traditional title 'philosophy'. To justify the use of these titles, certain conditions must be fulfilled. Unfortunately, far too often there is much cockle among the wheat, so that a critical attitude is indispensable in this matter.

Difficulty of this Chapter. The present chapter offered special difficulties to the author, because it is concerned with one of the most complex and most disputed problems of the philosophy of science— namely, the possibility and the nature of philosophy. Any view proposed in this matter and any argument proffered in defense of the proposed view is to some extent predetermined by one's implicit or explicit vision of man and world. For this reason it would not be easy to convince anyone who is already in possession of a different philosophical view. The difficulty becomes even greater because we can devote only a single chapter to the consideration of this problem, so that there simply is no room for a discussion with real or apparent opponents.

As any reader of this work will have noted, the personal philosophical attitude of the author is that of Thomistic realism. We did not consider it necessary within the context of the preceding chapters to defend this philosophical attitude in an explicit fashion. Even at present we shall not undertake such a defense or endeavor to refute the views of opponents. This reserve appears all the more justified, because we are convinced that, abstracting from the hidden philosophical background, the reader will be able to judge the content of this chapter upon its own merits and that adherents of any philosophical trend will be able to accept this content, even though they may give it a somewhat different interpretation. For we intend to limit ourselves to demonstrate that there are problems which lie beyond the reach of the special sciences and that these problems can be treated in a scientific way which differs from that of these sciences.

If we succeed in our plan, we will have shown that there is room for a science that differs from the above-mentioned special sciences. Such a science may be very suitably indicated by the term 'philosophy'. Because of the limitations proper to the purely introductory character of this work, we may consider ourselves dispensed from the task of discoursing on the nature of philosophy and from defending the choice to be made among the various philosophical systems which deserve to be considered in connection with the solution of the proposed problems. In other words, the reader should not try to find more in this chapter than the author considered possible within the limited scope of this book.[1]

We may end this introduction by pointing out that the philosophical sciences have been spoken of on several occasions in this book. We may refer the reader to these pages and more especially to the different degrees of abstraction considered in Part I, Ch. III, Sect. IV, pp. 26 ff. and the schema on page 42 of this volume.

The division of this chapter should be apparent from the preceding considerations. Sections One and Two will speak about the possibility of speculative and operative philosophy, and Section Three will demonstrate that this philosophy deserves to be called a science.

---

[1]We may refer him to the work of Dr. J. Hoogveld, *Inleiding tot de Wijsbegeerte,* Vol. 2 (revised by Dr. F. Sassen), Utrecht, 2nd ed., 1942. This volume is dedicated especially to a study of the nature and task of philosophy. It contains many important and clarifying considerations.

I. Speculative Philosophy

Preliminary Remarks

As we have mentioned above, to defend the possibility of a speculative philosophy, we must show that there is an object which can be scientifically treated in a fashion that differs markedly from the methods used by the special speculative sciences. Or to say it differently, we must show that even after the most extensive and intensive development of the special sciences there still remain problems which demand to be considered by the human intellect, and cannot possibly be treated by the methods of these special sciences, and therefore lie beyond the realm of these sciences.

It should be evident that there can be no question here of a material object which would lie outside the realm of the special sciences. Whatever exists in the world, whether it be lifeless, plant, animal, or man, and in some way is subject to experience belongs to the competence of the experiential sciences. As was pointed out in Chapter Six,[2] the object of the experiential sciences is the totality of reality which exists independently of man's thought, insofar as it can be known by man's natural cognitive powers. (The qualification excludes data that are known solely through divine revelation.)

There exists, moreover, a group of speculative sciences which are concerned with purely thought beings, i.e., with objects whose content and essence owe their existence to man's thought. They are called the ideal sciences (cf. Ch. VIII). Accordingly, leaving aside the realm of the supernatural, no object can be thought of which does not fall, at least in principle, within the competence of the special sciences, except those sciences themselves.

If, then, there hardly is a material object which could be reserved for philosophy, it follows that the right-to-exist of this intellectual discipline must be sought primarily in its formal object. In other words, philosophy owes its existence to the possibility of considering in an entirely different way the same material object that is studied by the special sciences. In the above-mentioned passage of Chapter Six we had already drawn attention to this difference between experiential and philosophical sciences. We may repeat it here in a slightly modified form: both the experiential sciences and philosophy study the totality of reality insofar as this reality can be known by man's natural cognitive powers, but they study it in different ways. The experiential sciences study real things in their specific and generic

[2] Section I, No. 3, pp. 124 ff.

essence, sometimes also in their concrete and individual essence, while speculative philosophy considers things from the viewpoint of being, i.e., as beings, and further also as human beings, as material beings, etc.

This formula, which is clear for anyone who is at home in philosophy, expresses the essential difference between the experiential sciences and speculative philosophy. Whoever is not, as a matter of principle, opposed to statements that cannot be empirically verified, will see in it the justification of the right proper to philosophy to exist at least alongside the experiential sciences. For such people it will be superfluous further to insist upon this point. Nevertheless, we will examine the object of philosophy somewhat more explicitly here, firstly, because the above-mentioned characterization does not do sufficient justice to the philosophical sciences in many respects and, secondly, because we hope that a more extensive consideration may convince some opponents that philosophy does have a right to existence.

As has been mentioned, we will attempt to show that there exist problems which differ from those of the special sciences. Some of them impress themselves upon the thinking mind even in a simple contact with reality. A scientific study of reality does not make them disappear but, on the contrary, often makes them even more urgent and raises additional problems which cannot be solved by the special sciences. The special sciences, moreover, have to admit, at least implicitly, all kinds of presuppositions which they themselves cannot justify.

In this section we will limit ourselves to the speculative sciences. Our efforts will perforce have to be of a fragmentary and incomplete nature. They will consist mainly of a few clear-cut examples of problems and questions in various fields of the special speculative sciences. Completeness would not be possible anyhow, because man is unable to grasp and describe in their totality all the problems which qualify for a philosophical study. Selecting only a few of the important questions that may constitute the object of a philosophical study, we will devote our attention to problems of the world of experience and of knowledge, as well as general problems of being. Keeping in mind the general scope of this book, we will concentrate on those philosophical questions which are raised by the general object proper to the various groups of special sciences and by the character of man's cognitive activity in these sciences but cannot be solved by these sciences themselves. They will provide us also with an opportunity to speak about the relationship between the special sciences and philosophy.

1. *Problems Raised by Observable Reality*

If the experiential sciences give rise to problems which they themselves cannot solve, the reason must lie either in the object of these sciences, i.e., in observable reality, or in the nature of these sciences themselves. As we will see, both contribute to this situation. We will limit ourselves here to the former and reserve the latter for consideration in the paragraphs devoted to the problems of knowledge.

To the extent that reality is either actually or at least in principle subject to observation by man's natural cognitive powers, it may be divided into lifeless things, plants, animals, and man. The sense experience which provides us with our first cognitive contact with these objects reveals to us how they present themselves to us in their concreteness and individuality and how they change, develop and influence one another. A more refined experience, through the subtle means and experimental methods used in the special sciences, supplies us with data that go far beyond primitive sense experience. These means enable us to penetrate profoundly into reality; they surpass all imagination in expanding the realm of experience both in the direction of the microscopically small and in that of the macroscopically large and distant.

Nevertheless, even this refined scientific experience remains subject to inherent limitation. It always remains primordially an experience of the concrete and individual in its actual situations and interrelations. Any statement which goes beyond the concrete constellation of data cannot be justified by these facts alone, but demands to be based also upon something else. Moreover, the actual data reveal aspects of observable reality which the research of the special sciences cannot solve and which demand a *sui generis* approach and study.

We will now enumerate some of these problems and questions in the following sequence: lifeless things, plants, animals, and man. In considering them, one should keep in mind that the series represents a gradation according to ontological perfection. Each level presupposes and implies in a more perfect fashion the preceding levels, and itself is implied in the next level. Vegetative life or life unqualified, for example, sensitive life, and even human life in its bodily aspect, is material life. For this reason the study of matter may investigate both the non-living and the living, including even man himself. It is even very desirable that the aspects that are common to the various grades of ontological perfection be viewed in the light of our knowledge of man. Animal life is life, but life endowed with the power of sense cognition and sensitive tendencies (whence it is called 'sense life'), while man's grade of being includes this sense life, raised to the intellectual or spiritual level. Accordingly, a reflection upon man in his totality must pay attention to matter, to life unqualified, to sense life and, of course, especially to the typical human element of intellectual life. Hence, for the above-mentioned distinction of four levels we may substitute the series: matter, life, sense life, and human life or man.

a. Problems of Matter

Ordinary sense experience shows us the material thing as something individual which is extended, temporal, endowed with quantities (properties, activities and passivities), subject to all kinds of change, etc. Intellectual wonder and reflection discovers in these aspects a number of problems demanding an answer. The following enumeration will sufficiently show this point, although there is, of course, no question of pretending that the list is exhaustive because completeness is beyond man's power.

First of all, we realize that the material world consists of things which have an existence of their own, distinct from that of other things. This realization leads us to reflect upon this autonomy of existence and thus toward such important concepts as individual and substance. These concepts, however, extend beyond the realm of matter and are even more perfectly realized in other realms. We will revert to this point later in this chapter.

Next, with respect to the individuality of material things there arise questions about the nature and degree of this individuality; as well as about the problem of the species-individual structure of material objects, for every individual material thing is known simultaneously as representative of a species. These two irreducible aspects point to a dualistic structure of matter, to its so-called hylomorphic composition.[3]

---

[3]Cf. Andrew G. van Melsen, *The Philosophy of Nature,* Pittsburgh, 1961, which speaks extensively about the species-individual structure.

The extended character of material objects raises another set of problems, e.g., concerning the nature of extension and the connection between extension and materiality. These problems evoke others regarding place and space, theories of localization, space and motion, continuous or atomistic structure of matter, natural minima, action at a distance, etc. The temporal character of things leads us to the difficult problems of time and duration, time and change, the reality of time, time and eternity, objective and subjective time, simultaneity especially in connection with the theory of relativity, etc.

The perception of qualities brings us face to face with the problem of the substance-accident structure. Taken in the broad sense, the term 'quality' applies also to all specific and individual properties and especially also to activities and passivities. The latter likewise have a number of problems of their own, such as that of the proper nature of the opposition between activity and passivity and that of the foundation which these two opposites have in the structure of matter. In addition, there are the historical questions regarding the difference between primary and secondary qualities and the possibility of measuring qualities.

The manifold changes which we observe in reality are of different kinds: qualitative, quantitative and local. Each of these raises its own problems which, however, may be partly classified also under the preceding categories of extension, quality, and so on. Nevertheless, there remain still numerous important problems demanding closer study. For example, what is substantial change? What is accidental change? Are such changes of matter real? And if so, what kind of structure must matter possess to be subject to such changes? From the occurrence of substantial change Aristotle deduced the matter-form structure or the hylomorphism of matter. Local motion likewise raises questions, e.g., about the nature and cause of motion, and, in addition, there are historical problems about the theory of impetus, inertial motion, and many others.

Finally, if the investigation is extended to the totality of material things, one encounters the problem of their interrelationship and the order of the universe.

All this shows that, even if we abstract from the different ontological degrees of perfection—lifeless, vegetative life, sensitive life, human life—the world of matter poses an abundance of problems which lie beyond the competence of the special sciences. The branch of philosophy which studies these problems of matter is known under various names, such as philosophy of inorganic nature, philosophy of matter, philosophy of nature, and cosmology. These terms, however, are not always used as if they were entirely synonymous.

We may add here the remark that some of the above-mentioned problems, e.g., those of substance, accident, individuality, activity, and passivity, are of such a general nature that they pertain more appropriately to general philosophy or metaphysics. We will revert to this point later in this chapter.

b. PROBLEMS OF LIFE

We will enumerate here a few of the questions arising with respect to the ontological degree of perfection pertaining to life in general, i.e., the life that is common to plants, animals, and man. To discover these problems, one could restrict oneself to a consideration of plant life, although various aspects of life are found more clearly and more perfectly in animal and human life.

New problems arising here are the question of life itself, i.e., the difference between living and non-living, and the problem of death. Among the general perceptible characteristics of life we may name the constancy of specific structure, but more especially the immanence of life, which from the time of Aristotle has served to describe life. This immanence reveals itself in the internal unity and the special kind of wholeness of the living body. It manifests itself particularly in the phenomena of life which we call self-preservation, nutrition, growth, and reproduction, which in varying degrees and forms are common to all living bodies. The immanence in question is realized in matter which of itself is characterized precisely by its transient activities. How can such immanence of life be explained?

This immanence, moreover, is connected with the fact that various aspects pertaining to matter-in-general reveal themselves more strikingly in living beings. Among these we may name, e.g., autonomy of existence, individuality and activity. This fact demands further study. Biologists, furthermore, point to the finality revealing itself very strikingly in the structure and function of living bodies. Finally, there is the problem of evolution and its various implications.

All such aspects inherent to life raise problems for the thinking and wondering man. Some of them were known even to the philosophers of antiquity, while others have come to light in modern times through more refined scientific experience. The biological sciences are able to learn more and more about the perceptible qualities and activities of living beings and they endeavor to explain them by means of causal factors which, in principle at least, are likewise subject to experience. Nevertheless, these sciences have to accept life as such, as something that is given. They are not able to explain life itself by means of their own methods and to investigate the fundamental aspects of life in its more profound causes. This investigation pertains to philosophy. It is usually performed in the part of philosophy called philosophy of life, philosophy of organic nature, or philosophical biology.

c. PROBLEMS OF SENSITIVE LIFE

The higher ontological grade of perfection which we find realized in animal life manifests itself through the sensitive character proper to the sensitive mode of knowing and tending, to estimative power and instinct, to sense memory and the power to learn from experience, etc. This sensitive mode of being implies at the same time a higher mode of self-autonomy, individuality, unity, and immanence. Accordingly, the aspects pertaining to life in general and even analogously to lifeless things are found here on a higher level and thus demand to be considered again.

All these and other similar qualities of sensitive life are accessible to simple experience, as is evidenced by the fact that they were known even in antiquity. The more refined experience rendered possible by the development of the zoological sciences has greatly enriched our knowledge of sensitive life insofar as this life is subject to an experiential approach. Nevertheless, here too it remains true that the fundamental problems which arose before the development of the special sciences still continue to exist and that new problems have been added to the old ones. While the special sciences have often made these problems even more manifest, they have contributed nothing to their solution. They would not even be able to do so, because of the limitation inherent in their methods. Accordingly, here also there remains room for the branch of philosophy which is called the philosophy of animal or sensitive life.

d. PROBLEMS OF MAN

Self-experience and interhuman contact make us know man as a being that is *sui generis,* a being that essentially differs from non-human beings. Prescientific experience suffices to provide us with this knowledge, and the problems which it raises again are not removed by the progress of scientific knowledge. There are many speculative sciences which study man in his bodily or mental aspects; for instance, anatomy, physiology, pathology, physical anthropology, and psychology. There are, in addition, many operative sciences which devote themselves likewise but in a different fashion to the sphere of the human: for example, various medical sciences, pedagogy, practical economics, and diverse technical sciences. The speculative sciences accept man as something given, they increase our knowledge of man in his perceptible aspects, but because of their bond with experience they cannot penetrate into the essence of man, into the deepest ground and source of his typically human properties and activities. The operative sciences are, of course, unable to teach us anything about man himself, because they presuppose this knowledge. It is precisely upon the basis of this knowledge that they endeavor to formulate norms for human activity in various realms. Thus throughout the centuries the problems pertaining to the typically human aspect of man have remained reserved to a different method of approach, which is called philosophy. Let us enumerate again a few of these problems.

The most important of the typically human activities are those of intellectual knowing and willing. Man appears capable of thinking about himself—which raises the problem of self-reflection and self-consciousness—and thus discovers himself as a subsistent being endowed with its own kind of individuality, as an ego, as remaining self-identical throughout all kinds of bodily and mental changes, as knowing and desiring, as subject to all kinds of feelings and moods. He discovers, moreover, that he is capable of determining his own activities with a measure of freedom, so that he has to accept being responsible for such activities. By means of his bodily being he lives in matter, nevertheless in many respects he appears to transcend matter.

Reflection upon these data of experience leads to long philosophical considerations in which man tries to penetrate into the proper character of the typically human activities and powers and to discover their most profound foundation. This philosophical reflection forces him to admit that there is in man a non-extended or spiritual principle called 'soul'. This inevitable conclusion, however, raises new problems regarding the nature of the soul, its origin, mode of existence and duration, its relationship to the body. For example, how must the unity of spirit and matter be explained? Many other problems could be enumerated here, such as the origin of man, the distinction between man and animal, the destiny and ultimate goal of man and of mankind.

The branch of philosophy which considers these and other problems of the same kind is usually called 'philosophical anthropology', but sometimes in a more restricted sense 'philosophical psychology'.

e. Problems of Human Culture

It is not only man considered in himself—insofar as such a consideration is possible—who gives rise to philosophical reflection, but also man insofar as he is the principle of the activities which are usually indicated by the term 'human culture'. We have considered these activities rather extensively in Chapter Six, Section Three, where we made a distinction between material culture, spiritual or social culture, and self-culture. Culture in general as well as its various forms are object of the special sciences called 'cultural sciences'. Culture, however, is the object of these sciences only insofar as it presents itself in specified and concrete forms, e.g., in determined nations or groups of people, or in various forms that are historically codetermined by all kinds of concrete situations. Alongside these cultural phenomena there are many general and more profound issues which transcend the intrinsic limitations of the special cultural sciences. Yet, their study is of great importance, because it provides us with a better understanding of man's cultural activity and consequently of man himself. It is especially in our time that the cultural aspect of human existence has been clearly emphasized—to such an extent that the resulting insight into man is sometimes expressed in the conclusion 'man is culture'. Others prefer to speak in this connection about the 'historicity of man'.

The many philosophical problems raised by man's culture find a place in the branch of philosophy called 'philosophy of culture'. This term may be understood in a broad sense and thus include many sections. It can be divided in accord with the various cultural sciences or groups of sciences to give rise to special philosophies of culture, such as philosophy of religion, speculative philosophy of law and of government, and speculative philosophy of art.

Because man's cultural activity is naturally always of an operative nature, i.e., directed to a goal man wants to attain or to realize, the philosophy of culture will often have to consider problems which are connected with the subject matter of the operative sciences as well as with these sciences themselves. Examples are provided by the philosophy of technique[4] and in a more general fashion by the philosophy of labor.[5] A clear-cut distinction is not easy to make here. Often it will be a question of personal taste whether this (operative) subject matter in question is classified as philosophy of culture or as operative philosophy (see below, Section Two, pp. 280 ff.). For this reason we do not wish to enter into discussions about this question. The important point is to realize that there are problems which lie beyond the realm of the special sciences and therefore may be the object of philosophical study.

f. PROBLEMS OF VALUES

Since the time when Lotze (1817-1881), Windelband (1848-1915) and Rickert (1863-1936), representatives of the Baden school of neo-Kantianism, directed special attention to the practical side of Kant's philosophy, the philosophy of values has acquired an important place in modern thought. While we do not intend to speak extensively about this philosophy, a brief consideration of it may not be omitted in connection with the philosophy of culture. We may add that we have already spoken about value judgments in Chapter Six.[6]

The term 'value' may have various meanings, even when it is used within the present context. For this reason it is good to clarify in a few sentences what we mean by it here. According to general metaphysics, every being is good in itself. Because of its inherent goodness, a being is capable of arousing the appetitive powers of one or the other category of sensitive or intellectual beings and of satisfying these appetencies. In this way it becomes a 'good' for this category, so that it can be desired as a purpose or as a means. Such a thing is said to possess 'value' for the category of beings in question. For this reason we may say that value is that aspect or quality of a good which confers upon this good the meaning of a purpose to be attained. Or, to express it differently, through its value, a good has a purposive character.[7]

Not every being possesses 'value' for every other being. Whether a thing has value for another being depends on both beings, yet is

---

4See, e.g., Andrew G. van Melsen, *Science and Technology,* Pittsburgh, 1961.
5E.g., Remy C. Kwant. *Philosophy of Labor,* Pittsburgh, 1960.
6Section V, No. 1, pp. 185 f.
7Cf. the classical formula: *id sub cuius ratione bonum ut finis appetitur.*

based upon an objective relationship. The one must be adapted to the nature of the other, it must be capable of serving to ennoble or perfect it. 'Value', therefore, is not an objective property which inheres in the object, taken in itself and independently of its relationship to one or the other subject. Value always implies a relationship, for it is based, on the one hand, on the goodness of the object which the value is attributed and, on the other, determined by its adaptedness to beings of various kinds or even to the need of an individual. Nevertheless, the 'value relationship' has an objective foundation in the object and in the subject, so that the theory of values must be built on the philosophy of being.

Value relations may be found on different levels. A lifeless object, a plant, or an animal may possess value, for example for another animal or for man. However, when there is question of values, it is customary to restrict the considerations to the sphere of man. There are two ways in which we may refer to values in the human sphere. First of all, a value judgment may be pronounced about something which exists already in reality and may constitute the object of research in a speculative science. As we have pointed out in Chapter Six,[8] in such a case it easily happens that one will relinquish the realm of experience and of the experiential sciences to make a judgment that is based only upon his philosophical background or upon his world view.

Secondly, the value aspect plays an important role in the realm of human activity and consequently also in the operative sciences. In these realms one must always keep in mind the purpose to be attained or realized, and the object derives its purposive character precisely from the value which it possesses for man; hence, it should be evident that in the realm in question the 'values' are of fundamental importance. Here also it remains true that the judgment about the values will be strongly influenced by views which are not based upon experience or upon the discoveries of the special sciences, but flow from the world view or the philosophical attitude of the man who makes the judgment.

Whatever interpretation is given to the concept 'value', it appears to be again something which, despite its close connection with the object of the special sciences, cannot be justified by these sciences themselves. Insofar as, therefore, considerations of value do not

---

[8]Section V, No. 4, p. 186.

have a theological foundation, we may attribute them to the realm of philosophy. The philosophical discipline dealing with these problems is called 'philosophy of values' or 'axiology'. As we have pointed out, the value aspect is restricted to the sphere of man, i.e., to the speculative appreciation of the value attached to a given being, or to the evaluation of something to be attained through human activities; hence, the philosophical considerations in question may be classified also partly under cultural philosophy and partly under operative philosophy (cf. Section Two, no. 2, p. 281).

A last remark. Some authors claim that the philosophy of culture is broader in concept than the philosophical speculation about values, while others maintain that the philosophy of culture is a subdivision of axiology or the philosophy of values. We do not wish to discuss this matter here and limit ourselves to pointing out that once more we have here a domain which the special sciences cannot explore by means of their own limited methods.

2. *Problems of Knowledge*

The problems of the perceptible world, spoken about in the preceding pages, give rise to the origin and development of various branches of philosophy which, as we will see, find their culminating point and terminus in general metaphysics. There are, however, also other no less important questions regarding man's cognitive powers, intentional and thought beings. We will devote a few pages to them, although here again we will have to be extremely brief and omit many important aspects. Within the framework of this book it should be sufficient to show that here also there exist problems which lie beyond the reach of the special sciences and which at least in part owe their very origin to reflection upon the way in which these sciences proceed. We will consider first cognition in general and then man's cognitive activity in science.

a. COGNITION IN GENERAL

It is hardly necessary to point out that human knowledge exists also outside and before all scientific activity. This knowledge has a very heterogeneous and complex structure. From earliest antiquity there have been thinkers who intensively studied man's cognition, discovered its problems and searched for their solution. In subsequent ages these problems have always remained the object of man's reflection. This situation did not change when special sciences, such as psychology, arose which study man's cognition insofar as it is a datum of experience and can be approached through observation and experimental methods. Because these sciences are experiential sciences, they have by their very nature limits which they cannot transcend. The limited powers of their special science are unable to solve the fundamental problems of man's knowledge.

Among these problems we may name the investigation of the proper nature of the various cognitive functions: sensitive knowing, which includes cognition through the external and internal senses; the functions of sense memory, estimative power, imagination and central sense; intellectual cognition and its capacities of self-reflection, of knowing reality, of forming concepts and judgments, of reasoning, etc.

Fundamental questions impose themselves all the time with respect to these functions. What is knowledge? What is sense cognition and intellectual cognition? How does the cognitive act obtain its content? Is this content perhaps purely subjective, wholly determined by an object that exists independently of the knowing subject, or dependent upon both the subject and the object? Are we capable of knowing reality? Is cognition active, passive, or both active and passive? What is the value of human knowledge? Is it limited to the concrete and individual or can it transcend this limitation and arrive at general statements having a universal validity? What is the value of the deductive and inductive methods? What is the relationship between faith and reason? What is true knowledge or, more generally, what is truth? Whence arise the general principles of being and knowing and what is their value? Many other questions could be added here, but let us not prolong the list unduly.

Such problems are studied in the branch of philosophy known as epistomology or philosophy of knowledge. Occasionally also it is called the ontology or metaphysics of knowledge, especially when cognition is considered as a mode of being (cf. p. 273). Sometimes it is referred to as criteriology or the critique of knowledge, but this term generally indicates a more restricted content, limited to the investigation of the value and limits of knowledge.

The enormous difficulties connected with the various aspects of man's cognition have had as their result that many of the cognitive problems have received entirely divergent and contradictory solutions. In epistemology there exists an almost endless list of philosophical trends: rationalism, empiricism, criticism, dogmatism, scepticism, positivism, idealism, phenomenalism, realism, and many others.

It is solely upon the basis of intellectual reflection and argumentation that man has to endeavor to discover the correct position in this realm. The experiential sciences are unable to make any direct contribution to this task. For the object of the philosophical reflection in question lies beyond the reach of any particular type of scientific knowledge. It is precisely knowledge itself which is at stake here. For this reason the adherents of the most divergent epistemological trends are capable of peaceful collaboration within the special sciences and of arriving, in general, at the same results. This fact shows *a posteriori* that the investigation of knowledge itself moves on another level than that of the special sciences.

b. COGNITION IN THE SPECIAL SCIENCES

Apart from the above-mentioned general problems of knowledge, there are also problems which flow from special modes of knowing and especially from the cognitive activities exercised in the special 'natural' sciences, whether speculative (experiential and ideal sciences) or operative sciences. We will omit here the supernatural or theological sciences, for their problems are *sui generis* and connected with the relationship of the divine or supernatural with the natural or with that between faith and reason. We have spoken about them previously in Chapter Five (Sections II and V), when we considered the theological sciences. We will omit likewise to speak about knowledge in the philosophical sciences, although there are special problems in this realm and one could justly claim that one of the primary tasks of philosophy is to reflect upon its own activities. As a matter of fact, this reflection is carried out in metaphysics or in the philosophy of knowledge.

As soon as man takes the special 'natural' sciences as the object of his investigation to reflect upon their scientific character, it should be manifest that he has left the realm of these sciences and entered an area which is known as philosophy. The branch of philosophy which performs this investigation is known under different names, such as, philosophy of science and critique of the sciences. All kinds of subdivisions are possible. We may name, e.g., philosophy of the ideal sciences or of the mathematical sciences, philosophy of physical science, of anthropological sciences, and of operative sciences. Because philosophy of science is always concerned with a special mode of knowing, it may, if necessary, be classified under the general philosophy of knowledge or epistemology.

The considerations of the philosophy of science may refer either to the character of a science or to its foundation. These two aspects, however, cannot always be sharply distinguished. A few remarks will be made here about both.

The Character of the Sciences. By the character of a science we mean the whole of properties and aspects which pertain to a science and at the same time distinguish it from others. Examples of such properties and aspects are the speculative or operative character of a science, the nature and limits of the knowledge proper to this science, the way in which it forms concepts, the type and degree of its abstraction, and the character of necessity and universality proper to its statements. Attention must be paid also to the various cognitive methods, such as, deduction, induction, analysis and synthesis, which the science in question uses as well as its method of demonstration. Another important point is provided by the nature of its hypotheses and theories, for they largely determine the entire structure of a science, especially in the case of the ideal sciences. We may refer here to Part One of this book, in which a number of these aspects have been considered fairly extensively.

The Foundation of Sciences. Each special science has a basis upon which it is founded. This basis contains all kinds of primordial elements and fundamental views which the science in question itself cannot justify. Although sometimes it may be possible to derive a part of these elements and views from a different special science, ultimately one will always arrive at foundations which no special science is capable of justifying. In other words, there exist here also problems whose scope lies beyond the limits of the special sciences. These problems may be concerned with the two aspects of foundation which we have distinguished in Chapter Six of Part One— namely, the starting point and the presuppositions of the sciences. To avoid repetition, we simply refer the reader to that chapter.

Many of the problems about the starting point are often considered in the general philosophy of knowledge; for instance, those concerning the nature and value of sense experience, which is the starting point of the experiential sciences, and those concerning self-reflection, which is indispensable in the acquisition of experiential knowledge of man. Self-reflection is considered also in philosophical anthropology. There are other problems which are connected with the general presuppositions common to all sciences. We may name the general metaphysical principles of identity, of contradiction, excluded middle, sufficient reason, and causality, which are considered in metaphysics. Finally there exist a number of general epistemological principles, which pertain to the subject matter of the philosophy of knowledge.

Thus, there would remain for the philosophy of science the investigation of the more particular presuppositions of the various sciences or rather groups of sciences. However, a complication arises here. To a large extent the special presuppositions are determined by the object of these sciences; hence, their investigation may be performed also in the special branches of philosophy which are concerned with the ultimate grounds of this object. Let us illustrate the point by means of an example. The speculations of physical science must be adapted to the proper nature of matter but, on the other hand, the way of knowing in the anthropological sciences is to a large extent determined by man's nature. The result is that the philosophy of physical science cannot be rigidly separated from the philosophy of the object studied by physical science, i.e., the philosophy of matter or of nature. And, on the other hand, the philosophy of the anthropological sciences cannot be strictly separated from philosophical anthropology. The following schema may serve to clarify the issue:

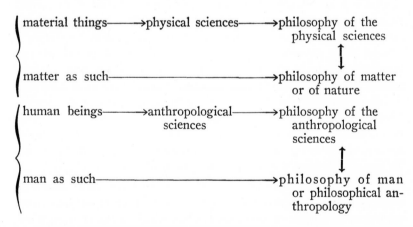

These complications explain why the terms 'philosophy of physical science' and 'philosophy of nature' are often taken in such a broad sense that one covers also the realm of the other, so that the two names can be used in a synonymous fashion. The term 'philosophy of culture' likewise is used sometimes to indicate the philosophical reflection upon culture as well as the philosophy of the cultural sciences. The same rule applies to other similar cases. Although we are generally in favor of a systematic distinction, it must be admitted that in practice it is extremely difficult to maintain a clear-cut separation of the problems in question and of the corresponding parts of philosophy. With respect to the philosophy of mathematics, such a distinction would even amount to a practical impossibility.

Operative Sciences. The preceding considerations were intended to apply to the special sciences in general, i.e., to both speculative and operative sciences. At first it may cause some surprise that the operative sciences are included, because one could think that reflection upon them would *per se* belong to operative philosophy. In reply, we may point out that reflection upon an operative science as a science, i.e., upon its proper nature, foundations, methods, etc., is a speculative endeavor, for in such a reflection the science in question is considered as something that is given. We may refer here to Chapter Seven, in which we have studied the operative sciences from a philosophical standpoint.

On the other hand, a philosophical reflection upon the *content* of an operative science may itself also have an operative character—namely, insofar as it serves to determine from a higher, philosophical, standpoint general norms which have to be followed in the derivation of special norms. Usually these general norms will be of an ethical nature. We will revert to this point in Section Two.

We may terminate with the remark that the name of a philosophical discipline does not always indicate exactly what it contains. For example, 'philosophy of education' may be a speculative reflection upon pedagogy, an operative foundation of general norms of education, or both. A sharp division, as we have pointed out, cannot always be made in this matter.

3. *General Problems of Being*

In the first part of this section we have spoken about different categories of beings—namely, material beings, living beings, sensitive beings, human beings, and cultured beings. All these beings have in common that in one way or in another they *are*. Thus, the plurality of things is at the same time a unity through the common bond of being. All kinds of questions arise here concerning the unity and plurality of being, its analogy, the structure of finite beings, the truth, goodness and beauty of being, the ultimate and definitive ground of being or absolute 'to be', etc. Concepts which have been partly considered in the preceding pages have to be reconsidered here from a general point of view; for instance, being, 'to be', essence, nature, autonomy of existence or subsistence, individuality, person, substance and accident, activity and passivity, potency and act, causality and finality. A number of principles concerning being which everyone accepts without great difficulty have to be examined to determine their content and scope; for example, the principles of identity and of contradiction, the principles of sufficient reason and of causality.

As should be immediately evident, such general problems of being are even less capable of being handled by the special sciences than are the problems of particular kinds of being. Of course, it remains true that these general principles are concerned with the objects studied in the special sciences, but they are considered now merely from the general viewpoint of 'being'.

The philosophical study which occupies itself with these general ontological questions is known as ontology, metaphysics, or the general philosophy of being. It finds its culminating point in the philosophy of God as the absolute 'to be'.

The search of metaphysics for the correct solution of its problems cannot, of course, expect any aid from sense experience, because its theories are not open to empirical verification. As a consequence, divergent and contradictory metaphysical views may and do exist side by side. To name only a few, monism, pluralism, materialism, spiritualism, and dualism; pessimism and optimism; theism, deism, and atheism. The correct solution can be found only by means of intellectual reflection, and this way reveals itself as extraordinarily difficult. For this reason the Christian philosopher will easily make use of ideas borrowed from revelation or from theology, at least as negative norms to avoid falling into error.

Being and Knowing. The preceding considerations could perhaps have caused someone to think that in the author's view being and knowing are juxtaposed as two irreducible dimensions. Such an impression, however, would be wholly wrong. 'To know' in general is 'to be-knowing' or the 'to be of a knowing being', and to know sensitively is a natural function of a sensitively living being, just as to know intellectually is a function of an intellectually living being.

Knowing evidently pertains to the general forms under which being reveals itself and which must be considered in metaphysics. 'To be-knowing' has to be viewed even as a higher grade of being than 'not to be-knowing'. Moreover, every being possesses the ability to be-known, as is expressed in the metaphysical principle: every being is intelligible.

Accordingly, the general problems of cognition pertain to the subject matter of metaphysics and could be considered in this branch of philosophy. For this reason some authors, as we have mentioned, speak of a metaphysics or ontology of knowledge. Usually, however, the philosophical study of cognition is classified separately as epistemology or the philosophy of knowledge.

4. Schematic Division of Speculative Philosophy and Concluding Remarks

The following schema endeavors to present a division of speculative philosophy which expresses a few important points that were made in the course of the preceding pages.

DIVISION OF SPECULATIVE PHILOSOPHY

special philosophical sciences	corresponding experiential sciences	object
A *philosophy of nature* (in the broad sense)	*physical sciences*	*non-human beings*
1. philosophy of inorganic nature or philosophy of matter — object: material being	1. sciences of matter e.g., physics and chemistry	1. (lifeless) material things
2. philosophy of (vegetative) life or philosophical biology — object: the living body	2. botanical sciences	2. (vegetative) living beings
3. philosophy of sensitive life — object: sensitive living being	3. zoological sciences	3. animals or sensitive living beings
B *philosophical anthropology* — object: man as a spiritual-material being	*anthropological sciences,* e.g. a. anatomy and physiological anthropology b. psychology	*man in his* a. material and bodily aspects and b. his spiritual aspects
C *philosophy of culture*	*cultural sciences*	*human culture*

A-1 extends to A-2 and 3 and even to B; A-2 extends to A-3 and B; A-3 extends to B. There are many points in which B and C are in contact or even overlapping. Cf. p. 269.

general philosophy of being or *metaphysics* culminating in the *philosophy of God* or *theodicy* — object: 'to be and the whole of beings culminating in 'absolute to be' or God

metaphysics contains *general epistemology* — object: 'to be knowing'

philosophical considerations about various modes of knowing (sense knowledge and intellectual knowledge); critique of knowledge (object: value and limits of knowledge); general philosophy of science (object: science in general and groups of sciences) with special branches: philosophy of physical science, philosophy of the ideal sciences, etc.

Concluding Remarks. It may not be entirely superfluous to point once more to the difficulties which, though common to all divisions, weigh especially heavy when there is question of dividing the philosophical sciences. For this reason the preceding schematic division should not be viewed as a proposal to draw sharp dividing lines and even less as the one and only possible division and orderly arrangement of philosophy. More than in any other intellectual discipline it is in philosophy that interconnections and overlapping abound.

As has been pointed out repeatedly in the preceding pages, all kinds of complications arise in the philosophical sciences. To name only a few, they occur in the demarcation of the realms proper to the philosophy of sensitive life, philosophical biology, and philosophy of nature; in the distinction between the philosophy of nature and the philosophy of physical science; in the relationship between philosophy of culture and philosophical anthropology as well as in the connection or subordination of cultural philosophy and axiology; in the relationship between philosophical epistemology and the philosophy of the sciences or between epistemology and metaphysics.

All this refers merely to the speculative philosophical sciences. Similar difficulties, however, occur also in operative philosophy, which we will consider in the following section. We will see there that there is not even a rigid separation of speculative philosophy from its operative counterpart. For instance, there are obvious connections between, on the one hand, operative philosophy and, on the other, philosophical anthropology, cultural philosophy and axiology.

These complications should not cause any alarm. They arise of necessity from the very nature of philosophy. In its different branches philosophy devotes itself to the most profound foundations of the objects studied, and these foundations always lie in the various participations of being. For this reason the different philosophical disciplines will always meet in one or the other mode of being or at least in being in general.

II. OPERATIVE PHILOSOPHY

Introduction

At the beginning of this chapter we pointed out that, in order to prove the right-to-exist of philosophy, one has to show that there are problems which cannot be solved by the special natural sciences. After doing this for speculative philosophy in Section One, we must now attempt to do the same for operative philosophy.

The idea could arise that it would be sufficient to pay attention only to the object of the special operative sciences[9] and to investigate whether there are here problems which cannot be treated within the limits of these sciences. This view, however, is not correct. As we have pointed out before and will make clear in this section, the speculative sciences also, insofar as they imply human activity, give rise to problems which offer subject matter for a philosophical reflection of an operative nature.

There is, moreover, a different way to show the right-to-exist of an operative philosophy. It is possible to center one's attention at once upon the various fundamental forms of human activity and to investigate in what way these forms can serve to formulate norms from a general viewpoint. In the following pages we will make use of both methods. The second of them appears most suitable for a general division of operative philosophy, while the first is particularly fruitful with respect to establishing more in detail the right-to-exist proper to the various parts of operative philosophy resulting from the division.

Division of Operative Philosophy. Operative philosophy has as its object the right order and the 'ought' of human activities; therefore, there exist as many branches of operative philosophy as there are distinct realms of human activities through which man is able to develop his inherent possibilities. Three general kinds of human activity may be distinguished, viz., thinking, intellectual tending or willing, and transient acting. By transient action we mean here the bodily activities through which man in a transient way executes his rational acts of will that are directed toward the realization of the good and the beautiful by means of matter. The distinction of the good and the beautiful indicates that there is a twofold tendency in this transient human activity, so that we would arrive at a four-fold division instead of a trichotomy.

The division is, of course, much too schematized to be adequate; for instance, transient action implies of necessity thinking and willing if it is supposed to be truly human activity. Nevertheless, this distinction is quite serviceable to arrive at a suitable subdivision of opera-

---

[9]Operative science, as a science, is considered in the philosophy of science, which belongs to the realm of speculative philosophy.

tive philosophy. Upon the distinction in question we may base the following fourfold division of operative philosophy, assigning to each a provisional name. Operative philosophy may aim at:

1. regulating man's thinking toward correct reasoning and knowledge of truth—*logic;*

2. regulating man's transient activities toward the making of the good—*poietics;*

3. regulating man's transient activities toward the making of beautiful things, the creation of beauty—*operative philosopy of art* or *aesthetics;*

4. regulating man's intellectual acts of tending or willing toward doing what is good, toward the attainment of man's ultimate end—*moral philosophy* or *ethics.*

Again, we do not intend to treat here fully each subdivision of operative philosophy. As we have done with respect to speculative philosophy, we will limit ourselves to the aspects which in our view fall within the scope of this work.

1. *Logic*

Any brief treatise of logic is faced at once with the difficulty that this term may have various meanings. Even if we restrict ourselves to the sense which assigns to logic a place within philosophy, we are far from finding unanimity. First of all, there is the philosophical view which identifies knowing or thinking with being and considers a process of thought as an evolution of being. If, next, we abstract from this view and use the term 'logic' to indicate the theory concerning the development of thinking, it acquires the broad meaning of 'theory of reason' or even of 'metaphysics of reason'. It is somewhat in this sense that the term is used in the philosophical system of Hegel.[10]

Even if the term 'logic' is restricted to the 'theory of human thought', it retains various meanings, and the choice of meaning determines whether logic is classified under philosophy or under the sciences in general. However, we do not intend here to treat logic exhaustively but merely to consider the right-to-exist proper to a particular part of operative philosophy. For this reason we will take

---

[10]For this survey we have made use of I. J. M. van den Berg's book, *De strijd om de logica.* Utrecht, 1935.

the term 'logic' here in the sense that is relevant to our question. It is the meaning which the term has in traditional philosophy and which may be described as "the science which is normative of discursive thought" or in a more classical fashion as "the science which makes it possible for man to think in an orderly way, with ease, and without error".[11]

Sometimes this science is called 'formal logic' or 'minor logic' to distinguish it from 'material logic', 'major logic' or 'critical logic'. The last three terms intend to indicate a science which investigates the conditions that must be fulfilled to arrive at a *true* conclusion, while formal logic is concerned merely with the *correctness* of the thought process and abstracts from its truth. When we speak here about logic without any qualification, we mean primarily formal logic in the above-mentioned sense, although a broader sense is sometimes implied.

a. The Right-to-Exist of Logic

Man is not a pure spirit but a spiritual-material being. Therefore, he cannot know essences in an immediate, intuitive way, but has to start from sense data and phantasms to arrive at concepts and judgments and to proceed step by step, by reasoning from one judgment to another, on the road to truth. The human activities in question, therefore, have to be directed in a correct fashion if they are to attain their purpose without error. Thus, there is need for a science having as its aim to study accurately man's way of thinking and to use this knowledge to arrive at the formulation of norms, capable of correctly guiding the process of thought. This science is known as 'logic'.

Its Operative Character. Because of its very aim, the science in question is of an operative nature. The speculative foundation upon which, like any other operative science, it has to be based, is always laid within logic itself; for instance, when man investigates the mode of knowing, the structure of a thought process and of the judgments and concepts constituting its elements. Thus, logic has the character of a speculative-operative science.

The operative character of logic should not be subject to doubt. For logic does not study a *being* given in experience, e.g., the way in which man's thought process actually takes place, but an *'ought'*—

---

[11]Cf. Thomas Aquinas, *In I Posterior Analytics,* lect. 1: "Scientia quae est directiva ipsius actus rationis, per quam scilicet homo in ipso actu rationis ordinate et faciliter et sine errore procedat".

namely, how discursive thought should proceed. This logic, therefore, must be clearly distinguished from psychology, even though it
may be true that certain data of psychology may be suitably treated
in the speculative part of logic.

Divergent Views. Although hardly anyone would doubt the necessity of logic in the sense explained above, opinions differ as soon as
questions are raised about the character of logic; e.g., is logic a genuine science or merely a skill? what is its content and scope? where
should it be placed among the sciences? and, how is logic related to
philosophy? We do not have room to consider all these and other
similar questions, but will make an exception for the view, mentioned
above, that logic must be considered a part of philosophy, albeit a
part with a *sui generis* nature.

b. Logic and Philosophy

It should be immediately evident that logic, in the above-mentioned
sense, may not be viewed as a special science, similar in nature to
other special sciences. For its purpose is to guarantee the correctness
of the thought process, and as such logic extends to all human activity
of thinking, including that of all sciences. Whatever the science may
be that man studies, his scientific activities must be directed by the
norms formulated in logic. Accordingly, logic does not limit its
endeavors to a particular realm of knowledge, but intends to be normative for all discursive thought. It extends its attention to the general
scientific methods which are used in the particular sciences or groups
of sciences. Consequently, logic has a universal and fundamental
function. In this respect, therefore, logic lies beyond or above the
special sciences, so that it is reasonable to assign it a place among
the philosophical sciences or more specifically among operative
philosophy.

That logic, in the traditional sense of the term, is not outside philosophy appears also from the fact that the view which one takes of
the content of logic, its nature, structure and value, depends to a
large extent upon his philosophical attitude. Let us illustrate the
point. Traditional or Aristotelian logic, for example, is strongly tied
to Aristotelian metaphysics. For instance, the categories into which
this logic divides concepts and the general principles—of identity,
contradition, excluded middle, etc.—have a metaphysical foundation
or at least a metaphysical meaning. Moreover, this logic usually contains purely philosophical speculations to explain the abstractness and

universality of the concepts which it utilizes. In addition, it silently assigns value to these logical concepts for the description of reality.

The Proper Character of Logic and Its Difference from Other Philosophical Sciences. Although logic should be classified under philosophy and is related to the other philosophical sciences, it certainly is not a philosophical discipline in the same sense as the others. Philosophical sciences in the 'proper' sense have being and real being as their object, which they consider either as given—speculative philosophy—or as to be realized through human activity—operative philosophy. Formal logic, on the other hand, especially if it is free from ontological intrusions, is concerned with beings of reason, such as concepts, judgments and their interrelationships, and reasoning processes, which as such cannot exist in reality, although they may be capable of representing realities in an intentional fashion. So far as pure logic is concerned, it is irrelevant whether or not its concepts indicate real things. It considers its concepts as 'variables' which, if so desired, may be expressed by symbols and these symbols may or may not be filled with real contents.

If symbols are used generously, a logical treatise begins to look like a mathematical text, especially when a logical system is constructed in a mathematical fashion according to axiomatic methods. In such a case the treatise is often referred to as 'mathematical or algebraic logic' and as 'logistics'. Such a logistics has the character of a formalized mathematical system: it starts from the smallest possible number of axioms or postulates to define the elementary concepts or symbols which it wants to use and deduces from them new propositions by means of pre-established rules. As much as possible, the mathematical logician abstracts from the meaning of the symbols used.

Mathematical logic or logistics, as developed since the middle of the nineteenth century, has produced rich results. First of all, it has managed to give a better foundation to classical logic and to treat its problems in a more complete and more differentiated fashion. Secondly, it has added entirely new areas to classical logic. However, much of what passes as logistics has not yet found any application in logic as the normative theory of correct thinking.

c. LOGIC AND MATHEMATICS

As we have mentioned above, there is a striking external resemblance between mathematics and mathematical logic or logistics which, moreover, unfortunately is often simply spoken of as logic without any further qualification. In addition, the two sciences are capable of fruitful interaction. Thus, there arises the problem of the relationship between logic and mathematics. The most divergent interpretations have been proposed in reference to this question. Some conclude that mathematics and logic are fully identical, others that mathematics is a part of logic, and others, again that logic is a part of mathematics. Without wanting to enter into these discussions, we would like to make here a few remarks that fit within the framework of a philosophy of science.

Firstly, in our view, logical calculus or logistics, considered in itself, belongs to the group of ideal sciences.[12] Just as a mathematical theory, so also a logical calculus has an 'ideal' value of its own, regardless of its practical usefulness for any purpose whatsoever. Sometimes, therefore, it will be merely a matter of taste whether a particular 'ideal' system is called logistics or mathematics.

Secondly, because of the special purpose its creators had in mind, a logical calculus may be very suitable for treating logical problems. However, this usefulness depends upon the possibility of substituting for the symbols used in the calculus contents which are meaningful in discursive thinking. If this possibility exists, then such a calculus may be correctly called 'logic', especially if a qualifier is added to this term.

Thirdly, a logic, in the traditional sense, and mathematics are two distinct sciences. Mathematics is an ideal science, usually a science of quantity as such, and therefore belongs to the speculative sciences. Logic, on the other hand, is an operative philosophical science which wants to establish rules for correct discursive thinking.

Finally, mathematics itself in developing its theories must follow the universal norms of logic. For this reason it may not be identified with logic.

2. *Poietics*

As we have mentioned in the introduction to this section, operative philosophy must pay attention also to the bodily activities by means of which man transiently executes the rational acts of will that are directed toward the material realization of ideas which mean the

---

[12]Cf. Ch. VIII, Sect. II, pp. 221 ff.

growth and perfection of man as a spiritual-material being. This growth and development must be understood as broadly as possible. It certainly should not be limited to man's intervention in lifeless matter and non-human living beings. Likewise, it should certainly include all spiritual-corporeal activities whose object in one way or in another is the world in which man lives as well as man himself, whether he is the acting individual or not. The important point is that it is a question of giving reality to what is fitting, useful or advantageous for man, or more briefly put, of 'making' what is 'good'.

There exists, of course, a formal distinction between a philosophical study of this subject matter and the way in which this matter is considered in the operative sciences of which we have spoken in Chapter Seven. These special sciences endeavor to discover methods and formulate norms for specific realizations in particular areas of human activity, while philosophy aims at the general aspects pertaining to all special operative sciences and at general problems which are raised by the object of these sciences but whose solution is usually presupposed in an implicit way. The part of operative philosophy with which we are concerned here has as its task to reflect upon the fundamental human attitude which is normative of operative activity insofar as this activity tends in one way or another to produce a realization in matter.

Man's being is a being-in-the-world. This means that man has as his task to make his being-in-the-world as successful as possible for himself and for his fellow men. Operative philosophy has to reflect upon this human orientation and task in their general aspects. It is possible to subdivide this philosophy according to man's fundamental tasks, such as education of the young, care for spiritual and bodily health and for the development of man's powers, organization of human society in the social, economic, cultural and other realms. In this way the special operative sciences or groups of such sciences receive their philosophical foundation in this branch of philosophy.

The preceding remarks show that the philosophical discipline in question is certainly not exclusively operative but speculative-operative, because of the speculative reflection upon which it must be based. This theoretical foundation could, of course, also be borrowed from various branches of speculative philosophy, such as philosophical anthropology, philosophy of culture, and axiology. The philosophy of values especially is of great importance in this matter, so much even that perhaps it should be considered to be an operative philosophy rather than a part of speculative philosophy. We may refer to our remarks on this question in the first section of this chapter (p. 265).

The Name of this Branch of Philosophy. The philosophical theory with which we are concerned here could be suitably called 'poietics' (from the Greek verb *poiein,* to make). An inconvenience of this term, however, is that it resembles too closely the term 'poetics', which is derived from the same verb, but whose meaning is restricted to the making of poetry, a non-philosophical occupation (see below).

A different name, which indicates at least an important part of theory in question is 'philosophy of labor', understood in a broad sense.[13] A more restricted part of it could be conveniently called 'philosophy of technique'.[14]

Frequently also philosophers treat the subject matter in question, without assigning a special name to it, in connection with the philosophy of culture or axiology. Others consider various problems pertaining to poietics in ethics. All this shows that it is not easy if not impossible to make a sharp division here.

3. *Operative Philosophy of Art*

Man has not only the capacity and the task of realizing what is good and useful or even necessary for a life worthy of man among his fellow men in this world, but he is also capable of transcending the sphere of the useful and the necessary and of attempting, by means of his spiritual-corporeal activities, to realize something that corresponds with his idea of the beautiful. Man possesses the power to know beauty. His power is not limited merely to discovering the beauty of nature and of the things given to him in his world, but enables him also personally to conceive objects of beauty and to realize them through artistic activities. The term 'art' is conveniently used to indicate the complex of these artistic activities and its products.

---

[13] An excellent study of this subject matter has appeared as Volume Ten in the philosophical series of DUQUESNE STUDIES: Remy C. Kwant, *Philosophy of Labor.* Pittsburgh, 1960.

[14] This subject matter is covered by Volume Thirteen of DUQUESNE STUDIES, *Philosophical Series:* Andrew G. van Melsen, *Science and Technology.* Pittsburgh, 1961.

As we have pointed out in Chapter Seven,[15] there exist sciences which aim at being normative of these artistic activities. The sciences in question, however, contain all kinds of aspects which give rise to problems that transcend their own competence. These problems demand philosophical reflection of both a speculative and an operative nature.

The realm of the beautiful is very large and complex. As a consequence, philosophical reflection on all aspects of the beautiful has its ramifications throughout various branches of philosophy. A few examples may serve to illustrate the point. Like the true and the good, the beautiful as such, as a transcendental idea, as a perfection of every being, is considered by metaphysics. Insofar, however, as the beautiful is or can be realized through human activities, its speculative philosophical aspects, its mode of being, belong to a special branch of speculative philosophy. This branch may be called 'speculative philosophy of art' and considered, if need be, as a subdivision of the philosophy of culture. The philosophical study in question endeavors to discover the general principles on which art and the creation of art are based. It attempts to find a reply to questions concerning the essence of beauty and the proper nature of art, concerning esthetic value, the relationship between art and beauty, the essence of artistic 'feeling' and esthetic emotion, the distinction between various arts, the social value of arts, and many other questions.

Alongside this speculative philosophical reflection there is room also for philosophical considerations of an operative or normative nature. Such an operative philosophy of art endeavors to arrive at general rules which govern the creation of beauty or the realization of artistic values. It has to be based upon the attainments of the speculative philosophy of art. Because it is difficult to separate the two philosophies of art in a systematic fashion, they are usually united into a single philosophy of art, having a speculative-operative character.

Moreover, it will not always be easy to make a clear-cut distinction between philosophy of art and science of art, because it is rather easy to pass from the consideration of one to that of the other.

---

[15] Section II, No. 4, p. 204.

Finally, for reasons of greater practical usefulness, treatises of the philosophy of art often consider also ethical questions, insofar as they are concerned with man's artistic activities.

4. *Ethics or Moral Philosophy*

Perhaps the introduction to this section has caused the impression that the various branches of operative philosophy, based upon the division of human activities, stand side by side as possessing all the same value. As we have pointed out, however, the division in question is too much schematized. This remark applies especially to appetitive intellectual activities or freely willing, to which we made ethics correspond. Activities of freely tending to something are unthinkable without intellectual knowledge and, moreover, find their natural complement in transient bodily expressions. These bodily expressions, at least insofar as they are truly human, cannot exist without rational acts of will. Even man's thinking, considered as a concrete human activity, does not occur without the influence of the will. The same applies to man's poietical and artistic activities.

Accordingly, we may certainly say that all deliberate human activities are initiated and guided by the free will through which man endeavors to attain or realize an intellectually known good. For this reason it is of the utmost importance that man's appetitive activities, taken in the broadest sense, be governed by correct norms. Consequently, the operative science which aims at formulating these norms, is the most important and the most fundamental of all operative sciences. Its statements have a kind of absoluteness, insofar as all human activity is subject to them, whatever the partial realm be in which this activity is exercised, whether it be in the realm of economy, technology, art, war, or any other area.

Insofar as the mental discipline in question abstracts from revelation, it is a philosophical undertaking and not a special non-philosophical study. This assertion should be sufficiently evident when one realizes that it is a matter of giving directions, not for man's activity in a restricted realm, but for human activity as such, insofar as this activity must be in conformity with the fundamental directedness or orientation of human nature. Such a science certainly transcends the special operative sciences spoken of in Chapter Seven, and these sciences have to take into consideration the conclusions of ethics when they formulate the norms proper to their own realms.

The Name of this Science. The operative philosophy which considers the subject matter in question is generally known as 'moral philosophy' or 'ethics' (from the Greek *êthikê,* which is derived from *êthos,* custom, usage). The term 'moral *philosophy*' indicates its distinction from moral theology. Ethics is the philosophical science which has as its object to realize the correct moral order and endeavors to attain this purpose by formulating general and fundamental norms or 'laws'.[16]

Ethics' Right to Exist. To justify the existence of the philosophical discipline in question, it is sufficient to start from the datum of experience that man has always and everywhere admitted moral views, expressing his conviction that human acts are bound by 'norms'. Man has always asked himself whether or not this or that action is permissible, ought to be done, or ought to be omitted. A simple norm universally recognized as such is the following: Man ought to do the good and avoid evil. The existence of such norms experienced as binding becomes even more evident when one pays attention to the emotional feelings and expressions which accompany man's conduct when it is in conformity with or deviates from the norms. Such conduct is accompanied by feelings of responsibility, satisfaction, consent, sorrow, remorse, purpose of amendment, etc.

Man generally recognizes, moreover, that such norms are not purely rules of conduct imposed by social conventions or the demands of a particular human society. He realizes that they have something to do with man's dignity as man, with the demands of human nature, the fundamental orientation and ultimate destiny of man, the meaning of human existence, or whatever other expression one prefers to use in this context. This datum of experience cannot be denied and demands closer philosophical reflection. Its philosophical consideration has as its task, on the one hand, to lay the theoretical foundation upon which the norms are based and from which they can be derived and, on the other, to discover and formulate the general norms which govern human activity. In this way moral philosophy, which under-

---

[16]If the term 'law' is used here instead of 'norm', its meaning differs evidently from the sense which 'law' has in the speculative sciences. In such sciences 'law' refers to the formula expressing a given ontological relationship, while in ethics there is question of the 'ought', the deontological aspect of human activity. Cf. Ch. VI, Sect. V, No. 2, p. 175.

takes this task, assumes a speculative-operative character. However, its speculative aspect is subservient to its operative task, and therefore ethics may be simply considered as an operative philosophical science. In the subsequent pages we will merely indicate a few features which clarify the proper character of this philosophy and connect these features with a possible division of ethics. Evidently, a full study of moral philosophy should not be expected here, for it would be far beyond the scope of this book.

Ethics is usually divided into generally ethics and special ethics, each of which permits further subdivisions. We will limit ourselves to a brief consideration of both and add a few remarks about the relationship of ethics to other sciences.

a. GENERAL ETHICS

As we have seen, the subject matter of ethics consists of the moral order required of human actions. The material object or that which has to be ordered are man's typically human acts, his rational acts of will, the actions which arise from man's typically human powers of understanding and willing. Such acts are known as 'human acts' in opposition to mere 'acts of man' as, e.g., digesting food. Only human acts qualify for a moral evaluation and can become formally object of ethics. The formal aspect which ethics evaluates in human actions is their moral goodness or evil, which consists in their conformity or lack of conformity with the ideal of morality or the absolute norm. Ethics, therefore, must study moral goodness in all its aspects.

Norms can be assigned only with respect to a purpose or end that is to be reached. For this reason the first task of ethics is to reflect upon the purpose to which man as man must direct his actions. It has to show that there is a purpose whose goodness and value is such that its attainment is a natural task for man, because the purpose in question is adapted to man's nature and therefore functions as the natural goal of man's integral activity. The recognition of such a total purpose at once supplies man with his universal norm of morality—viz., his human nature. Whatever harmonizes with, is demanded by human nature, considered in its integral structure, in all its relationships, both abstractly and concretely, is morally good, and whatever somehow conflicts with this nature is morally evil.

There is a host of problems here which ethics must endeavor to solve by means of a judicious reflection upon man's ultimate end and a careful analysis of 'human nature'. In actual fact, this ethical endeavor will be a reflection upon man's being itself, as a being which is at the same time a 'having to be', a destiny, a task. Accordingly, ethics as a normative science cannot originate as an isolated system, but is dependent upon general speculative philosophy and inseparable from it. Ethics can and must be based upon metaphysics and especially also upon philosophical anthropology. However, it has to consider these speculative data from the viewpoint of their suitability as a basis for the formulation of moral norms.

Thus, we see that it is the function of general ethics to reply to questions regarding the destiny and ultimate end of man, the essence of morality and the way in which human nature can be the general norm of morality, the meaning of objective and subjective morality, and other similar questions. It extends its considerations also to many questions which are connected with the fundamental problems of ethics. Among these we may enumerate moral freedom and its possible defects, the knowledge required for moral acts, responsibility, conscience, laws and duties, right in general, the relationship of the moral order and the legal order, virtues and vices, merit, reward, and punishment.

b. Special Ethics

Moral philosophy cannot be satisfied with the above-mentioned general considerations, but must also deduce the norms governing the various special realms in which man lives and works. In this task it has to seek the help of the speculative-philosophical studies which are concerned with these realms. In this fashion there arises a special ethics for each of the important sectors of human activity although, of course, there can be no question of a rigorous separation between these various special ethics. For a global view of these special ethics one may start by considering man first as a private individual in his various relationships, then man as a social being, as a member of different societies. In this way we obtain a schematic division of ethics which, although it is evidently not the only one, is at least very useful.

Man as a Private Individual. Man as a private individual may be considered in various ways; for example,

1. In his relationship to God. The philosophy of God shows that man must recognize God as his Creator; hence it follows that man

must be subservient to God and that his nature obliges him to worship God. In this way we arrive at norms of natural religion.

2. In his relationship to himself. Man's ethical duties toward himself may be derived from the speculative study of man's nature in philosophical anthropology or from special philosophical speculations regarding the meaning and value of life, of spiritual and bodily health. Examples of such duties are man's obligations toward his own life, his spiritual and bodily health, the development of his human powers, and also his ethical duties regarding his own artistic activities,

3. In his relationship to his fellow man as a private individual. The required speculative foundation is supplied again by philosophical anthropology. This basis allows man to derive two groups of ethical duties:

a. Duties of charity, in which our fellow man is considered primarily as our brother, as one who shares with us in human nature and in the dignity of man.

b. Duties of justice. These duties correspond with personal rights of our fellow men. With respect to obligations of justice, our fellow man is considered primarily as a competitor, as one who demands his share of the material goods of the world and who has the right to demand that we do not jeopardize his life, health, bodily or mental integrity, and human activities.

4. In his relationship to non-human beings. Respect for the Creator implies respect for His entire creation and, consequently, also for irrational beings. This respect allows us to deduce ethical norms for man's poietical activities on lifeless matter, plants, and especially animals.

Man as a Social Being. Partly by nature and partly by his own free choice, man is a member of various social organizations, the nature and structure of which are investigated in social philosophy or in various parts of speculative philosophy. Such a membership demands that man's social activities be regulated by norms. According to the type of society considered, various systems of norms come into existence.

1. Man as a child, parent or marriage partner is naturally a member of a family. To start and continue a family worthy of man, the corresponding human activities must satisfy certain ethical norms.

These norms are deduced by so-called 'domestic ethics', which considers marriage, the rights and duties of parents and children and, in addition, the duties and rights of masters and domestic servants.

2. Man is naturally a member of a civil society, such as a town, a county, a state, and a nation. The necessary speculative foundation of the ethical situation resulting from this membership is usually supplied by political philosophy or also by social philosophy. The corresponding operative discipline—so-called 'social ethics'—is often treated under the same name as its speculative foundation. It considers the rights and duties of governors and the governed, as well as the mutual duties and obligations of society's members. The ethical norms governing the co-existence and collaboration of human beings in a civil society must be directed toward the attainment and preservation of general welfare in the broad sense, i.e., including both spiritual and temporal welfare, at least insofar as this purpose can be reached by activities within the society in question. Their foundation, therefore, must be provided by a solid philosophical reflection upon the meaning and value of general welfare in the realms of economics, technology, agriculture, education, arts, sports, etc.

3. Our time shows clearly that man is also a member of a world-wide community. This fact implies a duty of reflection upon the mutual relationships between states and peoples and of deriving ethical norms governing just international relations and collaboration. These norms may differ in character according as they consider the juridical, social, economic, military or other aspects of the world-community.

4. Through free choice but also in consequence of his own inclinations and intellectual development, man may be a member of a professional society, such as a bar association, a medical society, a teacher or labor union. Special professional ethics determine the norms which govern the relations of such group members to one another as well as to their subordinates, and collaborators.

5. Man, moreover, may become freely a member of all kinds of other organizations, which are bound by rules of its own devising. Generally speaking, the social activities of such organizations have to satisfy not only these rules but also the norms of ethics. However, as a rule, there is no need for special norms, because the general norms of justice, charity, loyalty, etc. usually suffice for the purpose.

Remark Concerning Professional Ethics. When there is question of medical and juridical ethics or any other kind of professional ethics, these terms are usually understood in a broader sense than we have done in the preceding paragraphs. They are extended to include everything which in one way or another is ethically normative for a physician, a lawyer or other professional person. Thus, they contain also norms which we have classified differently and especially norms governing man's relationship to his fellow men as private individuals. Medical ethics, for example, will emphasize that the physician must follow the general norms governing the health, life and bodily integrity of our fellow man and that therefore he may not cause abortion, practice euthanasia, or sterilization (unless required by the patient's health), etc.

Moreover, treatises of professional ethics frequently contain all kinds of regulations which in themselves do not have an ethical character but prescribe what is to be done in certain situations that are met in the profession and which either arose from traditional practice or emanated from competent authority.

Moral Order and Legal Order. The parts of ethics which are concerned with man as a private individual are purely ethical, except insofar as they deal with obligations of justice based upon the personal rights of our fellow men. These obligations of justice as well as the entire section of ethics which considers man as a social being belong at the same time also to the legal order. In this realm the ethical norms are at the same time norms of justice, because the prescribed actions and duties correspond to the rights of our fellow man either as an individual or as a member of a society. For this reason these norms are often referred to as 'natural law', an expression which may be admitted provided it be taken in a narrow sense, because in its broad sense this term applies indiscriminately to all moral norms, including those that are purely moral.

Casuistry. Like moral theology,[17] so also ethics has as its complement so-called 'casuistry'. Even the norms of special ethics do not offer more than a general orientation in a particular area. To make these norms practically more useful, moral philosophers endeavor to render them more specific and to illustrate these specifications by means of concrete cases—whence the name 'casuistry'. Such cases are usually added to the different chapters of special ethics.

---

[17]Cf. Ch. V, Sect. II, No. 2, p. 96.

In his activity man finds himself always placed in a concrete and individual situation. For this reason he has to be guided not only by his knowledge of general and special ethics but also by prudence.[18]

c. The Relationship of Ethics to Other Sciences

As we have mentioned above, ethics has an absolute character and extends its concern to all human activities. It will, therefore, have to supervise the pursuit also of all sciences, whether speculative or operative. Insofar as certain sciences or groups of sciences themselves are operative and therefore concerned with norms governing human activities, ethics will have a special relationship to them. Although this question has been touched several times in a more or less passing way before, it will be useful to emphasize a few points somewhat more in detail here.

Ethics and Moral Theology. The term 'moral philosophy', which is synonymous with ethics shows that this science both resembles moral theology and differs from it in the way in which it handles the same object. The one is a philosophical study which endeavors to arrive at the fundamental norms of morality by means of natural reason alone, while the other seeks these norms in divine revelation (cf. Ch. V, Sect. III). In both cases the purpose intended is the same —namely, the orientation of human actions toward man's ultimate end. In various respects the two sciences are interdependent. There exists, moreover, a possibility of fruitful collaboration, to such an extent even that the terms 'ethics' and 'ethical' are often used in reference to a synthesis of moral theology and moral philosophy. For more details about their interrelationship we may refer to Chapter Five, Section Five (No. 1, pp. 108 ff.).

Ethics and Other Philosophical Sciences. The intrinsic connection of ethics with metaphysics or other parts of speculative philosophy has been sufficiently emphasized in the preceding pages. We have noted too, that certain ethical considerations are sometimes incorporated into appropriate parts of philosophy. This procedure will be followed rather easily in those branches of philosophy which themselves are of a speculative-operative character, because they spontaneously raise ethical problems. An example is provided by the philosophy of law, which does not merely study juridical situations as

---

[18]Cf. Ch. IV, Sect. II, No. 5, p. 71.

something that is given, as the existing order of law and rights, but also as something that ought to be realized. The last-named aspect belongs also to the ethical order (cf. above, p. 290). Other examples of philosophical disciplines possessing ethical aspects are provided by political philosophy, philosophy of economics, and operative philosophy of art.

Ethics and the Special Speculative Sciences. The object of the speculative sciences includes human activities only insofar as these activities are considered as something that is given and not insofar as they must be ordered to a definite goal under the direction of higher ethical norms. Thus, it might seem that with respect to their object there are no points of contact between the speculative sciences and ethics. This conclusion, however, is not quite correct, at least not insofar as the sciences of man and the cultural sciences are concerned. For these sciences often pronounce a value judgment about human achievements and conduct,[19] and the ethical values must certainly be counted among the values that are normative.

There is still another way in which the pursuit of speculative sciences may raise ethical problems—namely, insofar as man in his scientific research is bound by ethical norms. For example, he will have to ask himself whether or not certain experiments on animals and man[20] are ethically permissible, and the same applies to nuclear research, space travel, the creation of poison gas, explosives and other destructive means, when the man of research knows that they will probably be used in an unethical way.

Ethics and the Special Operative Sciences. The special operative sciences in particular will always have to pay attention to the norms of ethics. It is not sufficient to know that a particular way of acting is useful or desirable for the attainment of this or that purpose. Man has to see also whether or not this way of acting conflicts with the demands of human nature and fosters his integral and ultimate welfare. In other words, these sciences must always take ethical considerations into account. We may refer here again to the relationship of special operative sciences with operative philosophy of which we have spoken in Chapter Seven.[21] In addition, with due modifications, much of what has been said in Chapter Five[22] about

---

[19]Cf. Ch. VI, Sect. V, No. 4, pp. 185 ff.
[20]Cf. also Ch. VI, Sect. III, No. 2, p. 152 ff.
[21]Sect. III, No. 2, p. 205.
[22]Sect. V, No. 2, pp. 111 ff.

the dependence of the special sciences upon theology may be applied also to the relationship of these sciences to ethics.

III. PHILOSOPHY IS A SCIENCE

1. *Description of the Concept 'Philosophy'*

Sections One and Two have, we think, convincingly shown that there are problems which lie outside the realm of the special speculative and operative sciences and that these problems are often discovered precisely through a reflection upon these special sciences themselves or upon their object. Accordingly, alongside these sciences, another task presents itself to the questions of the thinking man. The mental activity which is devoted to the solution of these questions is said to be 'philosophical', and the systems which tend to pursue the solution in a methodic way are called 'philosophy'.

It is not easy to describe philosophy in the above-mentioned sense in such a way that the description meets with general approval. A still-current definition, which we continue to hold very suitable, says that philosophy is the science of everything which is, in its most profound foundations, insofar as such knowledge can be attained by man's natural reason. Or, in the slightly different formulation of Louis de Raeymaeker, "Philosophy is a body of natural knowledge methodically acquired and ordered, which undertakes to give the fundamental explanation of all things".[23]

A more analytical definition is given by Dr. Hoogveld: "Philosophy is the science which studies a) the first causes of being as such and whatever is connected with being as such, the first axioms of all being, the first causes of the various categories of beings in nature, in the mind, and in culture; b) the order of thought, its laws and their foundation, the general structure of science, the value and scope of human knowledge; c) the laws of moral obligation and their ultimate grounds, the nature of society and the ultimate grounds of its rules".[24]

Still in use is also Aristotle's definition of 'first philosophy', later called 'metaphysics': "the science which investigates being as being and the attributes which belong to this in virtue of its own nature".[25]

---

[23] *Introduction to Philosophy*, New York, 1948, p. 27.
[24] *Inleiding tot de Wijsbegeerte* (revised by F. Sassen), vol. II, p. 45.
[25] *Metaphysics*, bk. III, ch. 1; 1003a, 21.

This definition is applicable also to the other branches of philosophy, provided it be further specified by adding, e.g., material being or human being. Another definition of Aristotle describes philosophy as "a science which investigates the first causes and principles".[26] This definition is closely connected with the traditional description of philosophy as knowledge of the first principles and causes of all that is, acquired by natural reason.

An objection which may be raised against all such definitions is that they could mistakenly be conceived as clearly expressing the proper nature of philosophy. In reality it is only by the actual pursuit of philosophy that a person will be able to understand its character. Every philosopher, moreover, will impress his own personal seal upon his philosophy.

Despite the apparent differences between the various descriptions, they are fundamentally in agreement. Although the preceding sections have probably shown with sufficient clarity why we consider these descriptions satisfactory, we want to emphasize here a few points which in our view any good definition of philosophy should contain.

The 'Natural' Character of Philosophy. In contradistinction to supernatural theology, philosophy has a natural character. It is concerned only with knowledge attained by man's natural reason and extends only to realms that are accessible to man's natural cognitive powers. Its object, therefore, excludes everything which is known only through divine revelation and which as such constitutes the object of the theological sciences. On the other hand, theology as a science, as a pursuit or result of human thought, pertains to the object of philosophical reflection.[27]

God himself belongs to the object of philosophy, but only insofar as He is knowable to man's natural reason—namely, as the absolute ground of being which is required to explain the existence of finite beings. He is the object of theology as the God who reveals Himself to man. There is, therefore, a clear distinction in formal object.[28]

Material Object. The material object of philosophy is everything which is, every being, without any *a priori* exclusion. It contains both finite being and the infinite 'to be' which is God, the ultimate and

---

[26]Metaphysics, bk. I, ch. 2; 928b, 9.
[27]Cf. Ch. V, Sect. I, p. 80.
[28]Cf. Part I, Ch. V, p. 45.

absolute ground of being of all finite things. The material object of the philosophical sciences is the same as that of the totality of all non-philosophical sciences, whether theological or non-theological, which exist or will be developed in the future. For there is nothing among all that is which is not or cannot become the material object of one or the other special science. The difference between philosophy and the totality of the non-philosophical sciences, therefore, as well as that between a particular philosophical discipline and the corresponding special sciences, must lie in the formal object and the way of viewing the object.

Formal Object. The proper and integral object of a science is its 'formed' material object, its 'formal object.' Sciences which have the same material object are distinguished by their formal object.[29]

Because philosophy and all non-philosophical sciences are all concerned with 'to be' and beings, it is only through a further qualification of this material object that the proper object of philosophy can be determined. Aristotle, therefore, does not indicate being as the object of the 'first philosophy' but being as being. Instead of 'being as being', we may also say 'being as such' or 'being under the aspect of being'. The other descriptions of philosophy speak of knowledge of the most profound foundation or an investigation of the first principles and of the primary or ultimate causes. Such terms indicate the way in which philosophy investigates and knows, thus pointing to its essential and formal difference from other 'natural' sciences, although this difference does not manifest itself in the same fashion in all parts of philosophy.

From the preceding sections it should be apparent what is meant by the terms 'most profound foundations', 'first principles' and 'primary or ultimate causes'. These expressions certainly do not refer to a simple continuation of man's explanatory endeavors on the same level as that on which the non-philosophical sciences work. If philosophy were able to work in such a fashion, it would be merely a provisional extension of the special sciences, destined to be absorbed by their subsequent progress. The expressions in question refer to a method of explanation of being which lies on a wholly different level and proceeds by a different kind of abstraction and another mode of knowing than that of the special sciences. The philosophical way of explaining things is meaningful even before the special sciences

---

[29]Cf. Part I, Ch. V.

arise and grow. It is not made superfluous by the most refined development of these sciences. We trust that this point has been convincingly established in the preceding parts of this chapter.

2. *Philosophy Has the Character of a Science*

In this question we will proceed in two distinct ways. First we will endeavor to show that philosophy satisfies the demands which must be fulfilled by any genuine science. Secondly, we will devote our attention to a few deviating views for the purpose of showing that these views unjustly want to deprive philosophy of its scientific character.

a. PHILOSOPHY SATISFIES THE DEFINITION OF SCIENCE

It is rather strange that the scientific character of philosophy, as we understand this term, has to be defended against so many opponents. Former centuries practically never had any doubt about it, no matter how widely opinions diverged about the content of this science. Their definitions of philosophy nearly always formally used the term 'science' or 'scientific'. Most of the time philosophy was considered to be even the science *par excellence,* the 'mother of all sciences'.

Philosophy, in the sense in which we understand this term, undoubtedly satisfies the traditional definitions of science. The old description of science, which goes back to Aristotle, says that it is knowledge through causes. Philosophy certainly is this kind of knowledge, for it wants to give a 'fundamental' explanation, 'through first causes' or 'most profound foundations'.

Even a superficial confrontation of philosophy with the more analytic definition which we proposed in Part One (p. 14) shows that philosophy satisfies the requirements of science. Science, we said, "is a logically ordered system of true, or at least probably true, and universal statements concerning the essences, foundations, causes and finality in a definite field of knowledge, with reference to the investigations, arguments, and demonstrations upon which the conclusions are based". It would not seem necessary to show in detail that all the above-enumerated elements of science are present in philosophy, as this discipline has been described above. It goes without saying that this definition had not been proposed for the avowed purpose of making it fit philosophy.

Of course, one should keep in mind that a number of terms used in the definition of science are analogous and, therefore, cannot be used with respect to philosophy in exactly the same fashion as they apply to the special sciences. This point induces us to add here a few remarks which may serve to remove a number of objections that could exist against the scientific character of philosophy.

A Logically Ordered System. Philosophy, as we conceive it, certainly is a logically ordered system and, therefore, in this respect satisfies the decription of science. The systematic character, however, differs somewhat from that of the special sciences. In the latter the order of the system is usually determined by the nature of the science in question, e.g., by means of deduction or induction, although for pedagogical reasons it may be permissible to deviate from the historical order of its development. Philosophy, on the other hand, possesses the strange feature that its starting point may be chosen in a fairly arbitrary fashion. Of course, one will always have to start somehow with the world of experience of concrete man, but this world is inexhaustibly rich and offers a multitude of distinct starting points. Once, however, the starting point is chosen, one is bound by the demands of a logical process of thought, so that the required ordered system arises without any further difficulty.

It may not be superfluous to add that a philosophical system should never be closed and considered finished. Each and every part of it may and must always continue to be the object of philosophical reflection.

The Truth of Philosophical Statements. To be a science, philosophy must make statements which are true or at least probably true. It is this point which is most difficult and subject to most objections. Doesn't it seem rather obvious that philosophers can never agree about the truth and validity of their statements or even about the precise meaning of the terms in which they express their views? What one proclaims to be absolute truth, the other rejects adamantly as false. Nevertheless, the requirement of truth must be satisfied if what we call philosophy is not to degenerate into idle and useless speculations or possess at most a literary value.

The important point to keep in mind here is that the way in which the requirement of truth is or can be satisfied in philosophy differs from that of, e.g., the experiential or ideal sciences. Philosophy may not be put on the same line with the ideal sciences, which are concerned with beings of thought and, therefore, able to determine the nature of these beings to a certain extent in an arbitrary way. Such beings of thought allow the ideal science to construct a logically consistent system in which the statements deduced from their nature are true (cf. Chapter Eight). Philosophy, on the other hand, wants to present a fundamental explanation of real being. Its starting point, therefore, must lie in an irrefutable experience of real being. In this respect there is no room for arbitrariness, for one has to accept what experience shows. There may, however, still be a degree of liberty with respect to the actual choice of experiential data to be used as the foundation of philosophical reflection.

Like every science, such a philosophical study must proceed in a way that is intellectually justified. This demand implies two requirements, one of which refers to the concepts to be used and the other to the statements made by the science in question.

First of all, it has to explicitate the concepts it uses and to clarify them by means of other concepts. This clarification can hardly ever be made through a definition by genus and specific difference, because strictly philosophical concepts usually are primary and fundamental ideas that are not reducible to a more common genus. Moreover, philosophy mostly deals with analogous concepts, i.e., concepts whose meaning is not always the same. Nevertheless, these points should not be urged against the scientific character of philosophy, for in the special sciences also there are many ideas that cannot be sharply defined as well as many analogous concepts. This is especially the case in the human sciences.[30]

Secondly, philosophy must be able to verify its statements, make them be true. Its mode of verification differs, of course, from that of the special sciences, just as that of various groups of special sciences is also different.[31] Starting from an indubitable fact of experience and proceeding in a logically consistent fashion, philosophy must rationally justify its statements within its system in such a way that they can stand critical examination, possess an objective and real value, and thus may lay claim to general validity.

A new difficulty presents itself here, because philosophy does not lead an independent or quasi-independent existence and therefore, cannot be simply learned in the same way as one learns, e.g., a language. It is always the thinking man, the individual philosopher

---

[30]Cf. Ch. VI, Sect. V, No. 7, pp. 195 ff.

[31]Cf. P. Henry van Laer, *Philosophico-Scientific Problems,* Pittsburgh, 1953, Ch. III, Sect. III, pp. 47 ff.

with his own world view and his own conception of man and his world who has to build his own philosophy in his own way, even though he may resort to the aid of insights acquired by others or travel along trails blazed by fellow philosophers. For this reason philosophical views are nearly always connected with, and influenced by the—religious or non-religious—world view of their owner. The same, however, is true, at least in part, also of non-philosophical sciences and especially of the human sciences.[32]

Philosophy, of course, must proceed in a way that is so critically justified and shows so much reverence for the reality upon which it reflects that subjectivity and relativity are avoided as much as possible. The personally acquired insights must become intersubjectively acceptable as much as possible, because they must be based upon convincing rational arguments. In this respect philosophy resembles, as Gabriel Marcel says, a musical composition, which may be executed in various interpretations but always in such a way that the intention of the composer suffers no violence and the preferred interpretation is acceptable to others.

The philosopher who strives for objectivity and endeavors to verify the statements of his own system should become acquainted with divergent views and their supporting arguments. A careful inquiry into these views often makes it possible to point out the incorrectness of certain philosophical positions. For instance, the Cartesian concept of man must be rejected because it is clearly against the spiritual-material unity of man which is known to us from experience.

Moreover, it should be kept in mind that philosophical assertions which apparently contradict each other may still be both true in whole or in part and capable of being reconciled, because they may refer to different aspects of the same reality. We may think here, for example, of metaphysical statements regarding the unity and multiplicity, the absoluteness and relativity, the finiteness and infinity of being; the synthesis that can be made of conceptualistic, realistic and exemplaristic views of universals; the synthesis of anthropomorphic and agnostic views of man's knowledge of God; the possibility of incorporating certain idealistic ideas into a realistic philosophy; and the reconciliation of extremistic views in political philosophy.

---

[32]Cf. Ch. VI, Sect. V, No. 5, pp. 187 ff.

There is in this respect a great difference between, on the one hand, philosophy, which is always concerned with concrete totalities in their wealth of distinct inner and outer aspects and, on the other, various sciences, especially those of nature, in which the attention is centered on abstracted aspects which have been isolated from concrete totality. Because of this abstraction and isolation, it is much easier here to arrive at unanimity. Moreover, it may be pointed out that even in the experiential sciences, and especially in the human sciences, there are many statements which are far from receiving unanimous approval.[33]

Finally, we must add that the philosopher who believes in divine revelation is bound to take into account also revealed truths and theological statements that are certain. These truths and statements have to serve at least as negative directives. If a philosophical reflection leads to conclusions which cannot be reconciled with such truths, then he is certain that somewhere in his philosophical reflection he has made an error. Reversely, the agreement of philosophical statements with theological propositions, e.g., about God, creation, man, or the world, may also be a guarantee of their truth.

Universality of Philosophical Statements. Another difficulty may arise from the requirement that scientific statements be universal, because this condition may sometimes seem unsatisfied. For philosophy speaks of being, 'to be', material being, etc., which a non-philosopher could conceivably interpret as referring to singular subjects. Such statements, however, are at the same time singular and universal. Their unique status in this respect is connected with the proper nature of these concepts, which cannot be called abstract in the ordinary sense of the term. They arise through a *sui generis* process of abstraction, through so-called 'metaphysical abstraction'.[34] These concepts are singular insofar as they refer to the unity of being or to its totality, but also universal insofar as they apply to all that is or to everything human, everything material, etc. Moreover, again we may point out that even in the special sciences universality is not always present in the same fashion and that singular statements may also belong to the authentic subject matter of a science. This applies especially to the human sciences.[35]

---

[33] Cf. Ch. VI, Sect. V, No. 6, pp. 190 f.

[34] Cf. Henry J. Koren, *Introduction to the Science of Metaphysics,* St. Louis 1960, pp. 21 and 27 ff. See also Part I, p. 29.

[35] Cf. Ch. VI, Sect. V, No. 1, pp. 172 ff.

A Definite Field of Knowledge. The special sciences are concerned with a definite area of knowledge. This statement may be understood in the sense that a science is limited to a restricted, clearly circumscribed area of the knowable, so that different sciences can be distinguished by their material object. However, there are also sciences which consider the same material object but differ in their formal object.[36] This difference is even more decisive than a mere difference of material object, because it is precisely the formal object which determines the way the subject matter is considered, the choice of suitable methods, and similar features. Thus, it is the formal object which determines the proper character of a science, and it is this object especially which sets apart the 'definite field of knowledge' in question.

Because philosophy, in the broad sense of the term, is all-embracing, it cannot be set apart from the non-philosophical sciences with respect to its material object. In this sense, then, there is no area of knowledge which is reserved for philosophy. However, as we have seen above (p. 295), it has a formal object of its own and, therefore, possesses its own approach and its own methods in dealing with the problems falling under its attention. In this way, then, there arises a 'definite field of knowledge' for philosophy. So far as the various subdivisions of philosophy are concerned, there may also exist a partial distinction according to material object and consequently also a more limited area of knowledge.

b. Critique of Deviating Views

The preceding pages intended to show that philosophy, in the sense in which we understand this term, has every right to be called a science and even deserves to occupy a prominent position among all non-theological sciences. Nevertheless, this conclusion has not gone unchallenged during the past few decades. Especially neo-positivistic circles are opposed to it. Either they refuse to make any room at all for philosophy among the sciences or they distinguish between scientific and non-scientific philosophy and, in this case, they classify philosophy, as we conceive it, as non-scientific.

There must be some misunderstanding behind this rejection or—which is worse—a fundamental attitude which is wholly unacceptable. Although we do not have room for a complete consideration of the question, we must devote some attention to a few points that fall within the scope of our book.

---

[36]Cf. Part I, Ch. V.

Misunderstandings. The objections against the scientific character of philosophy arise in part from misconceptions about the requirements of science. The preceding pages which considered the demands made by science and how philosophy satisfies these demands may have been sufficient to remove the following types of objections:

Philosophy is not a logically coherent system (see p. 297).

Philosophy does not know what it is speaking about, because it is not able to define the concepts it uses, cannot verify its statements, and, therefore, cannot arrive at generally accepted assertions (see pp. 297 f.).

Philosophy cannot form any universal propositions (see p. 300).

Philosophy does not have any clearly-defined area of knowledge and no methods of its own (cf. p. 301).

Opponents of the scientific character assigned to traditional philosophy often formulate also more profound objections which need to be considered separately. The negative views usually have their foundation in an unduly restricted view of the concept 'science' and/or in a particular view of philosophy which deviates from the traditional understanding of this term. Many of these views find their basis in the fundamental attitudes of contemporary neo-positivism, although it cannot be denied that even in former times the scientific character of philosophy was occasionally denied, e.g., by Kant and the followers of the empiricism and positivism of David Hume, Stuart Mill, and Auguste Comte. We will limit ourselves here to a few characteristic contemporary views, presented without the delicate differentiations that are often attached to them. We do not want to enter into polemic discussions with the defenders of these views, but merely to point out certain aspects which in our opinion are highly vulnerable and incorrect.

Sometimes Philosophy is Rejected on the Basis of Too Narrow a View of Science. In neo-positivistic circles, the origin of which goes back mainly to the scientists of the Vienna Circle, there exists an exaggerated appreciation of mathematics and physical science and of the thought processes proper to these sciences. The exactness and the rigorously logical, axiomatic structure of mathematics, on the one hand, and the empirical verifiability of physical science, on the other, are simply considered as the criterion *par excellence* of scientific character. Whatever cannot satisfy these strict demands may not, or at least not fully, lay claim to the honor of being a science. It goes without saying that such a scientistic view must of course reject traditional philosophy (or that which we have qualified as philosophy in this book) as unscientific.

Against such views the following two remarks may be made. First of all, the demands which they impose are an arbitrary limitation of the concept 'science'. Mathematics and physical science are simply considered as the only genuine sciences, and other intellectual disciplines are excluded unless and insofar as they share in the character of mathematics or physical science. This arbitrary and irresponsible limitation results not only in the rejection of philosophy and theology but also in the bare tolerance of human sciences, at least insofar as these sciences lay claim to a character and methods of their own that are not the same as those of physical science. It is hardly necessary to point out that such a one-sided view mutilates and impoverishes the concept 'science.'

Secondly, the above-mentioned view of science stands or falls with the philosophical basis upon which it is founded—viz., the philosophy of neo-positivism, at least insofar as our time is concerned. It is really striking but nonetheless true that the rejection of philosophy finds its basis in a view of man and the world which itself is philosophical. As a matter of fact, many neo-positivists now admit that they proceed from a philosophical basis, as non-positivists have not ceased to demonstrate quite convincingly.[37]

Scientific and Non-Scientific Philosophy. Sometimes not all philosophy is rejected upon the basis of a onesided evaluation of a particular type of science, but only a certain type of philosophy, e.g., traditional or speculative philosophy and especially metaphysics, is disparaged because it is a 'world view' philosophy and, therefore, not scientific. It is reproached for occupying itself with insoluble pseudo-problems, with statements that do not have any meaning because they are against the correct use of language and contain concepts that cannot be defined. Such views are derived from the idea that the world of experience offers no area of knowledge which is outside that of the empirical sciences. They do not permit one to speak about being as such or about absolute values and absolute norms. All problems referring to such values and norms or to being as such are merely pseudo-problems, and all statements about these problems are merely pseudo-statements.

---

[37]Some of these points have been treated more extensively in our book, *Philosophico-Scientific Problems*, Pittsburgh, 1953, Ch. III. At the end of that chapter the interested reader will find a brief bibliography.

Nevertheless, proponents of these ideas recognize and defend the possibility of a scientific philosophy. Regarding the meaning of this term and the views which qualify as 'scientific', they differ among themselves. Each of them has his own opinion about this matter, an opinion which is based upon philosophy in our sense of the term.[38] The common element of these views is the demand of strict logical coherence and the rejection of any sentence which is subject to misunderstanding or cannot be accepted as universally valid.

According to many neo-positivists, the task of philosophy is exclusively logical or analytic, i.e., it must establish the meaning of sentences and problems and eliminate all meaningless statements. Philosophy, they claim, cannot be a system of truths or a science in its own right possessing an area of knowledge that is reserved for it alone. Philosophy is an activity "by means of which one establishes or discovers the meaning of statements. Statements are clarified by philosophy, and verified by the sciences. The latter are concerned with the truth of propositions, while the former considers merely the exact meaning of these propositions."[39] This view, therefore, closely connects philosophy with the special sciences: it is an activity within and on the outer shell of these sciences.

Another opinion, which is somewhat connected with the preceding view but more precise, limits the task of philosophy to the investigation and analysis of the language used by the special sciences and/or the foundations of these sciences, especially those of mathematics and physical science. Such a philosophy or 'logic of the sciences' would make only statements possessing a purely 'formal' character and, therefore, is supposed to be just as exact and reliable as, e.g., mathematics and physics. In this way, they think, it would be possible to arrive at universal statements, so that such a philosophy could justly be called 'scientific'. The subdivisions of traditional philosophy, such as, philosophy of nature, philosophical anthropology, and philosophy of history, would be replaced by the logical analysis of physical science, psychology, history, etc.

In addition, the proponents of 'scientific philosophy' sometimes admit also a general theory of being, not in the sense of classical meta-

---

[38]See the inaugural lecture of Dr. J. Loenen, "Over het onderscheid tussen een wetenschappelijk en een niet-wetenschappelijk deel der wijsbegeerte', Assen, 1959, in which he examines several views of 'scientific philosophy' and subjects them to a searching critique.

[39]Moritz Schlick, "Die Wende der Philosophie", *Erkenntnis*, vol. 1 (1930-31), p. 8. Cf. Viktor Kraft, *Der Wiener Kreis*, Vienna, 1950, p. 172.

physics but more as a comprehensive picture of reality, built exclusively upon the data of the empirical sciences.

Critique of this View. Several remarks are in order with respect to the above-explained concept of philosophy. First of all, much of what is contained in the various trends of 'scientific philosophy' undoubtedly possesses a certain value. Much of it also could be accepted as philosophy in the sense which we give to this term. However, in our view, such considerations pertain to various subdivisions of philosophy, such as epistemology, philosophy of science, logic, and philosophy of language.[40]

Secondly, when the proponents of 'scientific philosophy' speak about the opposition between scientific and non-scientific philosophy, they often reveal great ignorance of classical philosophy and ascribe to it all kinds of characteristics which it does not possess. To give an example, classical philosophy is supposed to be based merely upon feelings, upon irrational motives, upon religion and mysticism, or in general upon grounds which cannot be rationally justified. As we have explained above, however, philosophical statements can and must be based upon a rational foundation. For this reason philosophy deserves to be called a science.

Thirdly, those who reject philosophy, in the sense in which we understand this term, as non-scientific start from a concept of science that is too narrow and is arbitrarily restricted in such a way that only mathematics and physical science qualify as genuine sciences.[41]

Fourthly, the ideal pursued by the proponents of 'scientific philosophy' to create a philosophy which would be acceptable to all has never been attained, not even if we limit the acceptance to the circles of these proponents themselves. They have not even managed to agree about such fundamental concepts as foundations, acceptable methods, and the content of the term 'scientific'. This absence of unanimity clearly shows that the theoretical considerations in question differ in character from the explanations offered by mathematics and physical sciences, which were supposed to serve as the proper model to be followed.

Fifthly, the special view of science and of human knowledge in general which lies at the basis of the above-mentioned conceptions

---

[40]Cf. Sect. I, No. 2 (pp. 265 ff.) and Sect. II, No. 1 (pp. 276 ff.) of this chapter.

[41]Cf. above, pp. 296 ff. and 303 ff.

has just as much a philosophical nature as the positions taken by the defenders of classical philosophy. The books and treatises of 'scientific philosophers' manifest a character which closely resembles that of the classical philosophy which they abhor so much. Their view is based upon an arbitrary choice, an act of will which cannot be rationally justified. In this sense, therefore, so-called 'scientific philosophy' is likewise a world-view philosophy, for it is built upon certain views regarding man and his world.

Finally, a philosophy which wants to be good and lay claim to the honorable title of being a philosophy must certainly be scientific in the sense explained in the preceding pages (pp. 296 ff.). But in this case the qualifier 'scientific' becomes superfluous. It could at most serve to distinguish good philosophy from bad philosophy, from extreme subjectivism and from writings having a purely literary value.

CHAPTER TEN

THE UNITY OF THE SCIENCES

Nascitur ex variis radiis lux candida solis
Artibus ex variis unica fax radiat[1]

INTRODUCTION

For two reasons it appears desirable to terminate this work with a chapter about the unity of the sciences.

1. First of all, the preceding chapters considered the whole complex realm of the sciences and attempted to bring order in the complexity by means of various well-founded divisions; after which we proceeded to examine the resulting groups of sciences in a fairly extensive fashion. Thus a superficial reading could easily give the impression that the whole of the sciences constitutes merely a collection of sharply distinct groups almost devoid of mutual interrelationships. Such an impression would confirm the rather widespread conviction which favors this view and which originated from, or at least found support in certain historical developments and continues to be encouraged by the actually existing situation of our time. Let us illustrate this assertion.

Progressive Specialization and Estrangement. Until the late Middle Ages, despite all the distinctions that were made in the sciences (cf. Ch. IV), the idea of unity remained prevalent. Even Descartes (1596-1650) still held fast to the idea that the various sciences were branches of a single *sapientia universalis,* a single 'universal wisdom'. Nevertheless his time and especially the following centuries witnessed the rise of new sciences which seemed not to fit into such a totality and for which its pursuers passionately demanded a certain degree of autonomy. We may refer here, for example, to the new status assigned to physical science from the time of Galileo, Kepler and Newton.

As the sciences grew in number and development, it became less and less possible for anyone to be proficient in the totality of the sciences. The time was definitely past when anyone could be praised in the same fashion as a contemporary had eulogized St. Albert the

---

[1]"Even as the splendent light of the sun is born from different rays, so also a single flame bursts forth from the various kinds of arts" (Inscription above the entrance of the University of Utrecht).

Great: "totum scibile scisti" (thou didst know all that is knowable). Henceforth one had to limit himself to a determined group of sciences, a single science or even a restricted part of a single science.

Inevitable as this development was, it opened the era of specialization, the tendency to dominate a very small realm as fully as possible, which is sometimes somewhat ironically referred to as "knowing everything about nothing". The specialist, moreover, is often so dedicated to the object of his research, so absorbed by its scientific method and procedure, its specialized complex of ideas and its technical language, that the resulting scientific mentality makes it very difficult, if not wholly impossible, for him to remain intellectually open for methods or mental attitudes which deviate from his specialization.

Thus it is not surprising if the sciences and their pursuers have become strangers to one another and often even appear to be separated by an unbridgeable gap. Until fairly recent times universities comprised a number of more or less separate faculties, schools or departments, such as theology, law, mathematics and physical science, medicine, and philosophy, but nowadays the complexity has become so great that a single faculty or school needs an ever increasing number of institutes and laboratories, which lead a rather autonomous existence and are hardly capable of communicating scientifically with one another.

Desire for Unity. In recent times the above-mentioned tendency to separate the sciences by airtight compartments has met strong opposition both in theoretical studies and in the pursuit of science. On theoretical grounds as well as for practical reasons the tendency is judged to be incorrect and dangerous. There exists again an intense desire for the ideal of the university which dominated in former ages. Efforts are made to reach a synthesis which recognizes the unity of the sciences at least *de jure.* Moreover, attempts are made to remove the evil effects of the separation or to compensate for them. Some of these attempts move on a theoretical level. They consist in prescribing philosophy, especially philosophy of science in the broad sense of the term, and a studium generale or core courses which provide an orientation in different realms of science. Others are of a more practical nature and stimulate teamwork, i.e., they make specialists of different sciences collaborate in the study of a given object in order to consider all its aspects, implications and bearing upon the various sciences in their mutual interconnection and interaction.

As far as the philosophy of science is concerned, it is, of course important to study the unity of the sciences on a theoretical basis. In the first section of this chapter we will proceed in this fashion and show how and to what extent it is possible to speak of such a unity. This section will be relatively short, because it will consist mainly of putting together ideas which have been repeatedly formulated in the preceding chapters.

2. The second reason why we wish to terminate this work with a study about the unity of the sciences lies in the fact that certain groups, especially those of positivists, often propagate a kind of unification of the sciences which in our view must be received with great reservations and in its extreme forms even totally rejected. This kind of unification and the reasons why we cannot accept it will be considered in the second section of this chapter. The first, then, will defend the unity of the sciences, and the second will reject a proposed way of unification.

The Philosophical Character of the Reflection Upon the Unity of the Sciences. It should hardly be necessary to point out that reflection upon the unity of the sciences has a philosophical character. Just as was the case with the considerations devoted to the division of the sciences, the study of the unity pertaining to the sciences is an evaluation of the interrelationship, interdependence and inner connection of the various sciences and groups of sciences. Such an investigation, therefore, can never be performed within the restricted realm of a special science, but has to be made from a higher viewpoint and in the light of a more-embracing vision. As should be evident from the preceding chapter, such a study possesses a philosophical character, at least in the sense which we have constantly attributed to the term 'philosophy'. The reflection in question pertains, of course, to the branch of philosophy known as 'philosophy of science'.

Once the unity of the sciences has been established, it would be possible to investigate the way in which science, i.e., the totality of the sciences, is distinguished from other categories of human activities, such as religion, art, and technology. However, we will abstain from devoting much time to this question and restrict ourselves to a few remarks when we will speak about the unity of the sciences as resulting from the proper character of scientific activity.

I. A Defense of the Unity of the Sciences

Preliminary Remarks. To defend the unity of the sciences in spite of the distinctions that have been made, one could begin by pointing out that every distinction always refers to a totality which somehow is a unity. Distinction presupposes unity, as should be evident from the considerations presented in Chapter One. Despite the undeniable unity, however, there is distinction resulting in different groups of sciences, such as philosophy and physical science, as well as in different sciences, e.g., physics, history, and theology. It is even possible to make distinctions between the various parts of one and the same science. There are, moreover, unity and plurality with respect to individual and species, concrete-individual data and universal laws, experiment and theory, premises and conclusion, etc.

Distinction and unity, therefore, go hand in hand. Thus it could be a cause of surprise to see that the unity of the sciences is a matter of dispute, or that many reject it, while others accept it only after misjudging the differences between the sciences. For this reason alone it would be necessary to argue here that the sciences constitute a unity and to what extent. The argument in question, however, demands a further reflection capable of rendering our understanding of the point in question more profound and thus provides us with an added reason to discuss here the unity of the sciences.

The existence or non-existence of this unity has been the subject of many studies, especially in the past few decades. Generally speaking, the consensus is in favor of admitting a certain unity of the sciences, but there is no corresponding harmony about the nature of this unity. All kinds of arguments have been proposed in its favor.[2] While we cannot examine them here in any detail, we want to name two tendencies.

1. Some authors do not go beyond defending a kind of external unity, arising from all kinds of mutual relationships among various sciences or groups of sciences, such as similarity, interconnection, dependence, or subordination. The existence of such relationships is too obvious for comment and has been sufficiently pointed out in the preceding chapters.

2. Usually, however, the unity of the sciences is given a more profound foundation, mainly in one of the following ways: stress is

[2]Cf. R. Schwarz, *Wissenschaft und Bildung,* Freiburg, 1957, pp. 105-117.

placed upon the unity of the total object of all the sciences—namely, the one world (including man) or the unity of being, or upon man as both subject and object of the sciences. In our view both these lines of thought can serve to arrive at solid arguments for the unity of the sciences, although the line in which man functions as the central reference point is undoubtedly more important. We will pursue both lines here successively in arguing for the unity of the sciences.

1. *All Sciences Are Concerned With One and the Same Reality*

At first it seems that the assertion expressed in the preceding title is quite evident and not subject to dispute. Throughout the centuries man has sought the foundation upon which the unity of the sciences is built in the unity of their object, viz., being, which philosophy considered as such or in general, and the special sciences in its specific or generic manifestations. In this way the unity of philosophy and the special sciences is automatically maintained. Because the unity of being is extensively considered in metaphysical treatises, there is no need for us to dwell upon it here. We may be satisfied with referring the reader to such works and also to the first section of the preceding chapter.

True, this unity of being is often interpreted in line with idealistic trends of thinking, but it may be interpreted also, as we have constantly done in this book, in a realistic way. As a matter of fact, there have always been strong realistic currents of thought.

Nevertheless, this idea of unity is opposed by those who see the differentiation of the object precisely as the source which gives rise to the separation of the sciences in airtight compartments.[3] Is there not a clear-cut distinction and even separation of God and world (i.e., the whole of creation), and in the created world again of man and the non-human? Have we not used this separation precisely as the foundation of our distinction between theological and non-theological sciences, between sciences of nature and human sciences? Do not the ideal sciences lie wholly outside the realm of reality? How are the speculative and operative sciences to be united? These and other questions must receive satisfactory replies if one wants to speak legitimately about the unity of the sciences.

---

[3] According to some philosophers, e.g., Schwarz, *op. cit.,* pp. 106 ff., and especially according to some contemporary phenomenologists, one cannot justifiably argue from the unity of the objective world to that of science (*"Eine Welt—eine Wissenschaft"*). We cannot quite agree with this view, although we too consider the view which attributes to man the central place more fundamental than the argument used by the present line of thought. *Cf.* pp. 319 ff.

The answers would require extensive considerations if they had to be supplied at the beginning of a philosophy of science. However, since we have delayed raising the question of unity till the end of this book, we may simply refer to the preceding chapters in which the various difficulties have been met. All we have to do here is to stress a few points and to append a brief commentary.

Speculative and Operative Sciences

Chapter Four has indicated in a general way what the proper character is of the speculative and operative sciences and pointed out that these two groups of sciences are interrelated. Operative sciences always intend to establish norms for certain realms of human activity. No matter how varied they are, human activities always find their starting point in the one reality of man and his world. They arise from man, and therefore a very broad knowledge of man is required to arrange the manifold human activities in an orderly fashion. Insofar as these activities aim at the perceptible reality of man and his world, this arrangement demands extensive, and sometimes also very profound, knowledge of this reality. Insofar as these activities are directed toward establishing the right orientation toward God, there is need for theoretical knowledge of man in his relationship with God.

Thus it should be immediately evident that the operative sciences are intrinsically dependent upon the speculative sciences which supply the required knowledge of God, man, and world. On the other hand, the products of man's orderly activities themselves may become the object of speculative sciences, e.g., of cultural sciences. Accordingly, in spite of the well-founded distinction between operative and speculative sciences, these sciences are internally connected and interdependent, so that the two groups constitute an unbreakable unity.

The interconnection of the speculative and operative sciences is valid for all the groups of operative sciences which we have distinguished in the preceding chapters, whether they be theological, philosophical or special operative sciences. To avoid repetitions, we may simply refer here to the sections of this book where this point was considered in a different context—namely, Ch. V, Sect. III and IV; Ch. VII, Introduction, Sect. I and III, No. 2; Ch. IX, Sect. II.

Experiential Sciences

As we pointed out in Chapter Six (pp. 124 ff.), the experiential sciences together have as their material object the totality of reality which exists independently of man's cognitive activity insofar as this reality is knowable to man's natural cognitive powers. These sciences are formally distinct from the speculative philosophical sciences because they consider real entities solely in their specific and generic essence (and sometimes also in their individual and concrete essence).

The experiential sciences, therefore, find their unity per se in the unity of the world in which man is bodily rooted and has his living space. The differentiation of these sciences arises from the fact that the unity of man and his world possesses a complex structure and a plurality of knowable aspects, thereby offering a basis for different ways of formal study by man. This differentiation leads first of all to the broad distinction between sciences of man, sciences of nature, and sciences of culture. Each of these groups offers further opportunities for distinctions because of the complexity and variety of their respective objects but more even because man knows in an abstractive way, placing himself constantly upon different standpoints, so that he is continually introducing different formal aspects into the realm of his investigations. Such differences of formal object are necessarily accompanied by other differences, e.g., of method and mode of argumentation, and thus give each of the sciences its own character. All these distinctions, however, do not take away the inner connection and unity of the experiential sciences, for it is precisely against this background of unity that these distinctions are placed.

These general remarks may be followed by a few additional considerations regarding the unity of the sciences in reference to the various groups in which the experiential sciences may be divided. As we have seen in Chapter Six, these groups are the sciences of nature, of man, and of culture.

Sciences of Nature. These sciences, despite all their differences in objects, methods and modes of viewing their object, constitute a unity because they all are concerned with one and the same material world as a whole and in its parts. Although sometimes sciences of nature, e.g., geology and astronomy, botany and zoology, differ in their material objects, this difference does not result in an unbridgeable separation, because these objects themselves are integral parts of one and the same material reality, governed by the same fundamental laws, and therefore must always be viewed within the framework of this fundamental interconnection. The fact that a science

has a special material object does not make this science fully autonomous and independent of the other sciences. Although the earth,
for instance, in some respects allows a separate study, its actual condition and its situation in the whole of the material world can be
understood only in the light of the data gathered by astronomy,
physics, chemistry, and the sciences concerned with living bodies.
Zoology likewise makes use of the results attained by botany, and
both these sciences are connected with physics and chemistry.

To the extent that sciences of nature are concerned with the same
material object and differ only in their formal object, they may enjoy
a partial independence of one another in their working methods.
Nevertheless, any rigorous separation would be fatal for man's understanding of material reality, because the specialized approach of the
various sciences results in a one-sided view of reality. Each of them
provides, as it were, different photographs of the same reality, taken
from different standpoints, under different lights and in different parts
of the spectrum. One photo can be fully understood only by means
of a comparison with the others. We may even say that all photos
together do not give us an integral picture of concrete material
reality, for each of them is and remains an abstraction subject to
additional clarifications.

The interconnection of the various sciences of nature manifests
itself also by the fact that in more recent times some of these sciences
develop toward one another; for example, it is often no longer possible
to make a clear-cut distinction between certain branches of physics
and chemistry. In the same direction points also the rise of intermediary sciences, such as biophysics, biochemistry, physical chemistry,
medical physics and medical chemistry.

Sciences of Man. Similar considerations apply also to the sciences
of man. They have their unity from the fact that they are concerned
with one and the same material object—man—which they consider in
different aspects, in himself and in his manifold relationships with
his fellow men and the world. Insofar as man is a bodily living being,
he can be studied by means of the methods of the physical sciences,
and many data acquired by these sciences really do apply to man also.
It is interesting to note here that even in the Middle Ages man was
considered as a microcosm, because he contains the material, the
vegetatively living and the sensitively living, which through his
spiritual soul he fuses into a higher spiritual-material unity.

Sciences of Culture. The interdependence and unity of the cultural sciences, as well as their connection with the sciences of man, arise from the fact that they are all in a special way concerned with man and his activities. The realization of this interdependence manifests itself in the rise of new sciences, such as general linguistics and general literary science, which endeavor to throw light upon the subject matter in question from a more universal standpoint.

Insofar as human activities are directed toward non-human objects or find expression in matter or by means of matter, there often exists a possibility of approaching their object by means of the methods proper to the physical sciences. For example, techniques of physical science may be used in the study of manuscripts, and sound experiments can offer aid to the study of languages. In this way new bonds arise between these sciences and the sciences of nature. We may refer here also to the relevant parts of Chapter Six, Section Three.

We would like to add here a final remark about the unity of the experiential sciences—namely, that this unity manifests itself also in the possibility of using in part at least the same common methods, e.g., mathematical and statistical methods. We may refer here especially to the new science of cybernetics. True, the praise bestowed upon it and the expectations of its admirers are sometimes rather exaggerated. Nevertheless, it is certain also that the results of this science have found fruitful applications in a multitude of realms pertaining to the experiential sciences, not only to sciences of nature but also to those of man and his culture, such as physiology, neurology, psychiatry, linguistics, sociology, technology and production management. On the other hand, the possibility of using common methods should not deceive us into denying the distinction between, on the one hand, the sciences of nature and, on the other, the sciences of man and his culture. Cf. Ch. VI, Sect. IV, pp. 158 ff.

Philosophical and Non-Philosophical Sciences

Speculative Philosophy. Chapter Nine has extensively shown that speculative philosophy, as we conceive it, has as its object being, the whole of reality in its ontological aspects, and the special modes of being, such as being-man, being-alive, being-matter. Thus the material object of speculative philosophy coincides partially with the totality of objects studied by the experiential sciences. These sciences themselves, moreover, may become the object of philosophical reflection.

For both these reasons, therefore, there is an intimate bond between speculative philosophy and experiential science. The schematic plan appended to Section One of Chapter Nine (p. 273) clearly manifests this interconnection.

Philosophy finds its apex in the philosophical consideration of God, considering God as the absolute ground of being and the source of all finite and particular beings. For this reason there exists also an intimate bond between speculative philosophy and dogmatic theology. We have mentioned this point in Chapter Five, Section V, pp. 106 ff.

The interrelationship and unity of the various speculative parts of philosophy have been sufficiently emphasized in Chapter Nine. We may refer especially to the schema of Section One, p. 273.

Operative Philosophy. Section Two of the same chapter has spoken about operative philosophy and its relationship to other groups of sciences. This branch of philosophical thought endeavors to deduce, by means of man's natural reason, universal and fundamental norms in order to arrive at the right order of man's various types of activities, whether they be those of thinking and willing or transient activities. For this reason there exist intimate relations between operative philosophy and the special sciences, both in their operative branches and in their speculative parts. The same section (p. 291) pointed especially to the manifold relationships between, on the one hand, ethics and, on the other, moral theology, the various branches of philosophy, speculative and operative special sciences. These few remarks may suffice here, because the whole matter has been sufficiently discussed in the above-mentioned chapter.

Theological Sciences

As has been pointed out sufficiently in Chapter Five (see especially pp. 80 f.), the theological sciences should not be left out of the total edifice of science. The relations of theology to non-theological sciences, both philosophical and non-philosophical, likewise have been adequately considered in Section V of the same chapter, so that we need not repeat ourselves here.

However, in the present context the question could be raised to what extent God belongs to the one reality which is studied by science? Does He not infinitely transcend man and his world, so that God, man and world may not unqualifiedly be considered as a single totality?

In reply we must say that by virtue of His essence God infinitely transcends the created reality of man and world which is the object of the non-theological sciences. On the other hand, however, man and world are so utterly dependent upon Him that without His continuous creative action they would be unable to exist or to perdure in their existence. As creator, God is present in the totality of created beings in such a way that their existence without Him is simply unthinkable. The word of Saint Augustine applies here especially to man himself: "God is higher than the highest in me, but at the same time He is more intimate to me than my own inmost intimacy". With his natural reason man is capable of knowing this relationship to God and his duty to serve and honor Him. Moreover, he is able to know the fact of divine Revelation by means of this same reason and consequently the lifting of man to the supernatural order (cf. p. 86). Accordingly, man is not 'pure nature', and therefore he cannot be fully studied if one leaves this supernatural relationship to God out of consideration. We may add that *a posteriori* the sciences which study man and his culture, such as psychology, history and cultural anthropology, inevitably have to deal with the phenomenon of religion in either the natural or the supernatural sense of the term.

Thus it follows that the 'natural' or non-theological sciences cannot do without the help and complement of theology in the integral study of their object, of man and his world. For further consideration of this point we may refer the reader to Chapter Five, especially Section Five, and conclude by quoting a passage from an address of Cardinal Newman which very succinctly but also very clearly summarizes the ideas discussed above:

> Summing up, Gentlemen, what I have said, I lay it down that all knowledge forms one whole, because its subject-matter is one; for the universe in its length and breadth is so intimately knit together, that we cannot separate off portion from portion, and operation from operation, except by mental abstraction; and then again, as to its Creator, though He of course in His own being is infinitely separate from it, and Theology has its departments towards which human knowledge has no relations, yet He has so implicated Himself with it, and taken it into His very bosom, by His presence in it, His Providence over it, His impressions upon it, and His influence through it, that we cannot truly or fully contemplate it without in some main aspects contemplating Him.[4]

---

[4]*The Idea of a University,* in Longmans ed., New York, 1947, Discourse III, pp. 45 f.

Ideal Sciences

The preceding pages said nothing about the ideal sciences. Yet these sciences may not be omitted here precisely because of their peculiar character. As we have seen in Chapter Eight, the proper object of the ideal sciences is a product of man's thinking, while the object of the experiential sciences and of philosophy and theology is something which exists or can exist independently of man's thought. Superficially, therefore, it may seem that the ideal sciences have hardly anything at all to do with the other mental disciplines. However, as we have explained in the same chapter, despite the striking differences, there are also many bonds between the ideal and non-ideal sciences. In their origin and development the ideal sciences constantly need experiential contact with reality, albeit a very special kind of 'experiential contact' (cf. pp. 225 ff.). Moreover, it is upon this origin of ideal concepts in experience that is based the possibility of applying the results of the ideal sciences to appropriate problems of reality. For this reason these sciences cannot be dispensed with in the totality of the sciences.

Finally, the ideal and non-ideal sciences are connected by means of man, who as a spiritual-material being manages to form the fundamental concepts of the ideal sciences through a special abstraction from the data obtained from reality by means of his bodily being. This point will be considered more in detail in the second part of this section.

Summary

The preceding considerations should have made it clear that all groups of sciences are in one way or in another concerned with integral reality, i.e., with God, man, and world. Insofar as they are speculative, they endeavor to study this one reality in one or the other aspect or relationship. Insofar as they are operative, they attempt to formulate norms which intend to aid man in his various activities to know the true as well as possible and to realize the good and the beautiful in this one reality. In their attempts the operative sciences have to rely upon the results of the speculative sciences and, on the other hand, man's activities themselves and their results may become objects studied by speculative sciences.

Thus we may conclude that, no matter how varied the sciences are and how correctly their variety leads to their distinction into different groups, nevertheless they constitute a kind of unity because of their concern with one and the same integral reality. Once more Newman may be quoted here:

> Next, sciences are the results of that mental abstraction, which I have spoken of, being the logical record of this or that aspect of the whole subject-matter of knowledge. As they all belong to one and the same circle of objects, they are one and all connected together; as they are but aspects of things, they are severally incomplete in their relation to the things themselves, though complete in their own idea and for their own respective purposes; on both accounts they at once need and subserve each other.[5]

In this connection it may be useful to point to the danger which threatens everyone pursuing science—namely, the risk of becoming one-sided if he disregards the other groups of sciences and loses sight of the fact that the sciences are both diverse and one.

In the second part of this section we will consider another and, in our view, even more important factor unifying the sciences—namely, man insofar as he is concerned with them as their pursuer, their subject and their object. Meanwhile it should be apparent that the distinction between the two grounds upon which the unity of the sciences is based, between one reality and man, cannot be adequate in all respects. For man himself is included in this one reality and we may even say that he constitutes the most important element of finite reality, insofar as this reality is accessible to man's natural cognitive powers. The non-human part of the knowable world is divinely destined for man and oriented toward man, so that the world in a sense is a 'human world'. Nevertheless, the systematic distinction which we have made between man and world is fully justified with respect to our purpose, because the place and functions of man in the sciences, a matter to be considered now, are entirely different from those which pertain to him insofar as he is an element of the whole of reality.

2. *All Sciences Find Their Unity in Man*

We will investigate here in what way all sciences have unity because they find their origin in a certain type of human activity or because of another kind of intrinsic bond with man. For this purpose we will a) pay attention to the proper character of scientific activity; b) consider man as the subject of the sciences; and c) ask ourselves

---

[5] *Op. cit.*, p. 46.

to what extent man, as object of the sciences, can contribute to their unity.

a. UNITY BY MEANS OF THE PROPER CHARACTER OF SCIENTIFIC ACTIVITY

The pursuit of science is, obviously, a typically human activity. Science in the objective sense can exist only as the product resulting from man's scientific activity. Indisputable as these assertions are, they do not suffice to speak of the unity of the sciences. It is true, of course, that the various human activities manifest a certain inter-connection and unity because they find their origin in man and have their place in the one view of man, world and life held by the individual human being. Nevertheless, there is often sufficient reason to admit a profound or, if so desired, 'essential' difference between these various activities. Even if one abstracts from lower vital activities, such as vegetative and physiological functions, and limits himself to typically human activities, i.e., activities originating in man's reason and will or intellectual activities, it is unanimously agreed that there is sufficient reason for making fundamental distinctions because of the manifold intellectual powers of man. For this reason one may correctly distinguish various spheres of typically human activities, such as faith, science, art, purposive action, and technology, each of which require its own peculiar attitude.

The Proper Character of Scientific Activity

The characteristic element of scientific pursuits which distinguish them from the other spheres of man's activities consists in this that the purpose of science is always 'to know' i.e., 'intellectual knowledge with insight' (cf. Ch. I of Part I) or 'knowledge of truth'. This characteristic is connected with others, of which we will consider a few here after first saying a few words about 'knowledge of truth'.

Search for Truth. Scientific activity is always an intellectual search for truth, although in this context the term 'truth' does not always have a univocal meaning. In general, truth, at least in the sense of 'logical truth', means the agreement of the intellectual judgment with the situation judged by the intellect. In the speculative sciences it refers to a given situation which either exists independently of human thought or is produced by human thinking. The last-named case is found in the ideal sciences (Cf. Ch. VIII). In the operative sciences the situation in question is one that is to be brought about through man's activities. Here the intellect endeavors to arrive at a 'true' judgment of what ought or ought not to be done in connection with the situation that is to be realized (Cf. Ch. IV, Sect. I, pp. 47f.).

Methodic Procedure. As a rule, it is not possible for man to have an immediate insight into the truth of a particular situation. For this reason it is a common element of scientific pursuits that they have to make use of a method which, on the basis of a given or chosen starting point, is known or expected to lead gradually to new knowledge and to insight. Because the right approach is often not immediately known, one has to proceed gropingly, using hypotheses and theories which are subjected to verification. Whatever approach is used, man must attempt to base his new knowledge upon what he already knows by discovering the causal connection between the new item and previously possessed data and insights. Moreover, he will try to arrive as soon as possible at universal statements which supply him with a certain amount of understanding of the subject matter under consideration (Cf. Part One, Ch. II).

Scientific pursuits cannot proceed arbitrarily but are bound by general intellectual principles, the given data, and especially by the laws of logic (Cf. Ch. IX, Sect. II, pp. 276 ff.). There exist, of course, various scientific methods, such as deduction, induction, analysis, synthesis, hypothesis and theory, and different ways of proving a point. Each of them has its own value and possibility of application. Usually several methods have to be combined, even if one or the other will play a predominant role (Cf. Part One, Chs. VII-X).

General Principles. Precisely because all scientific activity is an intellectual judgment of an ontological situation that is present or to be realized, it has to develop according to the same general intellectual principles in the realm of ontology or epistemology, such as the principles of identity, contradiction, excluded middle, sufficient reason, causality, and intelligibility. Moreover, this activity has to rely on the trustworthiness of the intellect, the imagination and, at least in some cases, also of the memory and the senses. Thus the sciences possess unity insofar as all of them share the same intellectual principles and first foundations of knowing.

Critical Attitude. All pursuit of science demands a critical attitude with respect to the data and the correctness of the starting point, the suitability of the adopted methods, the right order of the successive steps of experimental research, argumentation, and reasoning process. The man of science must be able to justify fully for himself and for others the methods which he follows from the starting point until the final result of his pursuit. If such a justification cannot be stringently made, he will have to make an effort to determine the degree of probability proper to a particular intermediary step or to the final result.

Intellectual Honesty. The pursuit of science, moveover, demands that man be wholly honest in relation to the object of his research and with respect to other men of science. He has to see to it that his motives are pure, that he does not allow himself to be guided by wishes, faulty philosophical principles or world views, feelings of rivalry with respect to other pursuers of science, and similar unworthy factors. For such unworthy motives can easily lead to wrong interpretations of the actual data and to misjudging the results and views of others. Accordingly, the man of science must be critical of himself, his own attitude and motives. He must be ready to investigate the results and views of others, to accept them, if justified, and to revise his own ideas. In this way the pursuit of any science implies a common 'ethical' attitude, which may be considered another unifying bond (See also below, p. 324).

b. Unity in Man as the Subject of Scientific Activity

1. All sciences find their unity in man as the subject of scientific pursuits. First of all, the sciences arise from man, because man as a knowing being is the fountainhead of all knowledge. Every group of speculative sciences and, in a sense, even every particular science has its own way of representing reality, a way which cannot always immediately be combined with the represenations of the others. Nevertheless, all these representations are representations of and for man; they respond to his present preoccupations and can find their appropriate place only in man's integral vision of reality.

The same man who enters into scientific contact with nature and with culture, with himself and with his fellow men, and who in the ideal sciences with a certain freedom 'creates' objects to investigate them through his thinking, is capable also of taking the philosophical background of these sciences as the object of his study and to reflect philosophically upon the problems of being and knowing.

Finally, as a believer, he is capable of placing his natural knowledge in the light of the vision provided by his faith. This twofold mode of knowing, naturally and supernaturally, does certainly not result in a split existence. Faith and science do not contradict each other. The encounter with God and the acceptance of a self-revealing God does not eliminate man's natural knowledge, but supplies it with a new dimension which raises it up and incorporates it into a wider and higher whole. Man here does not function as a double subject of knowledge, but it is one and the same divinely illuminated spirit who, through his natural powers of knowledge and through the divine illumination, has at the same time an intellectual grasp of the natural and the supernatural order. In this way he is a principle of unity for the sciences pertaining to these two orders.[6]

Moreover, basing himself upon the knowledge gathered speculatively, man may proceed to think in an operative fashion, making plans for all kinds of possible realizations of good and beautiful things in either the natural or the supernatural order, and formulating norms governing the activities of man which are directed to these things.

Accordingly, with respect to all sciences, whether speculative or operative, theological, philosophical or non-philosophical, man is the fertile source, the cross road, both active and passive, in turn moving toward or away from this center in his scientific pursuits.

This brief sketch may suffice to show that all sciences, no matter how diversified they be, are united in man as their source and the subject of scientific pursuit. Insofar as sciences are speculative and in any way concerned with reality, they endeavor to bring to light whatever is more or less concealed in man's experience, and insofar as they are operative, they make use of this speculative knowledge to formulate sound norms for man's activity with respect to man and world.

2. The specifically scientific activity, of which above we have enumerated a few characteristics to distinguish it from other spheres of man's activities, is, of course, a human activity. No matter how varied scientific thought may be, it is always a 'human' thinking, subject to the great possibilities of man but also to his intrinsic limitations. Everything is known in a human fashion, whether man's knowledge is concerned with man and the world, with objects made or thought of by man, or even with the transcendent God. The infra-

---

[6]We may refer here to the pertinent parts of Chapter Five, Section Five.

human, the human as well as the suprahuman are known on a spiritual-material level, adapted to man's given cognitive powers. As the classical saying goes: "whatever is known is known in accord with the way of being of the knower". This fundamental principle has rather far-reaching consequences. We will mention a few here which are relevant to the question we are considering.

In his scientific pursuits the individual man stands together with his fellow men as an historical figure, carrying in his bosom the ideas of his time, his people, his own social group, formed and modelled by his sociological surroundings, his family milieu and his entire education. Moreover, each man is a person possessing his own inalienable individual ability and development, he has a personal view of the world and of life, as well as a philosophy which may deviate from those of his fellow men. All these and other factors make the individual living at a certain time and in a certain place or pertaining to a certain group or nation have a particular attitude toward the object of his scientific pursuits. In addition, there is the influence of his own personal qualities. All these factors exercise great influence upon the individual's realm of interest, upon his choice of scientific pursuits, and also upon the way in which he approaches and considers the chosen object. The way in which he formulates and couches his statements are influenced by all kinds of factors arising from his scientific, philosophical, sociological and religious background. Finally, the scientific interpretation and the sense attached to the data of experience are greatly influenced by the personal scientific and philosophical background against which these data are viewed. In a certain sense, therefore, as the old saying goes, attributed to the sophist Protagoras, "man is the measure of all things".[7]

All this goes to show that the pursuer of science must assume a critical attitude with respect to everything which he, as the subject of knowledge, could consciously or unconsciously add to the genuine content of his act of knowledge because of his own historical situation. The same critical attitude should prevail in regard of whatever could influence his interpretation of the actual data. Such additions or influences, which may be philosophical or non-philosophical, and even religious, could very easily deform the content of his knowledge in a considerable way. It may go so far that the genuinely objective ele-

---

[7] Pantôn chrêmatôn metron anthrôpos.

ments are simply buried below a deceptive overgrowth of subjective additions and that the individual considers as objective, as the result of his experiential research, something which in reality is purely the product of his own subjective fancies flowing from his personal philosophical or religious views, regardless of the question whether these views are true or false. Accordingly, genuinely scientific work, which aims at true and objective knowledge, absolutely demands a critical attitude and especially a high degree of self-critique.

3. In his experiential contact with the complex totality of man and world the person has the capacity of discovering all kinds of aspects and a plurality of meanings in accordance with the questions he asks and the standpoint he assumes. Knowledge therefore demands also a passive, questioning and receptive attitude with respect to whatever reality offers us as knowable aspects.

Contemporaries like to speak of the 'encounter' and 'dialog' of man and the world. These expressions may be very meaningful, provided the terms be correctly understood. A genuinely human 'encounter' with the world presupposes that man wants to respect the proper character of the other, e.g., the proper mode of being pertaining to the world which he wants to know better through his 'encounter'. In a genuine 'dialog' between man and world man may not be purely active, but must also be willing to listen to what the world replies to his questions. This reply in its turn may then inspire man to ask further questions. So far as the sciences of experience are concerned, perception and experiment may thus become the basis of theory, and the theory may become the occasion for new perceptions and new experiments.

The nature of the questions which man asks is, of course, strongly determined by man's actual knowledge and, as we have mentioned above, also by all kinds of philosophical, non-philosophical, and religious views, but the replies to these questions will always reveal ontological aspects which are proper to the object questioned by man.

Many more points could be raised in connection with man as the subject of science, especially in reference to the historical and personal influences which play a role in scientific pursuits. However, they lie beyond the scope of this chapter, which is limited to the aspects which are connected with the unity of the sciences. We may therefore conclude these remarks by repeating that the unity of the sciences cannot be properly founded if abstraction is made of man as the center of all scientific activity. Any further clarification that may be needed will be supplied by the consideration of man as the object of science.

c. Man as the Object of the Sciences

Is Man the Sole Object of the Sciences? In our times, even among groups in which one would not expect it at all, such as those pursuing physical science, one may often hear that, strictly speaking, the only object of the sciences is man himself. Usually also it is added that this unity of object is the only ground upon which the sciences can constitute a unity. The preceding considerations should have made it sufficiently clear that we can admit such a statement only with certain qualifications. Although this question could be viewed as an aspect of the problem of the relationship of object to subject in man's knowledge, it lies beyond the scope of our present work to treat this matter extensively. We will therefore limit ourselves to a few pertinent remarks.

As the preceding pages have indicated, man plays an important role in relation to knowledge in general and to scientific knowledge in particular. Knowledge is always a 'human' act of knowledge and, in addition, the content of this act is in many ways influenced by the proper character of the human knower.

On the other hand, one should beware of exaggeration. In our opinion, such an exaggeration is committed by those philosophers who claim that the knowing man produces the known object in all its aspects, or that man is able to give meaning to things independently of their objective meaning.

Proponents of such views declare that there can be no question of an 'objective world', of a *'monde-en-soi'*, a *'Natur-an-sich'*, or whatever other formula serves to express the same idea. We would be happy to subscribe to such formulae if they did not mean anything else than that there can be no question of contrasting, on the one hand, an objective world and, on the other, human consciousness which through the act of knowing would, as it were passively like a mirror, faithfully represent this reality. By means of his body man belongs to the material world and, as we have explained above, man's cognitive activities are of a spiritual-material nature, and therefore bound up with the world in an existential and historical way.

However, we cannot admit the above-mentioned formulae if they are intended to express that, independently of man, the world has no autonomous existence which man has to accept, no mode of being and properties which man through his act of knowing has to admit.

It is true, of course, that knowledge is not purely passive but a high level of activity and that, when man enters into cognitive contact with the world, human subjectivity will make its influence felt. This influence may be readily admitted to a greater or lesser extent in all sciences, but especially those which are concerned with man and human culture. Man is bound to be present in one way or in another in anything which would not be at all or at least not the same without his activity (Cf. Ch. VI, Sect. III, pp. 150 ff.). On the other hand, however, things have also manifestations and meanings which are independent of man's activity and which man to his surprise or even his dismay discovers; in other words, there are aspects and meanings which belong to the world-in-itself or to objective reality independently of man's cognitive activity. The world in which man finds himself located has a being of its own, which is prior in nature to its 'being-for-man' and therefore the ground of this 'being-for-man'. As such an 'objective' way of knowing, which endeavors to discover the proper mode of being belonging to things, one may consider especially the sciences of nature and more in particular the sciences which study non-living nature, because this nature is farther removed from man's own level of being and therefore offers less danger of being interpreted too humanly.

Sometimes it may happen that the properties and activities of the world will present themselves without 'being questioned'. Usually, however, they manifest themselves only when man 'questions' the world or nature in one or in the other way in accord with his own present situation or attitude. In such a case it is indeed 'nature questioned by man', to use a contemporary expression, which reveals itself to man, but the 'reply' is determined by nature and not by 'questioning man'.

It may be useful to point out here that the physical sciences constantly endeavor to eliminate as much as possible the 'human' element from their perceptions and experiments. The fact that the instruments used embody much human knowledge and human theories does not contradict this assertion. We may refer here again to the remarks made in Chapter Six, Section Three, pp. 156 ff.

The preceding remarks should suffice to show that in our view the often-repeated assertion about man as the sole object of the sciences is only partially correct and acceptable only with the necessary qualifications. In what sense it can be accepted will be indicated here below after a brief remark about the ideal sciences.

In the ideal sciences man's thinking produces and defines the elementary objects with a certain amount of arbitrariness. In other words, he is a 'giver of meanings'. Nevertheless, both in the undeniable origin of these objects in primary experience (cf. Ch. VIII, Sect. III, pp. 224 ff.) and in his subsequent viewing and investigation of these objects, the mathematician remains restricted by the originally given and known 'meaning' as well as the newly discovered 'meaning' of these objects.

The Sense in Which Man is the Sole Object of the Sciences. Some remarks will suffice to clarify the way in which man may be correctly called the only object of the sciences, thereby providing a new ground for speaking about their unity.

So far as the operative sciences are concerned, no matter what their nature be, they are always directed toward man, because they aim at formulating the norms of human activities. For, man's activity is always directed to something which somehow has 'value' for man.

The speculative sciences cannot be bundled together in the same fashion but need to be considered in groups. Philosophical and non-philosophical sciences which aim directly at man do not raise any special problem. The same, we think, may be said of the sciences concerned with human culture, for in them also in a more or less indirect way man endeavors to know more about himself—namely in his cultural activity and in his historical development.

The ideal sciences, on the other hand, do not directly have man as their object, for they are exclusively concerned with entities that can exist only in human thought (Cf. Ch. VIII, Sect. II). Indirectly, however, they may give rise to new knowledge about man, insofar as they invite man to reflect upon the thinking activity exercised in these sciences. As should be evident, such a reflection really belongs to the realm of speculative philosophy.

The remaining speculative sciences have as their object either the 'suprahuman'—God and created spirits—or the 'infrahuman'—non-human material beings, which may be indicated by the terms 'nature' or 'world'. As has been pointed out previously (pp. 322 ff.), both the suprahuman and the infrahuman are known from the level of the human. However, this human way of knowing does not make man the object of this knowledge. At first one would even feel inclined to say that man can know here only in an analogous fashion, ascending to a higher level or descending to a lower level, precisely because he is concerned with something non-human which is not directly adapted to his human cognitive powers.

Nevertheless, with respect to these ascending or descending modes of knowing there is a reason for claiming that in a certain sense man himself is the object of this knowledge. For in studying the suprahuman and the infrahuman man may discover points of similarity and of distinction in reference to his own essence as well as other relationships between himself and the non-human. Thus he may be led to a better understanding of his own nature.

The realm of the infrahuman comprises material living and non-living things, which may be collectively indicated by the terms 'world' or 'nature', although both these terms are used also in different meanings.[8] It would be possible to analyze extensively to what extent man discovers himself in nature. While we do not intend to present this analysis here, we would like to remark that the 'world' is correctly considered as a 'human world'. Even though this world exists autonomously and independently of man and originates long before man, nevertheless both as a whole and in its parts it has meaning only in reference to the future or present man, capable of gradually discovering and stating its human meaning. Spiritual-material being as he is, man needs a material milieu of living and lifeless things as the surroundings in which he can live and work, develop and display his powers. True, abstractly speaking, one may consider the world in itself and in its evolution without referring to man, but more profound research is bound soon to reveal the world's orientation toward man. Although man may have appeared only in a later phase of the world's development, one will easily acknowledge the fact that its long evolutionary pre-existence was necessary to prepare the world's phase which we may correctly term 'the era of man'. If the world is viewed in this way, it may be said with some justification that even in the sciences of this world or of nature man himself may be said to be the object. On the other hand, in our opinion such a view is possible only when man rises above the realm of these sciences and moves on to the level of world-view or philosophy.

The realm of the suprahuman comprises non-embodied spirits and the all-transcendent being known as God. Since the existence of non-embodied created spirits, usually called 'angels', is known directly only through Revelation, they do not normally constitute the object of non-

---

[8]Sometimes the terms are extended to comprise also man himself, e.g., in the expression 'God and the world'.

theological sciences. We will therefore limit ourselves here to the sciences which take God as the object of their study—viz., theology and the philosophy of God, which is the apex of metaphysics. This branch of philosophy endeavors by way of man's natural reason to acquire knowledge of the infinite or absolute Being, taking its starting point in the being of man and the world. It would appear difficult to us to maintain that the object pursued in the philosophy of God is man himself. In theology, on the other hand, the situation is somewhat different. The theological sciences speak of God as He has revealed Himself to man. This divine self-revelation is consequently directed to man and, in addition, shows us the special relationships of man with God, such as his elevation to the supernatural order, his fall and redemption. In this way, then, the theological sciences speak also of man himself.

A word may be added here about the speculative philosophical sciences insofar as they have not been included in the preceding considerations. Some of these sciences have man as their direct object, while others at most are indirectly concerned with man. Among the former we may name philosophical anthropology, philosophy of culture and epistemology, among the latter metaphysics and the philosophy of inorganic nature. In contemporary European philosophy man has occupied such a prominent place that not a few consider man the sole object of philosophical thought. It appears to us that this view is somewhat exaggerated and can be defended only by means of forced arguments.

A final remark to terminate this section. The foregoing pages should have clarified two points. First of all, the assertion that man is the sole object of all science can be admitted only with the necessary restrictions and qualifications. Secondly, philosophical reflection upon the various groups of sciences and their objects is capable of functioning as a unifying factor, especially because it may show that all knowledge, regardless of the realm to which it belongs, can contribute to a better knowledge of man.

II. Deviating Views About the Unity of the Sciences and Their Critique

As we have mentioned in the Introduction, frequent efforts have been made to defend the unity of science on other grounds than those considered in the preceding section.

The first of these efforts to come to our mind is, of course, that which is typical of every idealistic philosophical trend and which exaggerates the role of man as the subject of knowledge and of science to such an extent that man himself is held to produce the object known. Such views are defended by Kant, Fichte, Hegel and their followers. Many modern phenomenologists likewise lean in this direction. However, we will not examine the idealistic views of the unity of science here, for it would force us first to subject idealism itself to a thorough-going critique for which there is no room within the scope of this book. The question has been very briefly touched on pp. 326 f. Moreover, many of the ideas proposed in the preceding section would remain valid even in an idealistic conception of the unity of science.

A different unifying trend, which has enjoyed great vogue especially in the past few decades, is of positivistic orientation. Because of its wide-spread influence, it will be considered here. In our view the foundation upon which this positivistic idea of unity is based cannot be accepted. The reasons have been touched upon in the preceding sections, but for practical purposes it may be useful to clarify them here more extensively.

1. *Positivistic View of the Unity of Science*

Historical Remarks. While we cannot present here a complete history of the positivistic view, we will present some of the most striking high points that are important for the present question.

The first name to draw attention is that of Auguste Comte (1798-1857), the father of French positivism. According to Comte, all problems of nature and life are in principle capable of being solved by means of observation and experiment. Comte himself proposes a division of the sciences (cf. Ch. II, Sect. IV, pp. 24 ff.), but this division is more a convenient practical device than founded upon theory, for all sciences, says Comte, are 'positive' and part of a single 'natural philosophy'. Division through the character of their objects is not possible, because all objects, he holds, are objects of nature which agree in their fundamental properties and differ most in an accidental fashion. Moreover, the 'intimate nature' of these objects is not knowable anyhow.

Comte's view leaves no room at all for essential differences between man and non-human things. Even for the new sciences of sociology, which he himself originated and to which he gave its name, Comte preferred the term 'social physics', because his philosophy considered every science to be a physical science. Mathematics alone could in a sense be called an exception, because, according to Comte this science is the foundation rather than a constituent part of 'natural philosophy'. Arithmetics is nothing else than an extension of logic in a certain category of deductions, while geometry and mechanics in Comte's view are genuine sciences of nature, because they are based upon perception.

German positivism is represented by a philosopher who has written about the question concerning us here—namely, Wilhelm Ostwald (1853-1932), the successor of Haeckel (1834-1919) as leader of his Association of Monists (founded 1906). According to this 'monistic' view, everything—life and matter, spirit and body, world and God—can be reduced to a materialistic unit. So-called 'spiritual life' is merely an aspect of a bodily organism. Anything transcending matter is simply denied. Religion and metaphysics are combated in the name of science. According to Ostwald, in the realm of science this monism means that everything knowable must be treated with the methods of physical science, and the assertions of physical science are valid for all realms. Whatever cannot be discovered by means of these methods is bereft of all value. The 'monism' in question, therefore, is a monism of method.

Modern Positivism. The view of contemporary positivism about the unity of science has its source in so-called 'neo-positivism', a movement which originated as the 'Vienna Circle' in the third decade of the present century. In later years this philosophical current, which is especially widespread in English-speaking lands, split into different directions, partly at least because of the divergent interpretations given to the fundamental common principle of verification.[9]

These neo-positivistic currents have paid special attention to the unity of science. In 1939, the U. S. A. saw the former periodical *Erkenntnis* (founded 1930) replaced by a new journal having the significant title *Journal of Unified Science.* The year before work had started on an *Encyclopedia of Unified Science.* Thus it is evident that the unity of science lies close to the heart of modern

[9]Cf. our work, *Philosophico-Scientific Problems,* Pittsburgh, 1953, Chapter Three, which presents the origin of neo-positivism and the principle of verification. Much of what is said there is pertinent to the present question. In general we may refer the reader to the immense literature that has been published about logical positivism.

positivists. To achieve this unity, which is viewed as the crown on the work of neo-positivism, a new organization arose, bearing the name of *Unity of Science Movement*.

Main Features of the Positivistic View. Without entering into details, we will attempt to indicate the various ways in which the positivistic views try to arrive at the unity of science. The tendencies named may occur either separately or also jointly.

All positivistic currents limit the concept 'science' to the empirical sciences and, usually also, mathematics, excluding philosophy and theology. Among the empirical sciences they give great preference to the sciences of nature, which are considered to be the only ideal and genuine sciences, because they do not accept anything which cannot be verified experimentally. Sciences of man and of culture are recognized as sciences only insofar as their results are subject to verification by the methods of physical science. As long as such a verification is not possible, these sciences are second rank sciences. Some positivists see as the reason why these sciences have not yet reached the level of the sciences of nature, the fact that they are still young and have not yet sufficiently developed their methods. The tendency to reduce all sciences to physical science is sometimes called 'physicalism', but this term is also used in somewhat different meanings.

Certain groups of neo-positivists demand that all scientific explanations have the character of a 'structural description' i.e., characterize the object or situation by describing the total structure in which they fit. Such a structure does not necessarily have to be representable, but may be mathematical. The expectation is that even apparently totally different realms will reveal analogous structures, so that everything could be expressed in a single model or a single formula (*'Weltformel'*).

A requirement which is connected with the preceding demand but sometimes made independently of it is the rationalization of method, and especially of the axiomatic and formalistic structure, which all science must pursue in imitation of mathematics. Mathematics and logic[10] are seen here as the foundation and ideal of scientific method, although in themselves, as tautological structures without any content, they are not held to be sciences because they do not teach us anything about reality.

---

[10]These two are considered identical by many. See, however, Ch. IX, Sect. II, p. 279.

In addition, great emphasis is often placed upon the analysis of scientific language. Many modern positivists see the only possibility of survival for philosophy in this analytic function, which at the same time can fulfill a unifying role. The assumption is that a critical purification of language will show all sciences using one and the same clear and univocal concepts and symbols, the language and symbols, of course, of physical science. This requirement of analysis is often connected with a tendency to generalize the terms of physical science and to use them also in the sciences of man and of culture. The following quotation of Carnap may serve to illustrate the point: "There is a unity of language in science, viz., a common reduction basis for the terms of all branches of science, this basis consisting of the very narrow and homogeneous class of terms of the physical thing-language".[11]

2. *Critique of the Positivistic View of Unity*

Because we cannot present here a complete critique of positivism in its old and new forms, we may limit ourselves to a few remarks that are relevant to the question which concerns us here and as much as possible refer to the above-mentioned requirements. More-over, we cannot take into consideration all kinds of differentiations with which the positivistic views are shaded. For this reason we will abstain from attributing the above-mentioned requirements to any particular postivist. Those who do not hold the views rejected here, obviously do not have to feel hemselves under attack.

a. Its Starting Point

First of all, the starting point of positivism must be rejected. It wants to admit only that which can be verified empirically and usually thinks only about verification by means of the methods proper to physical science. This attitude is a fundamental denial of the much wider scope of cognitive possibilities man has, in the natural as well as the supernatural order, and the corresponding plurality of verification methods.[12]

b. Deformed Unity

Secondly, the unity of science which results from the positivistic view is a unity achieved, on the one hand, by rejecting whatever

---

[11]*Encyclopedia of Unified Science,* vol. I, no. 1, p. 61.
[12]Cf. our book, *Philosophico-Scientific Problems,* Pittsburgh, 1953, Ch. III.

does not fit into the accepted narrow framework, e.g., theology and philosophy in the traditional sense of the term, and on the other, by equalizing the remaining sciences with physical science, depriving e.g., the sciences of man and of culture of their proper character. This unity, therefore, is artificial simplification and uniformity rather than true unity. It implies arbitrary mutilation, restriction and impoverishment, because important sciences are not recognized as such and essential differences are either denied or disregarded.

As we have seen above, the unity of science can be justly defended, but it is a multiform and complex unity, a unity which retains essential distinctions, such as those which we have studied throughout this book: distinctions based upon purpose and character of knowledge, upon source and foundation, upon object, methods and viewpoint.

The uniformity which we reject here manifests itself in the above-mentioned positivistic views, e.g., in the limitation of scientific methods, in the demand of similarity of structure, in the unification of concepts and scientific language, which rejects the analogous formation of ideas. All these demands misjudge the multiformity of the knowable object and the breadth of man's cognitive possibilities. Thus they lead to a sad impoverishment of scientific knowledge, as we will see somewhat more in detail in the following paragraphs.

c. Inacceptable Consequences

The positivistic view of the sciences has to be rejected also because it leads to intolerable consequences. Although these consequences are implied or even mentioned in the preceding paragraphs, we may mention a few of them here more explicitly.

Entire Groups of Sciences Are Rejected. Several groups of sciences would have to be discarded, and they are precisely those which from time immemorial have been considered to be extremely important because of their value for man's knowledge of himself. Theology, for example, is rejected because it appeals to divine Revelation and leads to assertions which cannot be verified empirically. Such an attitude implies a denial or at least a misjudgment of the way God acts toward man and of man's elevation to the supernatural order.

Likewise, there would be no room for speculative philosophy in the traditional sense. Its problems, which were discussed extensively in the preceding chapter, are simply reduced to 'pseudo-problems', lying beyond the realm about which man can utter meaningful sentences. Operative philosophy also would have to be discarded. In the extreme positivistic view this rejection applies especially to ethics. All man can do is to make assertions about *de facto* relationships; hence he is certainly unable to establish norms governing man's activities in reference to his ultimate end.

Among the sciences of experience those which are concerned with man and his culture would be, as we have indicated above, either reduced to sciences of the second rank or accepted only in part—namely, insofar as they have been modelled after the sciences of nature. From our considerations in Chapter Six, Sections III-V it should be apparent that such a position multilates these sciences.

Dictatorship of Physical Science. The rejection of certain sciences and even of entire groups from the totality of science has serious consequences for man's view upon all kinds of problems which cannot fail to present themselves to the inquiring mind. The remaining recognized 'genuine' sciences, i.e., the sciences of nature, are declared competent to handle the objects formerly considered by the rejected sciences. The result is that these objects are distorted, that important and essential aspects of them are simply overlooked because the one and only recognized method—that of physical science—is unable to reach these aspects adequately. Such a procedure is wholly unjustified. It endeavors to proclaim the dictatorship of physical science because it is blind to any other kind of scientific knowledge. As Newman put it very aptly, "I observe, then, that, if you drop any science out of the circle of knowledge, you cannot keep its place vacant for it; that science is forgotten; the other sciences close up, or, in other words, they exceed their proper bounds, and intrude where they have no right".[13]

Dehumanization of Man. In connection with these consequences, the most important consequence, one may say, of the positivistic attitude is that no justice is done to man in many respects, because the typically human element of man is beyond the grasp of the methods and thinking of physical science. The great problems of human existence, the meaning of man's life, his orientation to God, his place in this world, his activity with respect to his fellow men and the world, and similar problems lie in their most essential aspects

---

[13] *The Idea of a University,* 1947, p. 65. See also Discourse III, nos. 2 and 4.

either totally or at least in part beyond the possibility of the approach proper to physical science. If, despite everything, they are nonetheless subjected to the grip of this science, the resulting knowledge is dehumanized. Human language, for example, is studied with disregard of the typically human element. Human events and man's psyche in the present and the past are considered fully approachable by means of their sense-perceptible and empirically verifiable expressions. In practice such a procedure amounts to the methodic elimination of certain human aspects from reality, followed by the declaration that nothing has been found which cannot be explained by the methods of physical science. The procedure makes one think of Eddington's fisherman who used only nets with a two inch mesh and afterwards, on the basis of his catch, declared that there are no fishes smaller than two inches.

The philosophical and non-philosophical sciences of man and human culture demand a human way of thinking and the use of methods adapted to the typically human element of man and his human activities, methods of self-reflection and introspection, of 'living-in-the-other', *'Einfühlen'*, *'Verstehen'*, or whatever other terms one wants to use to indicate these 'human' methods. The viewpoint to be taken, likewise, must be oriented toward concrete reality as it appears to man. Thus this realm cannot be adequately covered by means of the conceptual apparatus and simplified approach which performs such satisfactory services in physical science. The specifically human element cannot be caught fully in the categories of the sciences of nature. If anyone nonetheless wants to proceed here as is customary in physical science, he makes himself guilty of an arbitrary and serious mutilation. His procedure recalls to mind Procrustes, the Attican highwayman, who cut his victims down to make them fit the size of his bed.

Of course, our critique should not be taken to mean that the sciences of man and his culture in some of their parts cannot make fruitful use of the methods proper to mathematics and physical science. All we want to say is that these methods alone do not suffice (Cf. Ch. VI, Sects. IV and V). The sciences of man and culture will always have to retain their proper character and can never be absorbed by the physical sciences.

With these remarks we may terminate this final chapter. They once more emphasize a point which has been constantly referred to in nearly all chapters of this work—viz., the characteristic and irreducible value of man.

INDEX OF NAMES

INDEX OF SUBJECT MATTER

339

Objectivity, in physical and human sciences, 190 ff.; meaning of, 191, of world, 326 f.

Ontic Sciences, 55.

Ontological Sciences, 55.

Operative Sciences, applied, 70; special, 197 ff.; character of, 197 f.; division, 198 ff.; relation to other sciences, 205 ff.; to ideal sciences, 248 ff.; philosophy and, 206 f.; ethics and, 292 f.; unity of speculative and, 312.

Pedagogical Sciences, 199, 201 f.

Philosophy, 13 ff., 20 f., 40, 117, 251 ff.; theology and, 105 ff.; speculative, 40, 254 ff.; problems of, 257 ff.; of culture, 262 f.; of value, 263 f.; division of speculative, 273; operative, 40, 274 ff.; moral, 234 ff.; is a science, 252 f., 293 ff.; value of division for, 7 f.; theory as, 65; experiential sciences and, 188 f.; operative sciences and, 206 f.; applied science and, 207; possibility of, 251 f.; object of, 254 f., 294 ff.; operative philosophy of art, 282 ff.; moral, 284 ff., see also *Ethics;* ethics and other branches of, 291 f.; concept of, 292 f.; natural character of, 294; scientific, 303 ff.; unity of science and, 315 ff.

Physical Sciences, 25 ff., 155 ff., 164; differ from human sciences, 158 ff.; mathematics and, 167 ff.; laws of, 177 f.; value judgments and, 185 ff.; world view and, 187 f.; objectivity of, 190 ff.; necessity of, 242 f.; exactness of, 244 f., 246 f.; as positive science, 248 f.; science and, 268 f.; logic and, 278 f.; dictatorship of, 336.

Physics, 15 f.

Poetry, 19.

Poietics, 15, 45 f., 280 f.

Positive Sciences, 24 f., 246 ff.

Positive Theology, 98.

Positivism, philosophy and, 302 ff.; Comte's, 24 ff.; unity of science and, 302 ff.

Practical Thinking, 16, 43 ff.

Practical Sciences, 38 ff.; differ from theoretical, 56 ff.; connection with theoretical, 63 f.

Practice, 63, 72 ff. See also *Practical Thinking.*

Presuppositions, of speculative and practical sciences, 61 f.; of ideal sciences, 228 ff.; of experiential sciences, 228 ff.

Prudence, 71.

Psychology, 26, 30, 129, 134, 151, 164, 173, 194.

Purpose, of thought, 50 f.; science and objective, 58 f.; of physical sciences, 163 ff.; of human sciences, 163 ff.; of ideal sciences, 231; of operative sciences, 200.

Real, meaning of, 120 ff.; opposition to ideal, 210; concepts, 212 f.

Reality, meaning of, 120 ff.; problems of, 256 ff.; all sciences aim at the same, 311 ff.

Revelation, 78, 79 ff., 91 f.

Science(s), division, see *Division;* speculative and practical, 43 ff.; theological and non-theological, 79 ff.; experiential, 116 ff.; special, 110 ff., 197 ff.; ideal, 209 ff.; philosophical, 251 ff.; Comte's hierarchy of, 26 f.; philosophy and, 268 ff.; philosophy is a, 252 f., 293 ff.; unity of the, 307 ff.; reflection on the, 309 f.; unity of philosophical and nonphilosophical, 315. See also the entries for each of the various groups of sciences.

Schemata, of totality of science, 39, 42; of "natural", 40; of natural speculative science, 41; of place of theology in the whole of science, 114; of man and nature, 140; of nature and culture, 146; of object of experiential sciences, 147; of this object and of the experiential sciences, 148; of philosophy and the sciences of nature and of man, 269; of speculative philosophy, 273.

Scientific Activity, man as object of, 322 ff.

Scientific System, applied, 69 f.

Sense Life, problems of, 260.

Social Sciences, 151, 202 f., 203 f.

Sociology, 26, 151, 173. See also *Social Sciences.*

Somatic Aspect of Man, 151 f.

Somatic Sciences, 151 ff.

Species-Individual Structure, 222 f., 257.

Speculative Sciences, 15 ff., 38 ff., 43 ff., 117 f.; differences from practical, 56 ff.; connection with practical sciences, 63 f.; ethics and, 292; unity